CRISS-CROSS

CRISS-CROSS

ARCTURUS

ARCTURUS

This edition published in 2013 by Arcturus Publishing Limited
26/27 Bickels Yard, 151–153 Bermondsey Street,
London SE1 3HA

ISBN: 978-1-78212-579-2
AD003710EN

Printed in the UK

HOW TO SOLVE A
CRISS-CROSS PUZZLE

Criss-Cross puzzles can be great fun and solving them requires a keen eye for detail…!

Each puzzle consists of a grid of squares and a list of words, all of which must be placed, crossword-style, in the grid. Sometimes letters are already placed in the grid, to eliminate the chance of more than one possible solution to a puzzle.

Your task is to decide where each word fits, place one letter of the word into each square, then tick it off the list, continuing until every word has been found.

Here is an example of a finished puzzle:

	H	A	R	E					
		A				W		C	
		B	U	F	F	A	L	O	
		B		L		S		U	
	G	U	I	N	E	A	P	I	G
	E		T		A			A	
	R		W			W	O	R	M
	B	O	A	R		O			A
	I			E	A	G	L	E	R
	L	I	O	N		F			E

4 letters	WORM	GERBIL
BOAR	WREN	RABBIT
FLEA		
HARE	**5 letters**	**7 letters**
LION	EAGLE	BUFFALO
MARE		
WASP	**6 letters**	**9 letters**
WOLF	COUGAR	GUINEA PIG

Currencies of the World

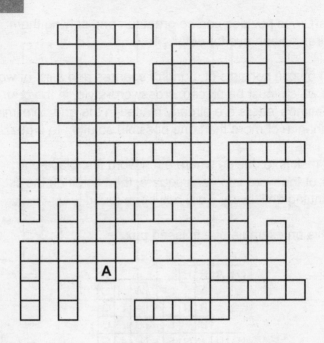

3 letters
LEK
LEV

4 letters
BAHT
BIRR
CENT
INTI
KYAT
RAND
REAL

5 letters
COLON
DINAR
FRANC
KRONA
KRONE
NAIRA
POUND
RUPEE

6 letters
BALBOA
DIRHAM

DOLLAR
FORINT
KORUNA
RUPIAH

7 letters
BOLIVAR
DRACHMA
GUARANI
RINGGIT

8 letters
RENMINBI

Animals' Homes

3 letters
DEN
PEN
STY
WEB

4 letters
BYRE
CAVE
COOP
DREY
HILL
HOLE
HOLT

NEST
POND
SETT
STUD

5 letters
EARTH
EYRIE
HUTCH
LEDGE
MOUND
ROOST
SHELL
STALL

6 letters
AVIARY
BURROW
KENNEL
WARREN

7 letters
PADDOCK

8 letters
DOVECOTE
FORTRESS

'A' Words

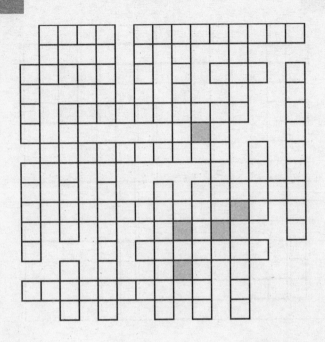

3 letters
ALB
ANY
ATE

4 letters
ARMY
AURA
AWRY

5 letters
ABOUT
ADDED
AGAPE

ANNUL
ASHEN
AZTEC

6 letters
ASTUTE
ATOMIC

7 letters
ADVANCE
AIMLESS
AMBIENT
ATELIER
ATTEMPT

9 letters
AEROPLANE
AVAILABLE
AVALANCHE

10 letters
ACCIDENTAL
ATTACHMENT
ATTENDANCE

11 letters
APPROXIMATE

Bunch of Flowers

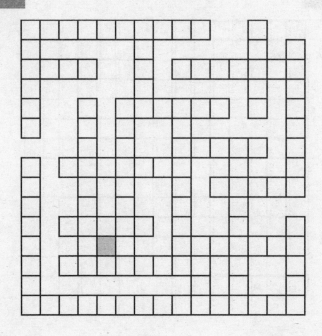

4 letters
IRIS
LILY

5 letters
ASTER
DAISY
LILAC
LUPIN
TANSY
TULIP

6 letters
CROCUS
SALVIA

7 letters
GENTIAN
NIGELLA
PETUNIA

8 letters
LAVENDER
SNOWDROP
XANTHIUM

9 letters
AQUILEGIA
CALENDULA
CELANDINE
COLUMBINE

10 letters
SNAPDRAGON

15 letters
MICHAELMAS
  DAISY

FUL to Finish

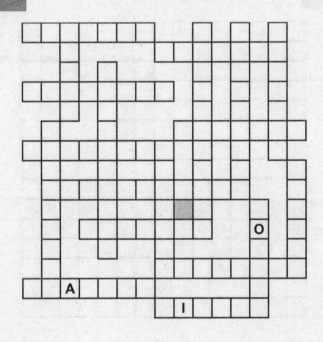

5 letters
AWFUL

6 letters
FITFUL
JOYFUL
MANFUL

7 letters
FEARFUL
GLEEFUL
LUSTFUL
PAINFUL

PLAYFUL
TACTFUL
TUNEFUL

8 letters
FORCEFUL
HOUSEFUL
LADLEFUL

9 letters
EFFORTFUL
WONDERFUL

10 letters
RESPECTFUL

11 letters
DISGRACEFUL
DISTRESSFUL

Holes and Spaces

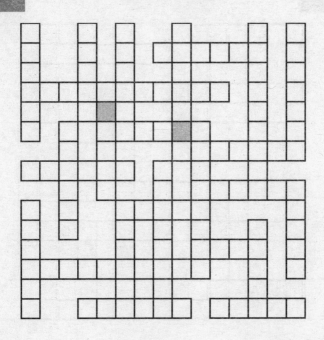

4 letters
RIFT
VENT
VOID

5 letters
BLANK
CLEFT
DRAIN
INLET
SPOUT
STOMA

6 letters
BURROW
CAVITY
CRANNY
CRATER
GROTTO
HIATUS
RECESS
TRENCH
WARREN

7 letters
CREVICE
SPYHOLE

8 letters
APERTURE
PEEPHOLE

9 letters
THUMB HOLE

10 letters
RABBIT HOLE

11 letters
INDENTATION

Little Things

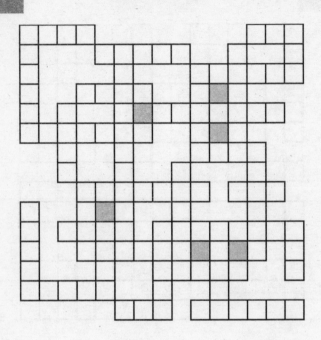

3 letters
ELF
FLY
JOT
TAD
TOY

4 letters
DOTS
FLEA
MITE
PECK
SLIM
SNIP
TICK

5 letters
DWARF
FLECK
PETTY
PINCH
SNIFF
SPECK
TEENY

6 letters
ATOMIC
DAINTY
MIDGET
MINUTE
PETITE

SECOND
SHRIMP

7 letters
DROPLET
GRANULE
SMIDGEN

8 letters
PINPOINT

11 letters
POCKET-SIZED

NEW Beginnings

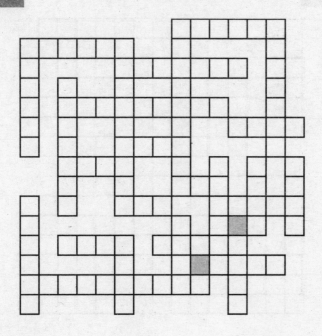

3 letters
AGE
TON

4 letters
GATE
LINE
LOOK
MOON
NESS
PORT
TOWN
WAVE

YEAR
YORK

5 letters
HAVEN
RIVER

6 letters
CASTLE
FOREST
JERSEY
MARKET
MEXICO

7 letters
EDITION
ENGLAND
FANGLED

9 letters
AMSTERDAM
CALEDONIA
TESTAMENT

10 letters
SOUTH WALES

Signs

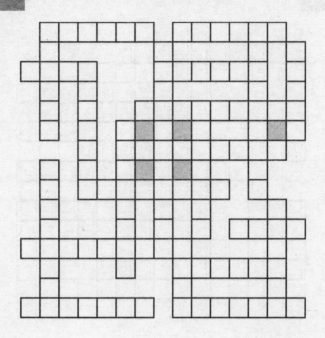

4 letters
SLOW
STOP
WALK

5 letters
GENTS

6 letters
DANGER
LADIES
POISON
SCHOOL

STAIRS
UNSAFE

7 letters
KEEP OFF
PARKING
STATION
WARNING

8 letters
ENTRANCE
FIRE EXIT
WET PAINT

9 letters
EMERGENCY
KEEP RIGHT
NO PARKING
VACANCIES

11 letters
QUIET PLEASE

Wild Cats

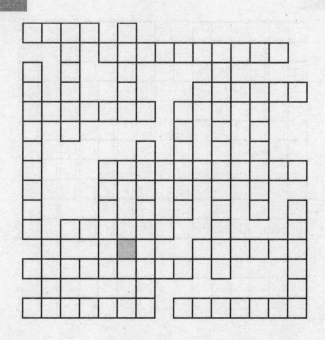

4 letters
LION
PUMA

5 letters
TIGER

6 letters
BENGAL
BOBCAT
JAGUAR
KAFFIR
KODKOD

OCELOT
SERVAL

7 letters
CARACAL
CHEETAH
LEOPARD
SAND CAT

9 letters
GOLDEN CAT
JUNGLE CAT
PALLAS CAT

10 letters
FISHING CAT

11 letters
BLACK-FOOTED

12 letters
GEOFFROY'S
CAT

Trees and Shrubs

3 letters
ASH
ELM
YEW

4 letters
ACER
BALM
DATE
LIME
PEAR
PINE
PLUM
TEAK

5 letters
ABELE
ALDER
APPLE
BALSA
ELDER
HOLLY
OSIER
ROWAN
SALIX

6 letters
ACACIA
BAMBOO

BANANA
ORANGE
WALNUT
WATTLE

8 letters
SYCAMORE

9 letters
QUICKBEAM
WHITEBEAM

10 letters
BLACKTHORN

Sharp Objects

4 letters
BARB
PINS

5 letters
ARROW
BLADE
SPEAR
SPURS
SWORD
TOOTH

6 letters
CACTUS
CHISEL
LANCET
POINTS
RAPIER
SCYTHE
SHEARS
SICKLE
SPINES
TALONS

7 letters
BAYONET
CUTLASS
MACHETE
PRICKLE

8 letters
SCIMITAR
STILETTO

10 letters
PROJECTION

Shapes

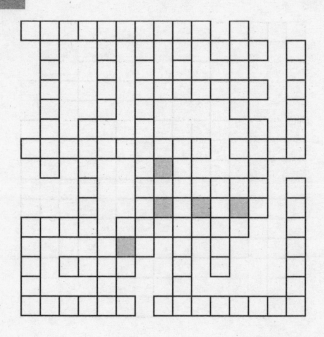

3 letters
ORB

4 letters
CONE
CUBE
KITE
OVAL
STAR

5 letters
CROSS
GLOBE
HEART

PRISM
ROUND

6 letters
CIRCLE
SPHERE
SQUARE

7 letters
DECAGON
ELLIPSE
HEXAGON
NONAGON

8 letters
CYLINDER
PENTAGON

9 letters
RECTANGLE

10 letters
HEMISPHERE
OCTAHEDRON

12 letters
DODECA-
HEDRON

Sporting Equipment

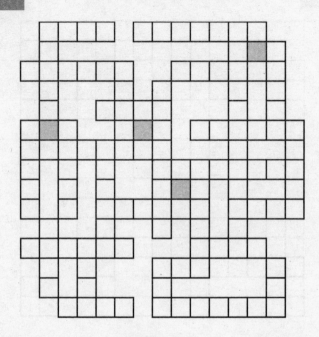

3 letters
BAT
BOW
CUE

4 letters
BALL
EPEE
JACK
LUGE
NETS
OARS
PUCK

5 letters
BATON
FRAME
RINGS
SCUBA
SKATE
WEDGE

6 letters
BASKET
DISCUS
ETRIER
MALLET
PADDLE

QUIVER
STUMPS

7 letters
NIBLICK
WHISTLE

8 letters
KNEE-PADS
SKI STICK
TOBOGGAN

12 letters
CLIMBING ROPE

Wedding Day

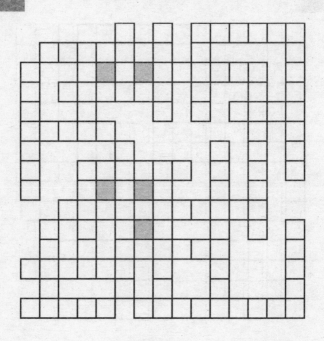

4 letters
CARS
WIFE

5 letters
ALTAR
BRIDE
DRESS
FEAST
PLANS
SMILE
USHER

6 letters
CAMERA
CHURCH
FLOWER
GUESTS
SHOWER
SPEECH
TOASTS

7 letters
NUPTIAL
WEDDING

8 letters
CONFETTI
HEN NIGHT
REGISTER

9 letters
LIMOUSINE
STAG PARTY
TROUSSEAU

11 letters
MORNING SUIT

King Henry VIII

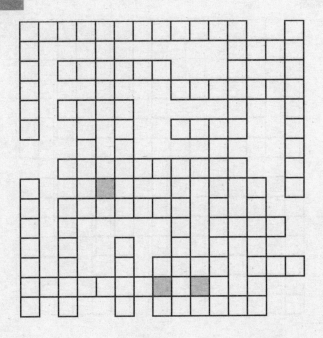

3 letters
SON

4 letters
ANNE
HEIR
JANE
KING
MARY
POPE

5 letters
TOWER

6 letters
ARTHUR
CLEVES
EDWARD
HOWARD
JESTER
THRONE
YEOMAN

7 letters
CLEMENT
CRANMER
DIVORCE
NONSUCH
WINDSOR

8 letters
MARRIAGE

9 letters
GREENWICH

10 letters
PARLIAMENT
THOMAS MORE

12 letters
HAMPTON
COURT

Not Very Nice

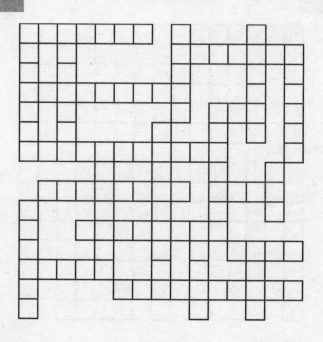

3 letters
BAD
SLY

4 letters
EVIL
FOUL
MEAN

5 letters
AWFUL
CRUEL
GROSS

6 letters
MOULDY
RANCID
SINFUL

7 letters
BALEFUL
CORRUPT
DEBASED
DECAYED
IMMORAL
RUINOUS

8 letters
CRIMINAL
SHAMEFUL

9 letters
ATROCIOUS
INJURIOUS

10 letters
DISGUSTING

11 letters
DETRIMENTAL

Pies

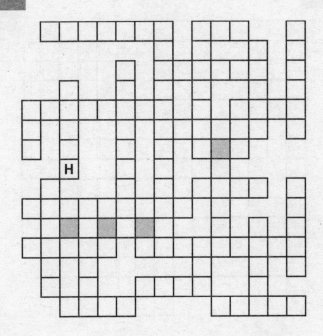

3 letters
MUD
PAN
POT
TIN

4 letters
MEAT
OVEN
PORK
TART

5 letters
CREAM
CRUST

DOUGH
FRESH
FRIED
LEMON
PECAN

6 letters
CHEESE
CHERRY
POTATO
RAISIN
TAMALE

7 letters
PUMPKIN
RHUBARB

8 letters
MERINGUE

9 letters
CHOCOLATE
SHEPHERD'S
VEGETABLE

12 letters
BUTTER-
SCOTCH

Let's Begin

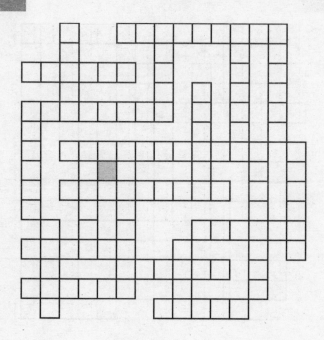

4 letters
OPEN

5 letters
ENTER
ERUPT
FOUND
START

6 letters
COME ON
CREATE

CROP UP
EMBARK
EMERGE
INCITE
KICK IN
PLUNGE
SET OFF
SET OUT

7 letters
USHER IN

8 letters
COMMENCE
GET GOING
SET ABOUT

9 letters
GET MOVING
INSTITUTE

11 letters
GET CRACKING

Knitting Pattern

4 letters
BALL
HOOK
PURL
ROWS

5 letters
CABLE
CHAIN
SOCKS
SPOOL
TWIST

6 letters
CAST ON
GARTER
REPEAT
STITCH

7 letters
BLANKET
COLOURS
COUNTER
CROCHET
FOUR-PLY
SLIP ONE

SQUARES
STRETCH

8 letters
KNITTING
PRESSING
STOCKING
TOGETHER

9 letters
INTERLACE

Punctuation Marks and Signs

4 letters
DASH
EURO
HASH
PLUS
TICK

5 letters
ARROW
COLON
COMMA
CROSS
MINUS
POUND

SLASH
TILDE

6 letters
EQUALS
PERIOD

7 letters
BRACKET
OBLIQUE

8 letters
ASTERISK
ELLIPSIS

LESS THAN

12 letters
QUESTION
MARK

13 letters
QUOTATION
MARK

14 letters
MULTIPLICATION

Things to Recycle

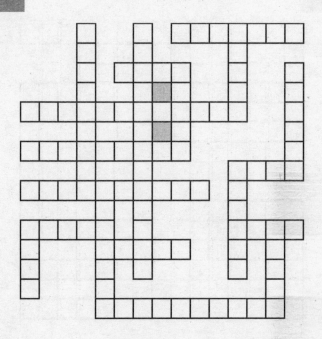

4 letters
BAGS
CANS
JARS
TOYS

5 letters
CHINA
GLASS
SHOES
STEEL
TYRES

6 letters
COMICS
TIMBER

7 letters
BOTTLES
PLASTIC

9 letters
CHEMICALS
MAGAZINES

10 letters
CATALOGUES
NEWSPAPERS

12 letters
MOBILE
PHONES

13 letters
WRAPPING
PAPER

Double 'S'

4 letters
HUSS
LASS

5 letters
ABYSS
MESSY

6 letters
ABBESS
ACROSS
DURESS

LESSEN
NASSAU

7 letters
DRESSED
ESSENCE
FINESSE
HESSIAN
IMPRESS
MASSAGE
MASSIVE
OPPRESS

RISSOLE
SESSION

8 letters
UGLINESS

9 letters
CESSATION
NECESSARY
WORTHLESS

Troubling Times

4 letters
BANE
BLOW
FALL

5 letters
CURSE
GLOOM
SLUMP
UPSET
WORRY

6 letters
BOTHER
MISERY
REBUFF

7 letters
BAD LUCK
DECLINE
FAILURE
PROBLEM
SCOURGE
SETBACK

8 letters
DISASTER

9 letters
ADVERSITY

10 letters
DIFFICULTY

11 letters
DISTRACTION

12 letters
WRETCHEDNESS

The Garden Pond

3 letters
KOI

4 letters
CARP
FISH
FROG
LILY
NEWT
POND
POOL
PUMP
TOAD

5 letters
DEPTH
LINER
NYMPH
ROCKS
SLABS
SPAWN

6 letters
DESIGN
GRAVEL
PEBBLE
RIPPLE
STONES

7 letters
BEETLES
CASCADE
GRASSES
INSECTS

8 letters
AERATION
FOUNTAIN

10 letters
REFLECTION

Winter

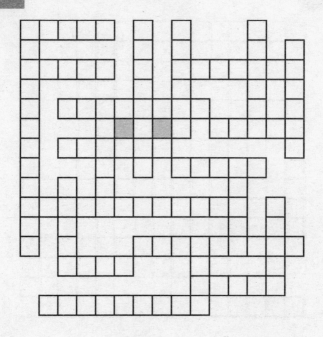

4 letters
LOGS
SNOW

5 letters
BLEAK
COALS
COLDS
COUGH
GALES
GUSTY
NIPPY
SLEET

6 letters
FROSTY
ICICLE
SKIING
SNEEZE
WINTRY

7 letters
NEW YEAR

8 letters
BLIZZARD
FREEZING

9 letters
CHRISTMAS
WOOLLY HAT

12 letters
BONFIRE NIGHT
GOOSE-
 PIMPLES

Spring-cleaning

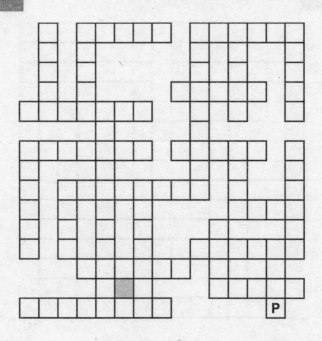

4 letters
MOPS
SOAK
SOAP
SODA
SUDS

5 letters
APRON
BROOM
GRIME
RINSE
SCRUB

SPRAY
WIPES
WRING

6 letters
BLEACH
BRIGHT
POLISH
STAINS
TOWELS

7 letters
BEESWAX

PLUNGER
TIDYING

8 letters
SANITARY
SWEEPING

9 letters
SPARKLING

11 letters
WHITE SPIRIT

Time for a Picnic

4 letters
BOWL
BUNS
CAKE
MUGS
PATE
SALT
WINE

5 letters
APPLE
CLOTH
FLASK

PLATE
SALAD
WATER

6 letters
BANANA
CHEESE
COFFEE
CRISPS
GATEAU
PEPPER
SWEETS

7 letters
CHICKEN
LETTUCE
PICKLES

8 letters
HAM ROLLS
LEMONADE

10 letters
MAYONNAISE

Weather Forecast

3 letters
DRY
WET

4 letters
FAIR
GOOD
HAAR
HAZY
SMOG
SNOW
THAW

5 letters
CLEAR
FOGGY
FRESH
GUSTY
SLEET
STORM

6 letters
CHILLY
DELUGE
SEVERE

7 letters
CLIMATE

THUNDER
TORNADO

8 letters
HEATWAVE
SCORCHER

9 letters
BAROMETER
LIGHTNING
PROSPECTS

13 letters
PRECIPITATION

Group Nouns

3 letters
LOT
POD
SET

4 letters
BALE
BODY
CAST
CLUB
GANG
HERD
HOST
KNOT

PACK
TEAM

5 letters
BATCH
BLOAT
CHARM
CLASS
CLUMP
FLOCK
GROUP
PRIDE
SWARM
WATCH

WHOOP

6 letters
FLANGE
GAGGLE
RAFTER
SCHOOL
SLEUTH

7 letters
MIXTURE

10 letters
EXALTATION

Holidaymaker

4 letters
TAXI

OUTING
VOYAGE

WALKING

8 letters
POSTCARD

5 letters
BEACH
COACH
GROUP
VIEWS

7 letters
AIRPORT
CAMPING
DAY TRIP
JOURNEY
LUGGAGE
PACKING
TOURIST
VISITOR

11 letters
TRAVEL AGENT

12 letters
TOUR
  OPERATOR

6 letters
BIKINI
CAMERA

Gemstones

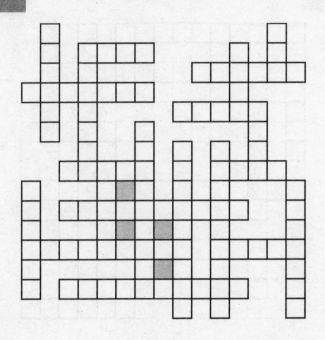

3 letters
JET

4 letters
JADE
ONYX
OPAL
RUBY

5 letters
AGATE
AMBER

PEARL
TOPAZ

6 letters
QUARTZ
SPHENE
ZIRCON

7 letters
KUNZITE
OLIVINE
PERIDOT

9 letters
CORNELIAN
HIDDENITE
MALACHITE
MOONSTONE

10 letters
CHALCEDONY
RHINESTONE

Happy Enough

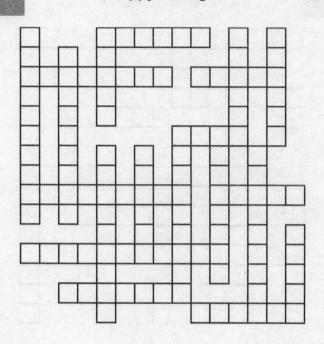

4 letters
GLAD

5 letters
JOLLY
LUCKY
MERRY
PERKY

6 letters
ELATED
JOCUND

JOVIAL
JOYFUL
LIVELY

7 letters
PLEASED

8 letters
ANIMATED
THRILLED

9 letters
EXUBERANT
FORTUNATE
FRIVOLOUS
GRATIFIED
OVERJOYED

10 letters
UNTROUBLED

11 letters
ON CLOUD NINE

Just Look

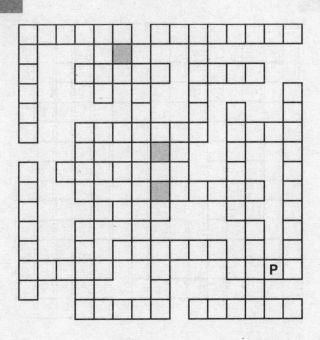

4 letters
ESPY
GAPE
GAWP
GAZE
LEER
OGLE
SCAN
VIEW

5 letters
CHECK
FOCUS

SNOOP
SPY ON
STARE
WATCH

6 letters
GLANCE
GOGGLE
REGARD
SEEING
SURVEY
TAKE IN

7 letters
GLIMPSE
INSPECT
OBSERVE

8 letters
REGISTER

10 letters
SCRUTINISE

11 letters
CONTEMPLATE

National Emblems

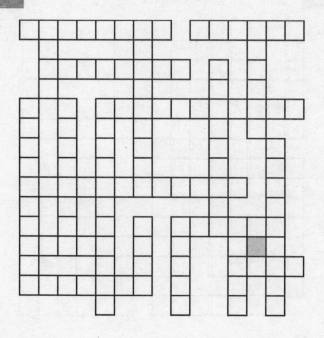

4 letters
HARP
LEEK
ROSE

5 letters
CAMEL
LLAMA
TULIP

6 letters
BAMBOO
BAOBAB

CASTLE

7 letters
SALTIRE

8 letters
MAGNOLIA
ROYAL OAK
SHAMROCK

9 letters
CROCODILE
IRON CROSS

MAPLE LEAF

10 letters
FLEUR-DE-LIS

11 letters
SNOW LEOPARD
STAR OF DAVID

12 letters
RHODO-
DENDRON

Jewellery

4 letters
CLIP

5 letters
BEADS
CAMEO
CHAIN
CHARM
CLASP
CROWN
WATCH

6 letters
ANKLET
BANGLE
BROOCH
CHOKER
COLLAR
DIADEM
HATPIN
LOCKET
PEARLS

7 letters
EARDROP
PENDANT

8 letters
CUFFLINK
EARRINGS
NECKLACE
SUNBURST

Grow and Grow

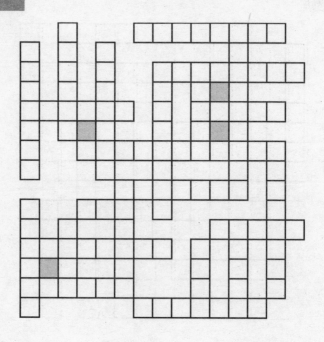

3 letters
WAX

4 letters
BOLT
BOOM

5 letters
RAISE
SURGE
SWELL
WIDEN

6 letters
DEEPEN
EXPAND
EXTEND
MATURE
SPROUT

7 letters
ACQUIRE
AUGMENT
ENLARGE
PROSPER

8 letters
ELONGATE
ESCALATE
MULTIPLY
MUSHROOM
SPRING UP

9 letters
GERMINATE

11 letters
PROLIFERATE

Newspaper Names

4 letters
ECHO
MAIL
POST
STAR

5 letters
GLOBE
PRESS
SPORT
TIMES
VOICE

6 letters
HERALD
RECORD
SKETCH

7 letters
COURIER
GAZETTE
JOURNAL
MERCURY

8 letters
EXAMINER
OBSERVER
REPORTER

9 letters
SPECTATOR
TELEGRAPH

10 letters
ADVERTISER

Pets

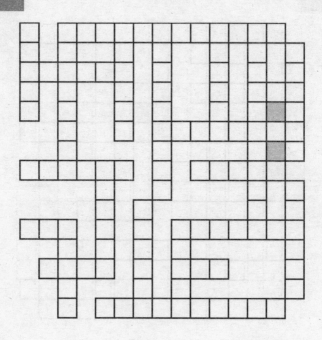

3 letters
CAT
DOG
RAT

4 letters
GOAT

5 letters
GOOSE
HORSE
MOUSE
PUPPY

6 letters
CANARY
FERRET
GERBIL
KITTEN
LIZARD
PARROT
PYTHON
RABBIT

7 letters
HAMSTER

8 letters
TERRAPIN
TORTOISE

9 letters
COCKATIEL

10 letters
BUDGERIGAR

11 letters
STICK INSECT

12 letters
TROPICAL FISH

Rivers

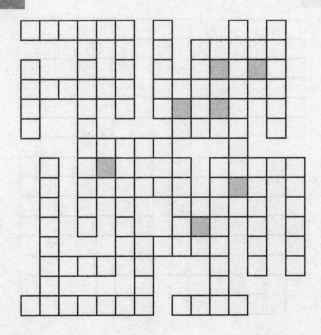

4 letters
ELBE
LENA
ODER
RHIW
RUHR

5 letters
DOURO
HAVEL
RHINE
RHONE
SEINE

SOMME
VOLGA
YUKON

6 letters
HUDSON
MEKONG
MURRAY
ORANGE
PARANA
THAMES
UBANGI
YELLOW

7 letters
ORINOCO
YANGTZE

8 letters
COLORADO
DELAWARE
SYR DARYA

11 letters
MISSISSIPPI

Shades of Green

3 letters
PEA

4 letters
ARMY
FERN
JADE
LIME
MOSS
PINE
SAGE

5 letters
APPLE
KELLY
KHAKI
OLIVE
PARIS

6 letters
BOTTLE
FOREST
RACING
SORREL

7 letters
AVOCADO
EMERALD
HUNTER'S
ISLAMIC

8 letters
SHAMROCK

10 letters
CAMOUFLAGE
CHARTREUSE

Security-conscious

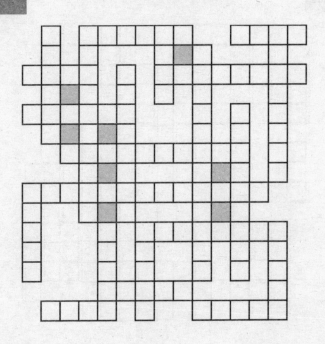

4 letters
CODE
DOGS
RISK
SAFE

5 letters
BOLTS
FRAUD
GUARD
SIREN
THEFT
VIRUS

6 letters
CAMERA
HACKER
TROJAN

8 letters
BARRIERS
FIREWALL
SCANNING
SHUTTERS

9 letters
MAG-STRIPE

10 letters
CHECKPOINT
MONITORING

12 letters
SURVEILLANCE

13 letters
VULNERABILITY

43 — Red Things

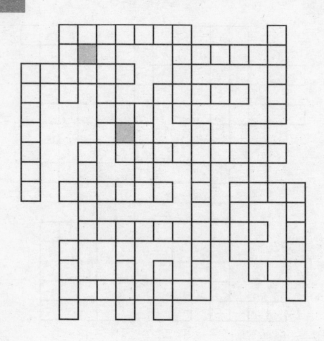

3 letters
ANT
INK
RAG

4 letters
FLAG
MARS
MEAT
ROSE
RUBY

5 letters
APPLE
BLOOD
BRICK
GRAPE
PLUMS
ROUGE

6 letters
CHERRY
CLARET
PEPPER
SUNSET
TOMATO

7 letters
CAMPION
FUCHSIA

8 letters
BURGUNDY

9 letters
CARNATION
RASPBERRY

10 letters
STRAWBERRY

Party Time

3 letters
FUN

4 letters
BALL
BASH
BEER
FETE
FOOD
RAVE
WINE

5 letters
GAMES

6 letters
LOVE-IN
SOCIAL
SOIREE

7 letters
SHINDIG
WEDDING

8 letters
BIRTHDAY
HEN NIGHT
JAMBOREE
OCCASION

9 letters
BARN DANCE
BEANFEAST

10 letters
SATURNALIA

11 letters
ANNIVERSARY
GET-TOGETHER

Lightweight

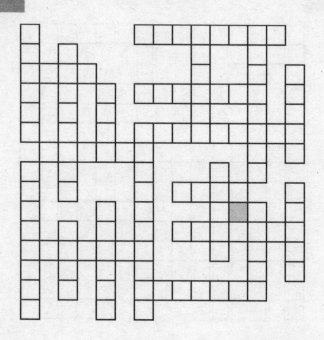

4 letters
AIRY
FINE
THIN
WEAK

5 letters
LOOSE
MINOR
PETTY
SANDY

6 letters
FICKLE
FLIMSY
SCANTY
SLIGHT

7 letters
BUOYANT
FRAGILE
SHADOWY
TRIVIAL

8 letters
ETHEREAL
GOSSAMER
NUGATORY
TRIFLING

9 letters
WORTHLESS

10 letters
WEIGHTLESS

Footwear

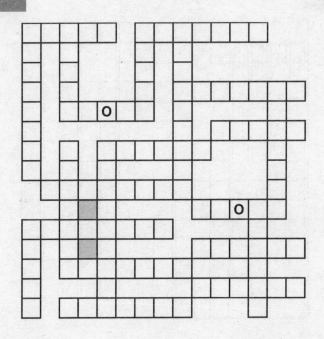

5 letters
BOOTS
CLOGS
FLATS
MULES
PUMPS
SHOES
SOCKS

6 letters
SABOTS
SKATES

TIGHTS
WEDGES

7 letters
CASUALS
HOSIERY
LACE-UPS
LOAFERS
PATTENS
SANDALS

8 letters
GALOSHES
PEEP-TOES
SNEAKERS

9 letters
STILETTOS
STOCKINGS

Feline Friends

3 letters
TOM

4 letters
CUTE
MANX
PAWS
TAIL

5 letters
CLAWS
FELIX
FLEAS

HAIRS
MOUSE
QUEEN

6 letters
BASKET
CATNIP
COLLAR
GINGER
NEPETA

7 letters
CATFLAP

FUR BALL
MOGGIES
SINGING

8 letters
FOOD BOWL
GARFIELD

9 letters
MARMALADE
NINE LIVES

Harvest Home

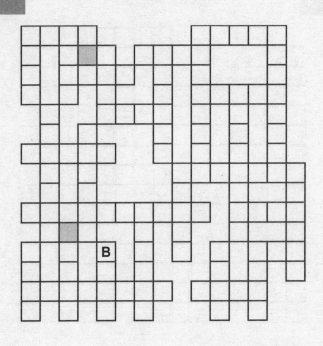

3 letters
RYE

4 letters
BALE
BARN
BEET
CART
CROP
FARM
HOPS
HUSK
LOAF
MILL
REAP

RIPE
SACK
SILO

5 letters
FEAST
FIELD
FRUIT
TITHE

6 letters
APPLES
BARLEY
BINDER
SUPPER

7 letters
BERRIES
FLOWERS

8 letters
CHERRIES
FESTIVAL
TEAMWORK
THRESHER

10 letters
VEGETABLES

Made of Paper

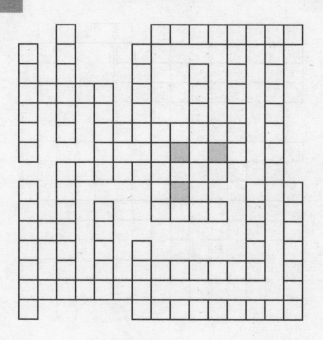

3 letters
CUP

4 letters
BILL
NOTE

5 letters
BOOKS
CHAIN
LABEL
PHOTO

PLANE
TOWEL

6 letters
FLOWER
LETTER

7 letters
COLLAGE
INVOICE
LEAFLET
PARASOL

RECEIPT
WRAPPER

8 letters
BROCHURE
DOCUMENT
ENVELOPE
PAMPHLET

9 letters
LAMPSHADE
WALLPAPER

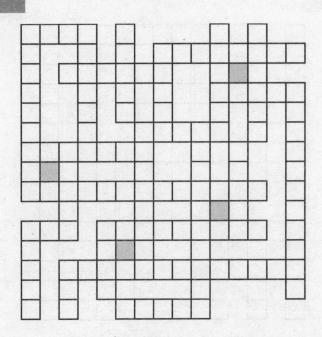

3 letters
BET
BIG

4 letters
BULB
BUOY

5 letters
BEANS
BIBLE
BIDET
BIRDS
BLURB
BLURT

BOXER
BRIBE

6 letters
BAMBOO
BLOUSE
BOBBLE

7 letters
BLANKET
BOBTAIL

8 letters
BLOCKADE
BROOKLYN

9 letters
BEELZEBUB
BRATWURST

10 letters
BINOCULARS

11 letters
BUCKTOOTHED

13 letters
BIDIRECTIONAL
BIODE-
   GRADABLE

Camping Trip

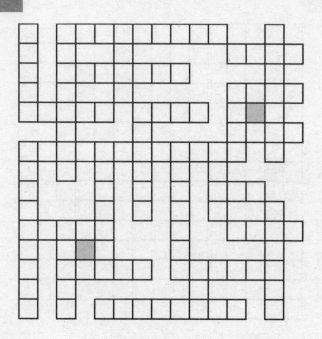

3 letters
AXE
OIL

4 letters
FIRE
MAPS
MATS
POTS
RAIN
SITE
TENT
WOOD

5 letters
PITCH
POLES
ROPES
STOVE
TORCH

6 letters
NATURE
STAKES
STREAM

7 letters
HATCHET
LANTERN

PROPANE
TRAILER

8 letters
FLYSHEET
OUTDOORS

9 letters
MOUNTAINS
OVERNIGHT

12 letters
MARSH-
  MALLOWS

Compost Heap

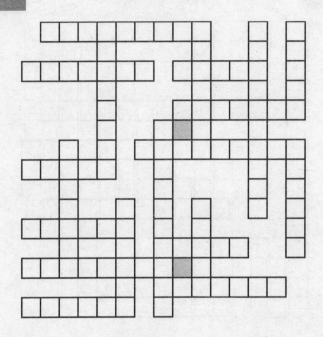

5 letters
EARTH
GRASS
PAPER
STRAW
WORMS

6 letters
DEBRIS
LEAVES
MANURE
SCRAPS

7 letters
BERRIES
FLOWERS
ORGANIC
SAWDUST
SEAWEED

8 letters
BACTERIA
PEELINGS

9 letters
CLIPPINGS
WOOD CHIPS

10 letters
BONFIRE ASH
FERTILISER

Farm Animals

4 letters
CATS
DOGS
EWES
KIDS
PIGS
RAMS
SOWS

5 letters
BOARS
BULLS

DUCKS
FOALS
GEESE
GOATS
LAMBS
SHEEP

6 letters
CALVES
CATTLE
CHICKS
DRAKES

HORSES
LLAMAS
PONIES

7 letters
GANDERS

8 letters
CHICKENS

9 letters
COCKERELS

Hello, Hello, Hello

4 letters
CIAO
HIYA
HOLA
S'MAE

5 letters
ALOHA
HELLO
HOWDY
SALVE

6 letters
HOLLOA
SALAAM
SHALOM

7 letters
BONJOUR
GOOD DAY
WELCOME

8 letters
GUTEN TAG

9 letters
GREETINGS
GRUSS GOTT

10 letters
BUON GIORNO
HOW-DO-YOU-DO

11 letters
GOOD EVENING

Distances

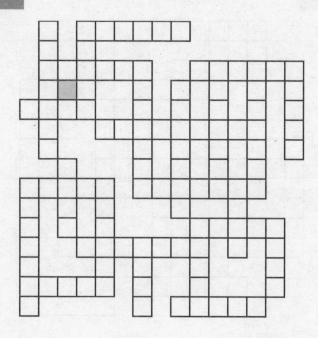

4 letters
FOOT
MILE
ROOD
SIZE
YARD

5 letters
CHAIN
CUBIT
LIMIT
METRE

REACH
RULER
SPACE

6 letters
EXTENT
FATHOM
LEAGUE
REMOTE

7 letters
ACREAGE
BREADTH
EXPANSE
EXTREME
FURLONG
HECTARE
MEASURE
STRETCH

9 letters
PLACEMENT

Household Items

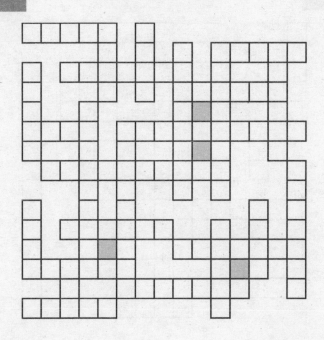

3 letters
RUG

4 letters
BOWL
DESK
LAMP
OVEN
SOFA

5 letters
CHEST
CLOCK
LIGHT

PIANO
STOOL

6 letters
CARPET
CARVER
LARDER
MIRROR

7 letters
DRESSER
OTTOMAN
TALLBOY
WHATNOT

8 letters
ARMCHAIR
CURTAINS

9 letters
DAVENPORT
HALLSTAND

10 letters
DISHWASHER
TELEVISION

Islands

3 letters
KOS
MAN

4 letters
EIGG
ELBA
GOZO
GUAM
JAVA
MAUI
MULL
RHUM

5 letters
ARUBA
LUZON
MALTA
NAXOS
WIGHT

6 letters
AZORES
DJERBA
LESBOS
SICILY
STATEN
UNIMAK

7 letters
ICELAND
PALAWAN

8 letters
BARLOCCO
GUERNSEY
KANGAROO

9 letters
ELLESMERE
NANTUCKET

Moons of the Solar System

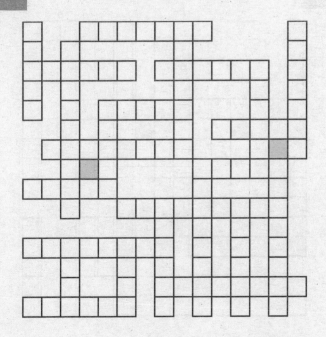

4 letters
LEDA
RHEA

5 letters
ARIEL
ATLAS
CUPID
JANUS
SKOLL
TITAN

6 letters
BIANCA
CHARON
DEIMOS
OBERON
PHOBOS
SKATHI

7 letters
CYLLENE
FORNJOT
OPHELIA

8 letters
AMALTHEA
CALLISTO
CORDELIA
DYSNOMIA
ORTHOSIE

9 letters
DESDEMONA
ENCELADUS

Pairs

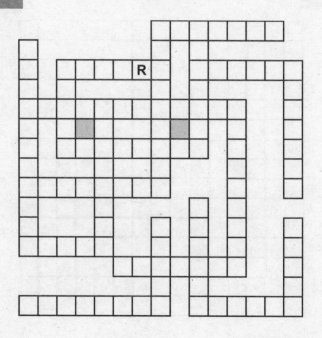

5 letters
BOOTS
PANTS
SOCKS
SPURS

6 letters
PLIERS
SHEARS
SHORTS
TIGHTS

7 letters
CYMBALS
MITTENS
PINCERS
SANDALS

8 letters
SCISSORS
SLIPPERS
TROUSERS
TWEEZERS

9 letters
CASTANETS
STOCKINGS

11 letters
WELLINGTONS

12 letters
LOUD-
SPEAKERS

Saints' Names

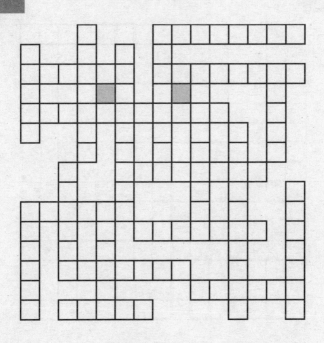

5 letters
ASAPH
BARBE
CLARA

6 letters
ANDREA
FERGUS
JEROME
JOSEPH
MAURUS
MONICA

7 letters
AMBROSE
BERNARD
SWITHIN
URSANNE

8 letters
DAMIANUS
DONATIAN
IGNATIUS
NICHOLAS

9 letters
CHRISTINA
VALENTINE

10 letters
GAUDENTIUS

11 letters
BONA VENTURA

Rodents

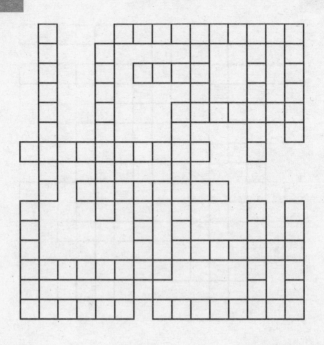

4 letters
CAVY

5 letters
COYPU

6 letters
AGOUTI
GOPHER
JERBOA
MARMOT

NUTRIA
RABBIT

7 letters
HAMSTER
LEVERET
MUSKRAT

8 letters
CAPYBARA
DORMOUSE

HEDGEHOG
MUSQUASH

9 letters
GROUNDHOG
PORCUPINE

10 letters
CHINCHILLA
FIELDMOUSE

Marine Life

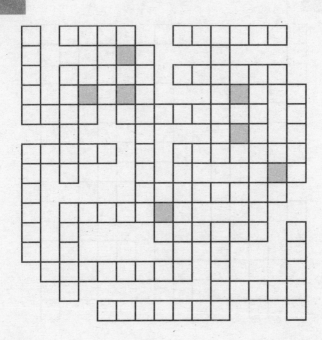

4 letters
CLAM
KELP
ORCA

5 letters
CONCH
CORAL
KRILL
LAVER
MUREX
SHARK
SQUID

WHALE
WHELK

6 letters
COCKLE
LIMPET
SHRIMP
WALRUS
WINKLE

7 letters
ABALONE
ANEMONE

MANATEE
NARWHAL

8 letters
BARNACLE
PLANKTON
SEAHORSE

9 letters
JELLYFISH
LANGOUSTE

63

Keep in Touch

4 letters
CALL
TALK
TEXT

5 letters
GREET
ORATE
SPEAK
UTTER
WRITE

6 letters
ANSWER
CHAT TO
CONVEY
GOSSIP
LETTER
LIAISE

7 letters
ADDRESS
COMMUNE
ENQUIRE

8 letters
CONVERSE
EXCHANGE
INTERACT
QUESTION

9 letters
TELEPHONE

11 letters
COMMUNICATE

Palindromes

4 letters
DEED
OTTO
PEEP
SEES

5 letters
MADAM
PUT UP
RADAR
ROTOR
SEXES
SHAHS

STATS
TENET

6 letters
REDDER

7 letters
RACE CAR
REVIVER

9 letters
EVIL OLIVE
LATE METAL

NURSES RUN
SEVEN EVES

11 letters
SEE REFEREES

12 letters
PUPILS SLIP UP

13 letters
RISE TO VOTE
  SIR
SENILE FELINES

Musical Instruments

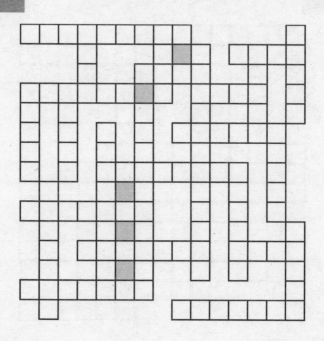

4 letters
BELL
DRUM
LUTE
MOOG
OBOE
TUBA

5 letters
BUGLE
CELLO
ORGAN
REBEC

TABOR
VIOLA

6 letters
CORNET
RATTLE
VIOLIN

7 letters
CELESTA
CLAPPER
CLAVIER
MARIMBA
PICCOLO

8 letters
RECORDER

9 letters
KEYBOARDS
VIRGINALS

10 letters
CONCERTINA

12 letters
HAMMOND
 ORGAN

Full of Fruit

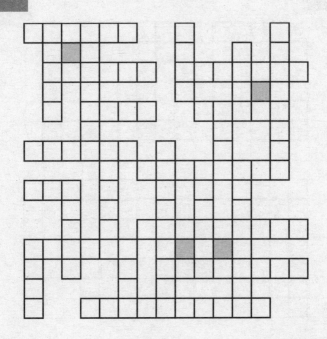

3 letters
FIG

4 letters
AKEE
DATE
KIWI
LIME
PEAR
UGLI

5 letters
APPLE
GRAPE
OLIVE

6 letters
BANANA
CHERRY
PAPAYA
PAWPAW
POMELO
QUINCE

7 letters
PUMPKIN
TANGELO

8 letters
BILBERRY
MULBERRY

PLANTAIN
RAMBUTAN

9 letters
CARAMBOLA
PINEAPPLE

10 letters
CLEMENTINE

In Flight

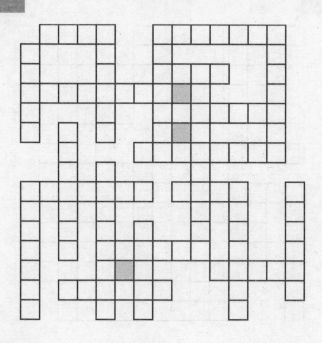

4 letters
CREW
GATE
MEAL

5 letters
AISLE
CABIN
PILOT

6 letters
BRIDGE
LOCKER
PILLOW
WINDOW

7 letters
ARRIVAL
BAGGAGE
BLANKET
CHECK-IN
LANDING

TAKE-OFF
TICKETS
TROLLEY

8 letters
BOARDING
SEAT BELT
SECURITY

10 letters
TURBULENCE

Perfect Puzzle

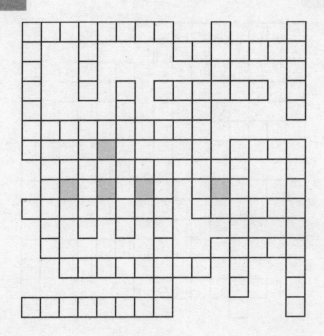

4 letters
FINE
PURE
TRUE

5 letters
CLEAR
MODEL
SHEER

6 letters
ENTIRE
EXPERT

SUPERB

7 letters
CORRECT
PRECISE
SKILFUL

8 letters
ABSOLUTE
COMPLETE
PEERLESS
TEXTBOOK
THOROUGH

ULTIMATE
UNMARRED

9 letters
EXCELLENT

10 letters
CONSUMMATE

11 letters
SUPERLATIVE

London Underground

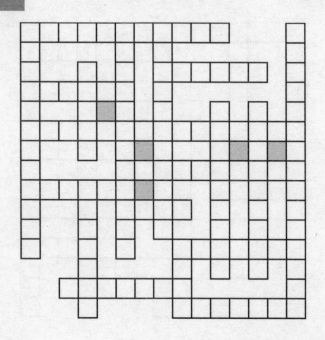

4 letters
BANK
OVAL

5 letters
UPNEY

6 letters
EPPING
PINNER
TEMPLE

7 letters
BARKING

BECKTON
KILBURN
NEASDEN

9 letters
EAST INDIA
STRATFORD

10 letters
NORTH ACTON

11 letters
PRESTON ROAD
WEMBLEY PARK

12 letters
ELVERSON
 ROAD
WEST
 BROMPTON

15 letters
RAVENSCOURT
 PARK
SOUTH
 KENSINGTON

Our Favourite Things

4 letters
CATS
DOGS

5 letters
CAKES
CANDY

6 letters
GRANNY
HORSES
SWEETS

7 letters
FLOWERS
INCENSE
KITTENS
SEAFOOD
WALKING

8 letters
DIAMONDS
GOOD FOOD
WEDDINGS

9 letters
CHAMPAGNE
CHRISTMAS
OPEN FIRES
SURPRISES

10 letters
TELEVISION

11 letters
SANDCASTLES

Nursery Words

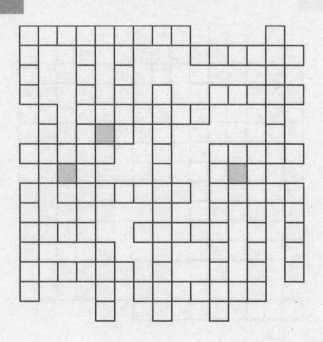

4 letters
COTS
PRAM
TEAT
TOYS

5 letters
COLIC
DRINK
NAPPY
POTTY
PUREE
SLEEP

6 letters
BOTTLE
CUDDLE
LOTION
RATTLE

7 letters
BEDTIME
BLANKET
LULLABY
WEANING

8 letters
TEETHING

9 letters
PUSHCHAIR
TEDDY BEAR

11 letters
DEVELOPMENT

12 letters
TALCUM
  POWDER

Making Movies

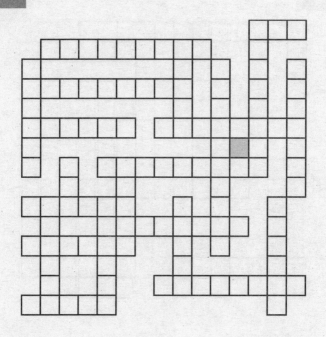

3 letters
CUT
SET

5 letters
ACTOR
BUYER
EXTRA
PROPS

6 letters
ARTIST
GAFFER
LOADER
MAKE-UP
PROMPT
READER
SCENES

7 letters
STAND-IN

8 letters
CABLEMAN
COSTUMER
PRODUCER
STUNTMAN

9 letters
BIT PLAYER
CAMERAMAN
RECORDIST

10 letters
MOULD MAKER

Time for Bed

4 letters
BATH
COSY
LAMP
REST
YAWN

5 letters
COCOA
QUILT
RELAX

6 letters
DOZING
DROWSY
PILLOW
SLEEPY
SNOOZE

7 letters
LULLABY
PRAYERS
PYJAMAS
SNORING
WASHING

8 letters
MATTRESS

9 letters
UNDRESSED

10 letters
ALARM CLOCK
NIGHTDRESS

Round Objects

3 letters
ORB
WOK

4 letters
BOWL
DISH
DOME
HOOP
TYRE

5 letters
BERET
PENNY

PIZZA
PLATE
QUOIT
TOKEN
WHEEL

6 letters
BANGLE
GIRDLE
HUB-CAP
TABLET

7 letters
BISCUIT

CYMBALS
EARRING
FRISBEE
LENS CAP
LETTER 'O'
MONOCLE

8 letters
PLANCHET

10 letters
TAMBOURINE

The Nobility

4 letters
DUKE
EARL
RANK

5 letters
BARON
LAIRD
REALM
ROYAL
TITLE

6 letters
ESTATE
GENTRY
LADIES
NOBLES
PALACE
PRINCE
THRONE

7 letters
DYNASTY
KINGDOM

MAJESTY
PAGEANT
STATELY

8 letters
CEREMONY
MARQUESS

9 letters
ETIQUETTE

Trucks and Vans

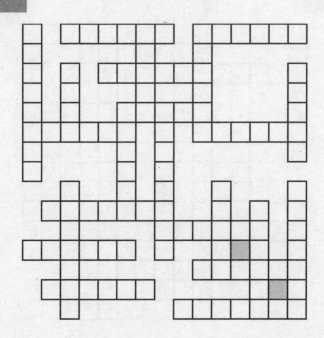

4 letters
JEEP

5 letters
DODGE
ISUZU
IVECO
RHINO

6 letters
COMMER
DENNIS

DUCATO
ESPACE
RASCAL
SCANIA
SHERPA
SHOGUN
SUZUKI
THAMES
TRAFIC
VITARA

7 letters
BEDFORD
BRISTOL
LEYLAND
TRANSIT

8 letters
DAIHATSU
SCAMMELL

Silent 'G'

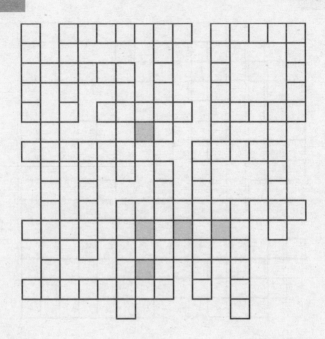

5 letters
COIGN
DEIGN
FEIGN
GNASH
GNOME
MIGHT
NEIGH

6 letters
ASSIGN
ENSIGN

GNOSIS
HIGHER
RIGHTS
SLEIGH
SLIGHT

7 letters
COLOGNE
CONSIGN
GNARLED
SIGNING

SYNTAGM
THOUGHT

8 letters
FIGHTING
STRAIGHT

9 letters
FORTNIGHT

10 letters
APOPHTHEGM

Motoring

3 letters
CAR

4 letters
BOOT
GEAR
SUMP

5 letters
AMBER
CHOKE
CRASH

6 letters
BYPASS
CLUTCH
CORNER
DIESEL
DRIVER
LIGHTS
SIGNAL

7 letters
CHASSIS
EXHAUST
LICENCE

PARKING
TRAFFIC
TURNING

8 letters
JUNCTION
MECHANIC

10 letters
CRANKSHAFT
SUSPENSION

How Are You Feeling?

4 letters
DOWN
GLUM
LAZY
WARM

5 letters
HAPPY
MOODY

6 letters
DISMAL
DREARY

GLOOMY
JOVIAL
SOMBRE
SULLEN

7 letters
AMIABLE
EXCITED
FRETFUL
MAUDLIN
SUBDUED
TEARFUL

8 letters
FRIENDLY
MOURNFUL
PETULANT

9 letters
IRRITABLE

11 letters
DISGRUNTLED

Items of Clothing

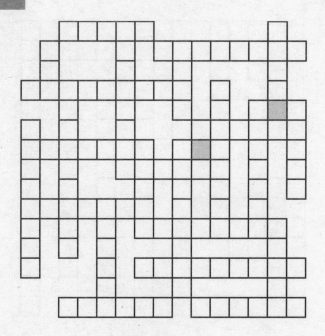

3 letters
HAT

4 letters
SARI
VEST

5 letters
BOOTS
JEANS
SHIRT
SKIRT

6 letters
BLOUSE
FEDORA
SHORTS
TABARD
TIGHTS

7 letters
MUFFLER
SWEATER
WARMERS

8 letters
GALOSHES
OVERCOAT
SWIMSUIT
TRAINERS
TROUSERS
WRAPOVER

9 letters
DRESS SUIT
OVERDRESS
STOCKINGS

Hobbies and Pastimes

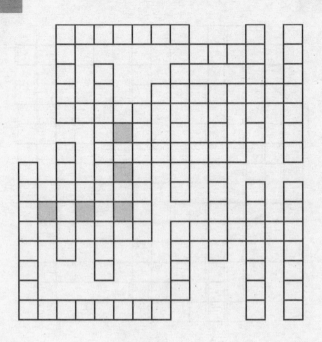

4 letters
JUDO
YOGA

5 letters
CHESS
MUSIC

6 letters
CAVING
SKIING

7 letters
DANCING
FISHING
JIGSAWS
JU-JITSU
MACRAME
ORIGAMI
SAILING
SINGING
WEAVING

8 letters
JUGGLING
KNITTING
SKITTLES
WOODWORK

9 letters
GENEALOGY

11 letters
DRESSMAKING

Shades of Blue

3 letters
SKY

4 letters
BABY
DARK
NAVY
TEAL
TRUE

5 letters
ALICE
AZURE

LIGHT
ROYAL
TUFTS

6 letters
BRIGHT
COBALT
OXFORD
POWDER
PURPLE

7 letters
CELESTE

TIFFANY

8 letters
EGYPTIAN
ELECTRIC
PRUSSIAN
SAPPHIRE

9 letters
TURQUOISE

11 letters
ULTRAMARINE

Under the Ground

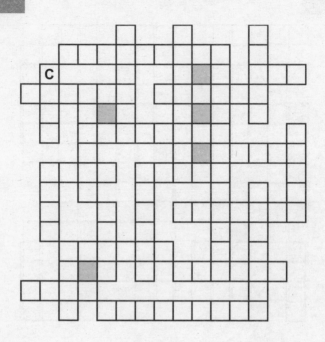

3 letters
OIL

4 letters
CAVE
COAL
CORM
GOLD
WELL
WORM

5 letters
CRYPT
RIVER

ROOTS
TUBER

6 letters
BUNKER
CELLAR
FOSSIL
RABBIT
SUBWAY
TUNNEL
WARREN

7 letters
CONDUIT

CULVERT

8 letters
BOREHOLE
CATACOMB

9 letters
MINESHAFT
UNDERPASS

12 letters
SUBTER-
RANEAN

Girls' Names

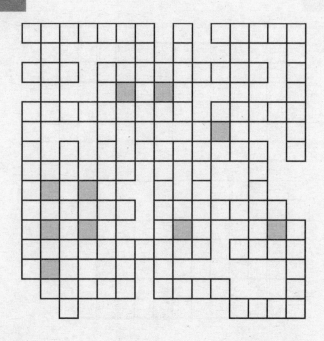

3 letters
NIA
ZOE

4 letters
DAWN
ROMA
ZENA

5 letters
AGNES
ANITA
OLIVE
RHODA

VIOLA
WANDA

6 letters
AMELIA
ELAINE
SHARON

7 letters
ABIGAIL
ARIADNE
CANDICE
FRANCES
GILLIAN

SABRINA
SHELAGH

8 letters
ROSALIND

9 letters
CATHERINE
CONSTANCE
GABRIELLE
MADELEINE

10 letters
CLEMENTINE
GWENDOLINE

Floral Clock

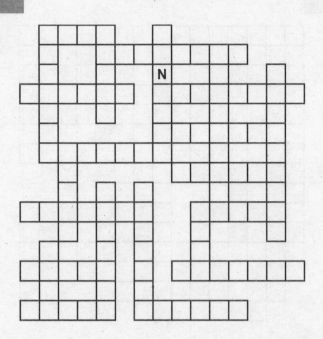

4 letters
MOSS
SAGE
TIME

5 letters
HANDS
HERBS
SEDUM
SLOPE
THYME

6 letters
FORMAL
SALVIA
TULIPS

7 letters
ALYSSUM
LOBELIA
MINUTES
NUMBERS
PANSIES
SHAPING

TENDING
WEEDING

8 letters
DIVISION
LAVENDER

9 letters
EDINBURGH
HOUSE LEEK

'C' Words

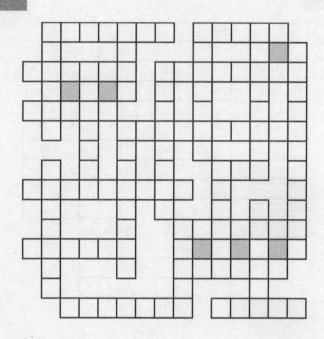

3 letters
COY

4 letters
CYST

5 letters
CACHE
CAULK
CLOCK
CURVE

6 letters
CAESAR

CEREAL
CHEESE
CORPSE
CRAVEN
CROCUS

7 letters
CAPTAIN
CELLIST
CERTAIN
CODICIL
COTERIE
CYANIDE

8 letters
CEREBRAL
CEREMONY
CLIMBING
COLANDER

9 letters
COSTUMIER

10 letters
CLAVICHORD

11 letters
CLANDESTINE

Breakfast Menu

3 letters
EGG
JAM
TEA

5 letters
BACON
BREAD
HONEY
TOAST

6 letters
BAGELS

CEREAL
COFFEE
MUFFIN
YOGURT

7 letters
KIPPERS
SAUSAGE

8 letters
KEDGEREE
ROAST HAM
TOMATOES

9 letters
CROISSANT

10 letters
BAKED BEANS
CORNFLAKES

12 letters
BLACK
  PUDDING

Electrical Appliances

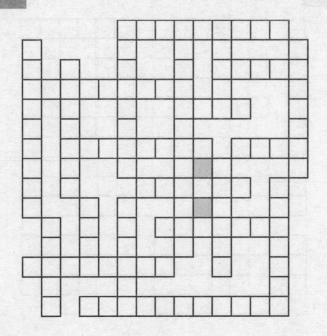

4 letters
FIRE
IRON
LAMP

5 letters
CLOCK
DRILL
RADIO

6 letters
GUITAR

HEATER
KETTLE

7 letters
BLANKET
CHARGER
FOOT SPA
IONISER

8 letters
COMPUTER
HI-FI UNIT

STRIMMER

9 letters
COFFEE POT
FOOD MIXER
HAIRDRYER

11 letters
SCREWDRIVER

12 letters
REFRIGERATOR

Films

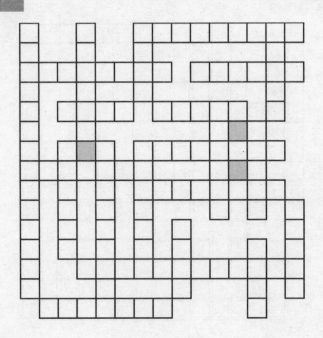

4 letters
DUNE
FAME
TMNT
ZULU

5 letters
BABEL
RAMBO
SHAFT
TOMMY

6 letters
BEN-HUR

HARVEY
TOP GUN
ZODIAC

7 letters
HOT FUZZ
RAIN MAN
SHAMPOO

8 letters
AIRPLANE
HIGH NOON
THE MUMMY

9 letters
DEATH WISH
SPIDER-MAN

12 letters
AMAZING
GRACE

14 letters
BLAZING
SADDLES

Goddesses

5 letters
DIANA
DURGA
FREYA
FRIGG
IRENE
VENUS
VESTA

6 letters
ATHENE
AURORA

HECATE
HESTIA
ISHTAR

7 letters
ARIADNE
ASTARTE
DEMETER
MINERVA
PANDORA
SALACIA

8 letters
MORRIGAN
PERTUNDA

9 letters
KUNDALINI

10 letters
AMPHITRITE

House…

4 letters
BOAT
CALL
COAT
LEEK
MAID
ROOM
WIFE
WORK

5 letters
BOUND

CRAFT
MATES
MOUSE
PARTY
PLANT
SNAKE

6 letters
ARREST
KEEPER
MASTER

7 letters
BUILDER
CLEANER
PAINTER
SPARROW
SURGEON
TRAILER
WARMING

8 letters
BREAKING

It's So Hot

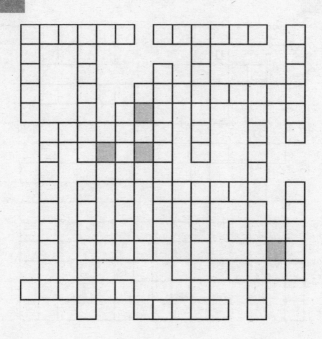

4 letters
KILN
LAVA

5 letters
ASHES
COALS
FORGE
GRILL
ONION
STEAM

6 letters
DESERT
HEARTH
PEPPER
RADISH
SUMMER

7 letters
BONFIRE
FURNACE
INFERNO
MUSTARD

PAPRIKA
TROPICS

8 letters
RADIATOR

9 letters
FIREPLACE
MICROWAVE

10 letters
FIRE ENGINE

Double 'P'

5 letters
APPLE
GUPPY
POPPY
PUPPY
ZIPPY

6 letters
APPEAL
APPEAR
COPPER
KIPPER

NIPPLE
OPPOSE
SUPPLE
YIPPEE

7 letters
CLIPPER
GRAPPLE
STEPPED
TOPPLED

8 letters
APPARENT
LIPPIEST
SHOPPING

9 letters
KIDNAPPER

11 letters
APPROPRIATE

New Year

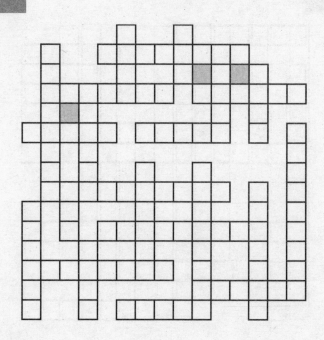

3 letters
EVE
JIG

4 letters
DRAM
REEL
WINE

5 letters
CLOCK
HAPPY
PARTY

TOAST

6 letters
CHIMES
FUTURE
SPIRIT
WHISKY
WISHES

7 letters
FUN TIME
NEW YEAR

8 letters
GOOD LUCK
HANGOVER
MIDNIGHT
STREAMER

9 letters
COUNTDOWN
FIREWORKS

10 letters
RESOLUTION

Pub Names

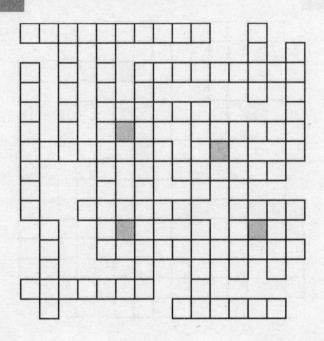

4 letters
BULL
LAMB
SHIP

5 letters
ANGEL
CROWN
EAGLE

6 letters
ALBION
ANCHOR
BEACON

CASTLE
NEW INN
PLOUGH

7 letters
OAK TREE
RED LION

8 letters
BLUE BOAR
GREEN MAN
TOWN GATE

9 letters
RIVERSIDE

10 letters
CROSS FOXES

11 letters
DROVER'S
 ARMS

12 letters
ROSE AND
 CROWN
SARACEN'S
 HEAD

Fractions

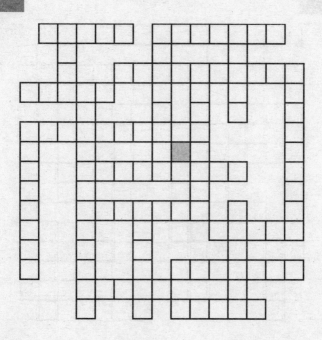

4 letters
HALF

5 letters
FIFTH
MIXED
NINTH
SIXTH
TENTH
THIRD

6 letters
EIGHTH
SIMPLE

7 letters
COMPARE
QUARTER
SEVENTH

8 letters
ELEVENTH
QUOTIENT
SIXTIETH

9 letters
HUNDREDTH
TWENTIETH

10 letters
EQUIVALENT
THOUSANDTH

12 letters
THIRTY-
  SECOND

Fire

4 letters
FUEL
GLOW
HEAT

5 letters
ARSON
ASHES
BLAST
BLAZE
SMOKE

6 letters
ALIGHT
EMBERS
FUMING
SPARKS

7 letters
BURNING
CRACKLE
FURNACE
IGNITED
INFERNO

8 letters
KINDLING
SCORCHED

10 letters
INCENDIARY

11 letters
DESTRUCTION

In the Shed

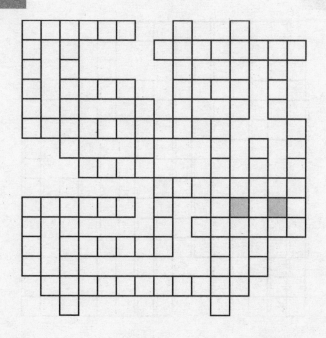

4 letters
BAGS
HOSE
MICE
POTS
RAKE
SACK
TRUG

5 letters
MOWER

6 letters
BOWSAW
BUCKET
DIBBER
HAMMER
LABELS
LADDER
OILCAN
TROWEL

7 letters
CHOPPER
TOOLBOX

8 letters
BIRD FOOD
SAWHORSE

10 letters
WEEDKILLER

11 letters
BAMBOO
   CANES
WHEELBARROW

Ghosts

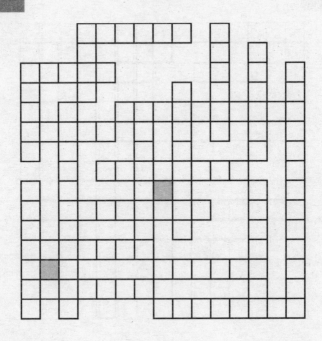

4 letters
SOUL

5 letters
GHOST
GHOUL
SPOOK

6 letters
SHADOW
SPIRIT
WRAITH

ZOMBIE

7 letters
BANSHEE
ESSENCE
PHANTOM
SPECTRE

8 letters
BOGEYMAN
HAUNTING
PRESENCE

REVENANT
VISITANT

10 letters
APPARITION

11 letters
POLTERGEIST

13 letters
MANIFESTATION

Coin Collection

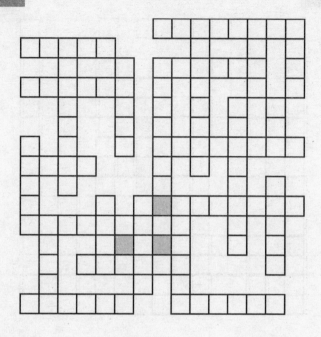

3 letters
SOU

4 letters
DIME
EURO
OBOL
REAL

5 letters
ANGEL
CROWN
DUCAT

GROAT
PENNY
POUND

6 letters
BEZANT
COPPER
FLORIN
GUINEA
ROUBLE
STATER

7 letters
GUILDER
SOLIDUS

8 letters
DENARIUS
FARTHING
NAPOLEON
SESTERCE
SHILLING

9 letters
DANDIPRAT

Countries of the World

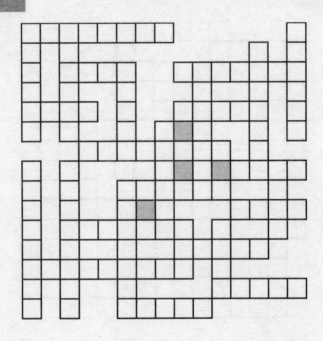

3 letters
USA

4 letters
GUAM
IRAN
IRAQ
LAOS
MALI
OMAN

5 letters
EGYPT
ITALY

NIGER
SPAIN
YEMEN

6 letters
BRAZIL
KUWAIT
RUSSIA
TAIWAN
UGANDA

7 letters
BELARUS
ENGLAND

ERITREA
URUGUAY
VANUATU

8 letters
BOTSWANA
MALDIVES
PORTUGAL
SLOVENIA

9 letters
VENEZUELA

Film Stars

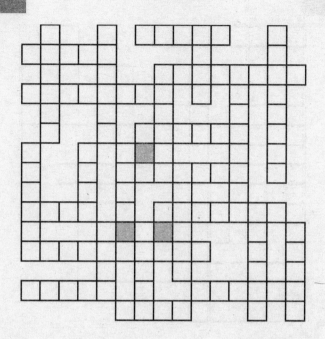

4 letters
CHOW
DEAN
DIAZ
GERE
PITT
WEST

5 letters
CHASE
CLOSE
FLYNN

FONDA
TANDY

6 letters
ATKINS
BENING
BOGART
CARREY
SNIPES
STREEP
WEAVER
WILLIS

7 letters
ANDREWS
HEPBURN

8 letters
BANCROFT
KINGSLEY
LAWRENCE
STALLONE

10 letters
SUTHERLAND

Indoor Games

4 letters
DICE
LUDO
POOL
SNAP

5 letters
CHESS
FIVES

6 letters
AIKIDO
BO-PEEP

BRIDGE
PELOTA
SEVENS

7 letters
CANASTA
MAH-JONG
MARBLES

8 letters
CHECKERS
PING-PONG
SCRABBLE

9 letters
BILLIARDS

10 letters
BASKETBALL

11 letters
TABLE TENNIS

13 letters
POSTMAN'S
KNOCK

Occupations

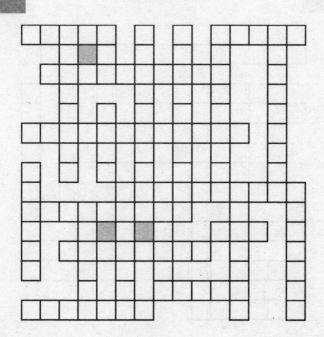

3 letters
NUN
VET

4 letters
CHEF

5 letters
BOSUN
BOXER
NURSE

6 letters
SAILOR
SEAMAN
TYPIST

7 letters
CLEANER
COURIER
REFEREE
RIVETER

8 letters
LINESMAN
SURVEYOR

9 letters
BARRISTER
EXECUTIVE
PLASTERER

10 letters
IRONMONGER
PROGRAMMER
RESEARCHER
SIGNWRITER

12 letters
PSYCHIATRIST

Diary Dates

3 letters
MAY

4 letters
JUNE
WEEK

5 letters
APRIL
MARCH
MONTH

6 letters
ADVENT
AUGUST
EASTER
FRIDAY
SHEBAT
SUNDAY

7 letters
HARVEST
TUESDAY
WHITSUN

8 letters
DECEMBER
EPIPHANY
FEBRUARY
SATURDAY

9 letters
LOW SUNDAY

12 letters
CHRISTMAS
DAY
CHRISTMAS
EVE

Geographical Features

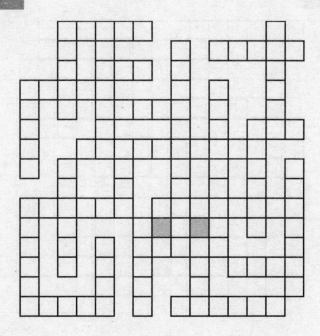

3 letters
SEA
TOR

4 letters
CAPE
HILL
LAKE
MOOR

5 letters
ATOLL
BEACH
BROOK
CANAL

CLIFF
DELTA
MARSH
OASIS
SHOAL

6 letters
CAVERN
DESERT
RAPIDS
RAVINE
STEPPE
STREAM

7 letters
ESTUARY
ISTHMUS

8 letters
CATARACT

9 letters
WATERFALL

10 letters
ESCARPMENT

11 letters
ARCHIPELAGO

Pirates

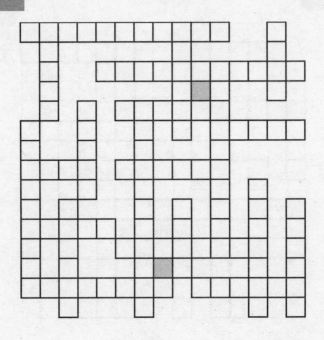

4 letters
GOLD
LOOT
SHIP

5 letters
BOOTY
CHEST
OCEAN
PLANK

6 letters
CANNON

JEWELS
PARROT
RAIDER
VESSEL
YO HO HO

7 letters
GALLEON

8 letters
EYE PATCH
KEELHAUL

9 letters
TELESCOPE

10 letters
HISPANIOLA

11 letters
BOTTLE OF
 RUM
EDWARD TEACH
SPANISH MAIN

Common Signs

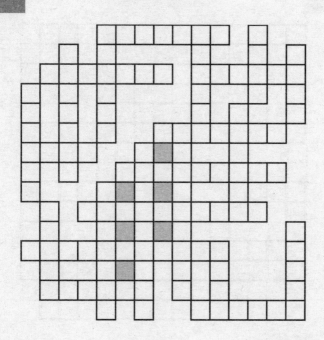

4 letters
HALT
SLOW
STOP
WALK

5 letters
BENDS
FLOOD

6 letters
DANGER
DETOUR

ONE WAY
POLICE
SCHOOL
STAIRS
UNSAFE

7 letters
CAUTION
DON'T RUN
FOR SALE
KEEP OFF
NO ENTRY

9 letters
DIVERSION
EMERGENCY
FIRE ALARM

10 letters
SALE AGREED

11 letters
GONE TO
LUNCH

All Together

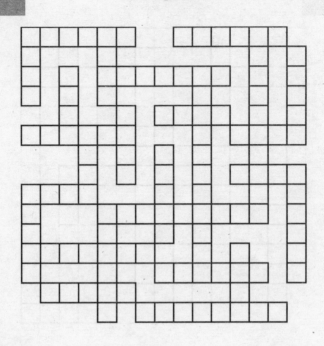

4 letters
BAND
CLUB
CREW
GANG
HEAP
HERD
MASS
PACK
TEAM
TUFT

5 letters
BATCH
CLUMP
PARTY
SHEAF

6 letters
BUNDLE
CLUTCH
GATHER
MUTUAL
STRING
TROUPE

7 letters
CLUSTER
COLLECT

8 letters
ASSEMBLE

9 letters
MULTITUDE

10 letters
CONGREGATE

11 letters
CONJUNCTION

Boys' Names

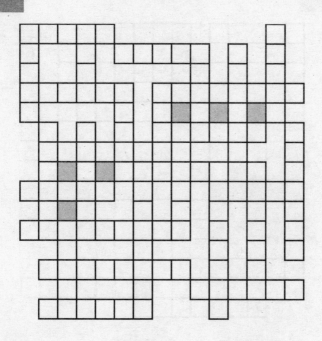

4 letters
OMAR

5 letters
BRIAN
CALEB
CLIVE
EDGAR
ENOCH
LANCE
LEROY
RAOUL
ROGER
WALLY

6 letters
ARNOLD
CEDRIC
ELIJAH
GARETH
GEORGE
GERALD
LIONEL

7 letters
ANTHONY
SOLOMON

8 letters
BARNABAS
BENJAMIN
EBENEZER
JONATHAN
REGINALD
RODERICK

9 letters
FERDINAND
ZACHARIAH

Cheeseboard

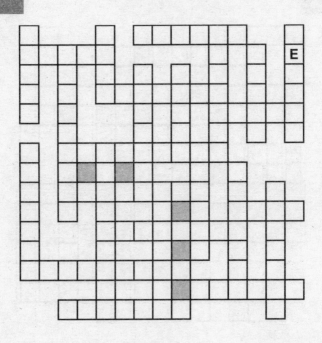

4 letters
EDAM
YARG

5 letters
CABOC
DERBY
QUARK
TEIFI
ULLOA

6 letters
COJACK
EMLETT
PROVEL
VENACO

7 letters
CABECOU
CHEDDAR
COTTAGE
GABRIEL
GRUYERE
GUBBEEN

IBERICO
TYN GRUG

8 letters
EMMENTAL
MUENSTER

9 letters
CAMEMBERT
LIMBURGER
RICHELIEU
ROQUEFORT

Countries of Africa

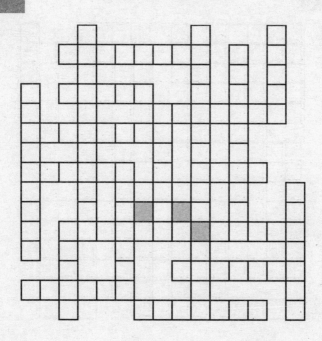

4 letters
CHAD
TOGO

5 letters
BENIN
GABON
KENYA
LIBYA
SUDAN

6 letters
ANGOLA
UGANDA

7 letters
ALGERIA
COMOROS
LESOTHO
NAMIBIA
NIGERIA
SENEGAL
TUNISIA

8 letters
BOTSWANA
ETHIOPIA

9 letters
THE GAMBIA

10 letters
MADAGASCAR
MAURITANIA

11 letters
COTE D'IVOIRE

Coughs and Sneezes

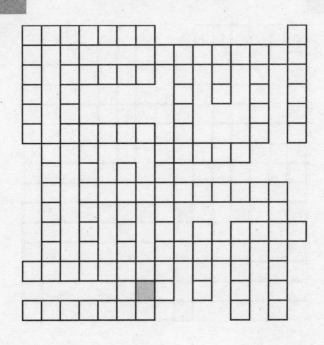

3 letters
FLU

4 letters
COLD
DUST

5 letters
CHILL
COUGH
HANKY
SMOKE

SYRUP
VIRUS

6 letters
ASTHMA
CHESTY
TROCHE
TUSSIS

7 letters
ALLERGY
CATARRH

HACKING
RED NOSE

8 letters
FEVERISH
HAY FEVER
HEADACHE
MEDICINE
REACTION

11 letters
IPECACUANHA

Early

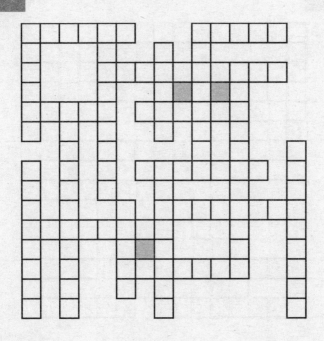

5 letters
FIRST
PRIOR
READY
YOUNG

6 letters
FORMER
FUTURE
UNRIPE

7 letters
SUNRISE
TOO SOON

8 letters
IMMATURE
IMMINENT
INCOMING
ORIGINAL
PREVIOUS

9 letters
EMBRYONIC
FORESTALL

10 letters
BEFOREHAND

11 letters
AHEAD OF TIME
APPROACHING

Flowing Things

3 letters
FOG
GAS
SAP
TAR

4 letters
BEER
LAVA
MIST
WINE

5 letters
BLOOD

CREAM
GRAVY
MAGMA
RIVER
SMOKE
STEAM
TIDES
WATER

6 letters
CLOUDS
GEYSER
PETROL
SALIVA

8 letters
FOUNTAIN
GASOLINE

9 letters
WHIRLPOOL

11 letters
ELECTRICITY

12 letters
VEGETABLE OIL

Hallowe'en

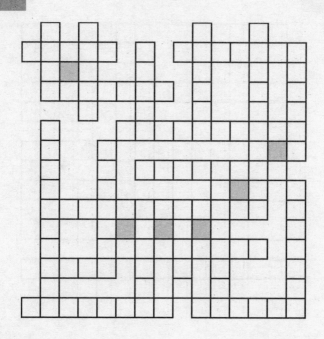

4 letters
BATS
IMPS

5 letters
EERIE
MAGIC
PAGAN
TOADS

6 letters
FLYING
OCCULT

POTION
SPELLS

7 letters
GOBLINS
SCARING
SPIDERS
WITCHES

8 letters
INITIATE
SPECTRAL
TALISMAN

9 letters
ENCHANTER

10 letters
DEMONIACAL
LEVITATION
WITCHCRAFT

12 letters
TRICK OR
  TREAT

Breadboard

3 letters
COB
RYE

4 letters
NAAN
OVEN
SALT

5 letters
BAGEL
BAKER
BOARD

BROWN
DOUGH
FLOUR
KNEAD
SAUCE
STICK
TOAST
WHEAT
WHITE

6 letters
CRUMBS
FRENCH

GARLIC
MILLER
RISING

7 letters
BRIOCHE
CROUTON

8 letters
CHAPATTI

9 letters
WHOLEMEAL

US States

4 letters
IOWA
OHIO
UTAH

5 letters
IDAHO
TEXAS

6 letters
ALASKA
HAWAII

NEVADA
OREGON

7 letters
FLORIDA
INDIANA

8 letters
ARKANSAS
DELAWARE
ILLINOIS
MISSOURI

9 letters
NEW JERSEY
NEW MEXICO
TENNESSEE

10 letters
CALIFORNIA

11 letters
MISSISSIPPI
NORTH DAKOTA

A Game of Chess

4 letters
KING
PAWN
ROOK

5 letters
BLACK
BOARD
BOX UP
MOVES
QUEEN
TEMPO
WHITE

6 letters
BISHOP
BYKOVA
CASTLE
GAMBIT

7 letters
FISCHER
KRAMNIK
SPASSKY
SQUARES

8 letters
KASPAROV

9 letters
CHECKMATE
EN PASSANT

10 letters
TOURNAMENT

Bingo

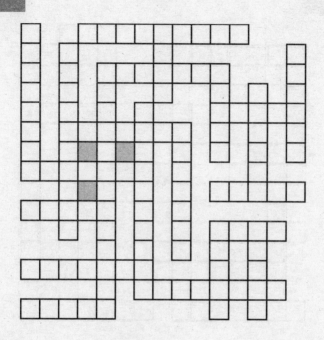

4 letters
HALL
LOST

5 letters
BLIND
BREAK
CARDS
LOTTO
MONEY
SHOUT
TABLE

6 letters
RANDOM
WINNER

7 letters
CALL OUT
NUMBERS
SEASIDE
SESSION
TICKETS

8 letters
NIGHT OUT

ON ITS OWN

9 letters
FULL HOUSE

10 letters
EXCITEMENT
LEGS ELEVEN

13 letters
CLICKETY-
CLICK

END at the End

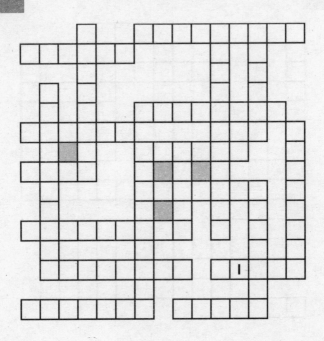

4 letters
WEND

5 letters
FIEND
TREND
UPEND

6 letters
ATTEND
DEPEND
EXTEND
INTEND

7 letters
CONTEND
DESCEND
PRETEND

8 letters
BEFRIEND
DIVIDEND
MISSPEND
REVEREND

9 letters
APPREHEND
RECOMMEND
TRANSCEND

10 letters
CONDESCEND

11 letters
SUPERINTEND

Double 'F'

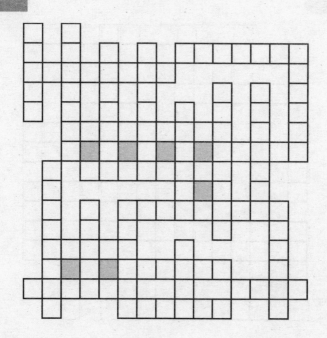

4 letters
DUFF
OFFA

5 letters
AFFIX
CLIFF
QUIFF
STAFF

6 letters
BAFFLE
COFFEE

EFFACE
EFFLUX
FLUFFY
REBUFF
SCOFFS

7 letters
BUFFALO
SHUFFLE
SNUFFED
SUFFICE
SUFFOLK

8 letters
AFFLUENT
OFFICIAL
PARAFFIN
WOODRUFF

9 letters
CHAUFFEUR
CUFFLINKS

In the Post

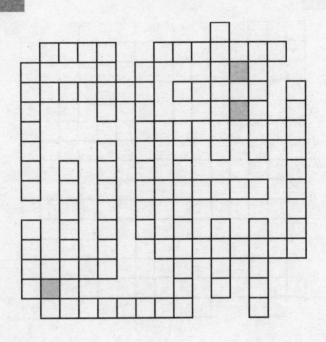

4 letters
BOOK
CARD
FORM
MAIL

5 letters
BILLS
OFFER
ORDER

6 letters
PARCEL

7 letters
INVOICE
LEAFLET
MISSIVE
PRESENT
RECEIPT
VOUCHER

8 letters
BROCHURE
MAGAZINE
REMINDER

9 letters
CATALOGUE
NEWSPAPER
STATEMENT

10 letters
ACCEPTANCE

In the Air

3 letters
FLY
FOG

4 letters
DUST
HAZE
KITE
MIST
MOTH
WIND

5 letters
AROMA
BLIMP
PLANE
SCENT
SMOKE
STEAM

6 letters
BREEZE
BUBBLE
OXYGEN
POLLEN
ZEPHYR

7 letters
BALLOON

8 letters
NITROGEN

9 letters
PARACHUTE

10 letters
HANG-GLIDER
HELICOPTER

Enough Is Enough

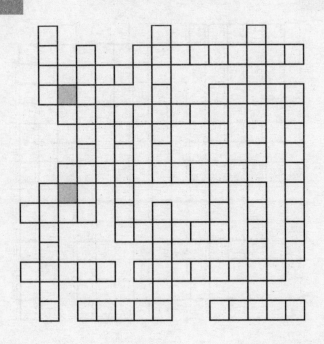

4 letters
FULL
WIDE

5 letters
AMPLE
BROAD
GREAT
LARGE
ROOMY

6 letters
GALORE
PLENTY

7 letters
LIBERAL
PROFUSE
RAMPANT
TEEMING

8 letters
ADEQUATE

ENORMOUS
EXTENDED

9 letters
EXTENSIVE
EXUBERANT
GRANDIOSE
UNSTINTED

10 letters
COMMODIOUS

Cycling

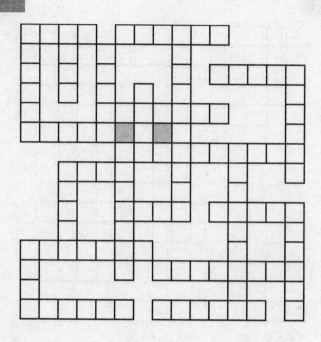

4 letters
BELL
CLIP
LOCK
NUTS
PUMP
SEAT

5 letters
BOLTS
CHAIN
GEARS

TYRES
WHEEL

6 letters
BASKET
HELMET
LEVERS
LIGHTS
PEDALS
SADDLE

7 letters
PANNIER

SPANNER
TOECLIP

8 letters
MUDGUARD

9 letters
INNER TUBE

10 letters
HANDLEBARS
STABILISER

Civil List

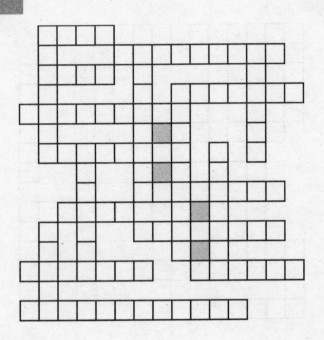

4 letters
GOOD
KIND
NICE

5 letters
SUAVE

6 letters
GENIAL
URBANE

7 letters
AFFABLE
AMIABLE
DUTIFUL
GALLANT
GENTEEL

8 letters
GRACIOUS
LADYLIKE
OBLIGING
WELL-BRED

9 letters
AGREEABLE
COURTEOUS
WELCOMING

12 letters
WELL-MANNERED

Brainbox

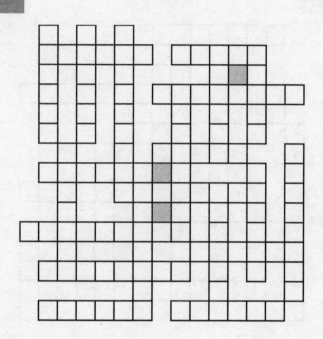

5 letters
ACUTE
LOBES
SKULL

6 letters
ACUMEN
BRAINY
BRIGHT
CLEVER
CORTEX
GENIUS

MEMORY
PINEAL
WISDOM

7 letters
BELIEVE
NOTIONS

8 letters
APTITUDE
DELIRIUM
PERCEIVE

RATIONAL
SAGACITY
STIMULUS

9 letters
BEHAVIOUR
SPECULATE

Back to School

4 letters
DESK
EXAM
KIDS
PASS

5 letters
GAMES
LATIN
LINES
MARKS
NOTES
SPORT
TESTS

6 letters
FRENCH
SHORTS

7 letters
ALGEBRA
MONITOR
OUTINGS
SCHOLAR
SPANISH
UNIFORM

8 letters
EXERCISE
REGISTER
SWOTTING

9 letters
DETENTION
SCHOOL BUS

12 letters
BUNSEN
BURNER

Dressmaking Pattern

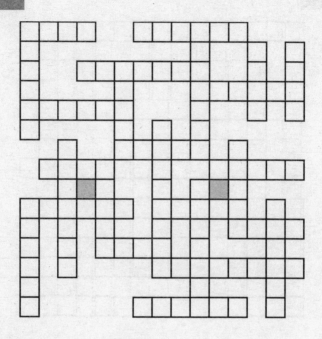

4 letters
EYES
LACE
PINS
SEAM
SILK
YARN

5 letters
CHALK
HOOKS
MODEL
REELS

SATIN
SPOOL

6 letters
BOBBIN
BUTTON
EDGING
FABRIC
NEEDLE
TAILOR
THREAD
ZIPPER

7 letters
FITTING
GARMENT
MACHINE
PATTERN

8 letters
SCISSORS
STITCHES

Card Games

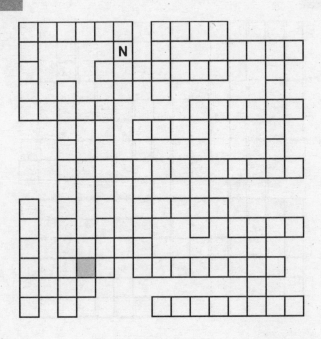

4 letters
BRAG
FARO
FISH
GRAB
SKAT
SNAP
SOLO

5 letters
BUNKO
DEMON
HI-LOW

RUMMY
WHIST

6 letters
BRIDGE
HEARTS
PIQUET
RED DOG

7 letters
CANASTA
PONTOON
STREETS

8 letters
GIN RUMMY
KLONDYKE

9 letters
TWENTY-ONE

12 letters
NINE-CARD
BRAG

13 letters
CONTRACT
WHIST

Birds

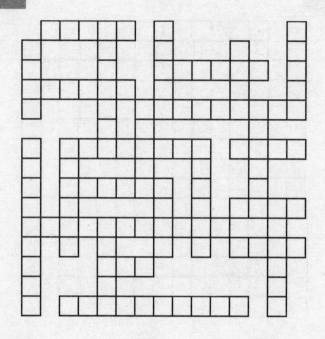

3 letters
AUK

4 letters
CROW
GULL
KITE
RHEA
ROOK
SWAN

5 letters
BOOBY
CRANE

GREBE
HERON
HOBBY

6 letters
AVOCET
BULBUL
CURLEW
DIPPER
LINNET
PLOVER
TURKEY

7 letters
BLUE TIT

8 letters
DOTTEREL

9 letters
DOWITCHER
GYRFALCON

10 letters
SHEARWATER

11 letters
TREE CREEPER

ARM First

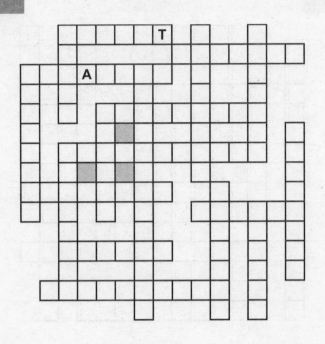

5 letters
ARMET

6 letters
ARMADA
ARMFUL
ARMING
ARMLET
ARMPIT

7 letters
ARMLESS
ARMORIC
ARMY ANT

8 letters
ARM CANDY
ARMAGNAC
ARMATURE
ARMCHAIR
ARMENIAN
ARMOURED

9 letters
ARMISTICE

10 letters
ARMAGEDDON

11 letters
ARMED FORCES

13 letters
ARMED
SERVICES

ALL Up Front

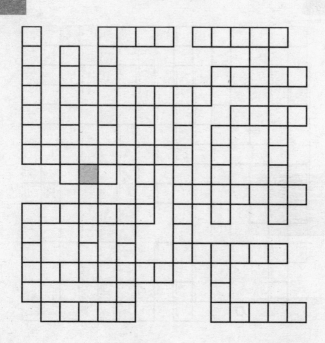

4 letters
EARS
STAR
TOLD

5 letters
ALONG
IN ALL
NIGHT
PARTY
RIGHT
SORTS

SPICE
YOURS

6 letters
AROUND
SEEING
THE WAY

7 letters
HALLOWS
PURPOSE
TELLING

THE BEST
THE SAME

8 letters
ELECTRIC
TIME HIGH
TOGETHER

9 letters
IMPORTANT
SYSTEMS GO

'D' Words

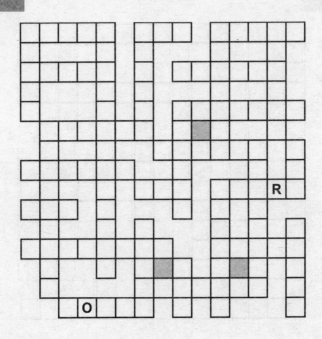

3 letters
DAB
DEW
DIP
DRY
DUO

5 letters
DADDY
DAIRY
DAISY
DEEDS
DODGE
DOLLS
DREAD

DUNES
DYING

6 letters
DAINTY
DAMPLY
DASHED
DIBBER
DRAGON
DRONES
DURESS

7 letters
DARKEST
DEBORAH

DIETING
DISDAIN

8 letters
DOMINOES
DRINKING

9 letters
DORMITORY

13 letters
DISCON-
    CERTING

Farming

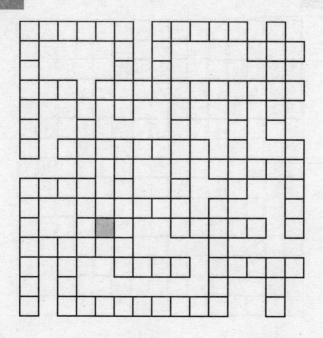

3 letters
EWE
RYE
SOW

4 letters
BYRE
CORN
EGGS
RAMS

5 letters
BARNS
DAIRY
GEESE

PEARS
SHEDS
SWINE

6 letters
APPLES
ARABLE
CALVES
CHEESE
FODDER
MEADOW

7 letters
ACREAGE
CHICKEN
MANAGER

8 letters
CHERRIES
DRAINAGE
FARMYARD

9 letters
SCARECROW

11 letters
INSECTICIDE

A Day at the Seaside

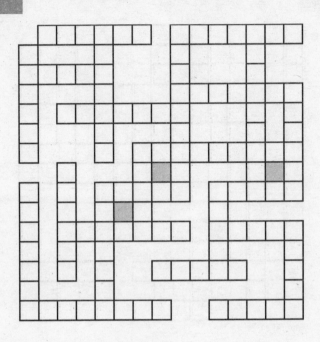

5 letters
BOATS
BRINY
INLET
POOLS
SPADE
SPRAY
TIDES
TOWEL
WAVES

6 letters
BIKINI
LIMPET
SHELLS
SUNBED

7 letters
BATHING
MUSSELS
PARASOL
PEBBLES
SANDALS

SHINGLE
SHRIMPS

8 letters
SOFT SAND

9 letters
BEACH-BALL
LIFEGUARD
PROMENADE

Cake Baking

4 letters
EGGS
SALT
TRAY

5 letters
CAKES
CREAM
FLOUR
FRUIT
ICING
MIXER

SPOON
SUGAR

6 letters
GRATER
RECIPE
SPONGE

7 letters
BEATING
FILLING
LOAF TIN

RAISINS
SPATULA
TESTING

8 letters
CURRANTS
DECORATE
SULTANAS

9 letters
PARCHMENT

The White Stuff

4 letters
GOLD
LIES
NILE
RICE

5 letters
BROOM
CEDAR
DWARF
MAGIC
NOISE
PAPER

SAUCE
SHARK
SHEEP
WATER

6 letters
CLOVER
FUNGUS
ORCHID
PEPPER
POTATO

7 letters
CURRANT
FEATHER
PUDDING

8 letters
ELEPHANT

9 letters
BLOOD CELL
CHOCOLATE
CORPUSCLE

Scotland

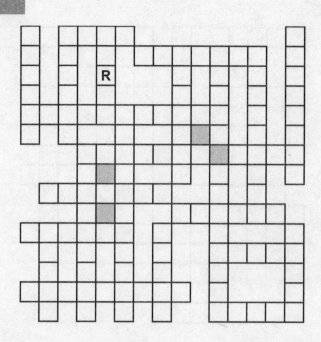

4 letters
FIFE
OBAN

5 letters
ANNAN
ARRAN
ISLAY
LEWIS
PERTH
RONAY
TIREE

6 letters
DUNDEE
HAWICK
ORKNEY
THURSO

7 letters
BORDERS
KINTYRE
LYBSTER
MELROSE

8 letters
BEN ALDER
DUMFRIES

9 letters
CAPE WRATH
KILNINVER
ROYBRIDGE

11 letters
BANNOCKBURN
SPEAN BRIDGE

Novelists

5 letters
BOWEN
HARDY
MARSH
SCOTT
SWIFT
WOOLF
YATES

6 letters
ARCHER
BARRIE
HUXLEY
LEASOR
MARTEL
SAYERS
SEWELL

7 letters
BAGNOLD
BECKETT

FRANCIS
HERBERT
LE CARRE
MITFORD
RUSHDIE

9 letters
STEINBECK
STEVENSON

Italy

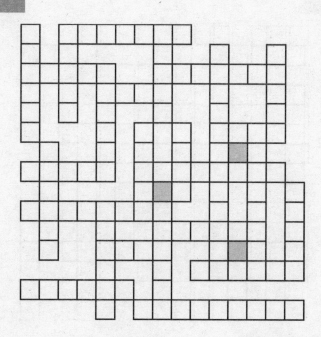

4 letters
ELBA
NOLE
PISA
ROME

5 letters
GENOA
MILAN
PADUA
PARMA
PIAVE
TIBER
TURIN

6 letters
ANCONA
MARCHE
MOLISE
NAPLES
PESCHE
RIMINI
TRENTO
VENICE

7 letters
BOLOGNA
TRIESTE

8 letters
BRINDISI
LA SPEZIA
PIEDMONT

9 letters
MONTE ROSA

12 letters
MONTE
  CERVINO

Names: G-I-R-L-S

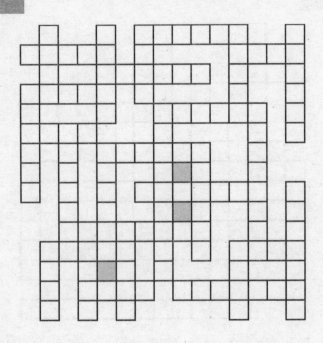

4 letters
GAIL
GWEN
IONA
IRIS
LILY
LISA
ROMA
RUBY

5 letters
LIBBY
LINDA
LYDIA

RHODA
ROSIE
SADIE
SARAH

6 letters
GLENYS
INGRID
ISABEL
LILIAN
LILITH
RACHEL
ROBINA
SANDRA

7 letters
GILLIAN
LYNETTE
SHELAGH
SHELLEY

8 letters
GRISELDA
SAMANTHA

9 letters
GABRIELLE

Names: B-O-Y-S

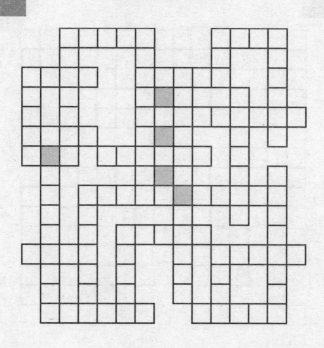

3 letters
YUL

4 letters
BART
OMAR
OWEN
SEAN
YVES

5 letters
BARRY
BASIL
BRETT

BRIAN
BRUCE
BRUNO
OSCAR
SHANE
SILAS
SIMON

6 letters
OLIVER
SAMUEL
SIDNEY
STEVEN

7 letters
BERTRAM
BRENDAN
STANLEY

8 letters
BARNABAS
BENJAMIN

9 letters
SEBASTIAN
SIEGFRIED

Have a Beer

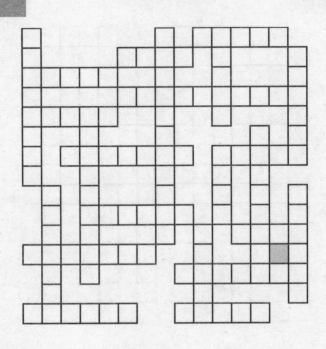

4 letters
HELL
HOPS
MALT

5 letters
ATLAS
BROWN
HOOKY
LAGER
LIGHT
STOUT
YEAST

6 letters
BARLEY
BITTER
PANAMA
TETLEY

7 letters
BOHEMIA
LAGONDA
PALE ALE
PILSNER

8 letters
GOLD BEST
SOBERANA

9 letters
WHITE BEER

10 letters
UNCUT AMBER

11 letters
SPECKLED HEN

Baseball Terms

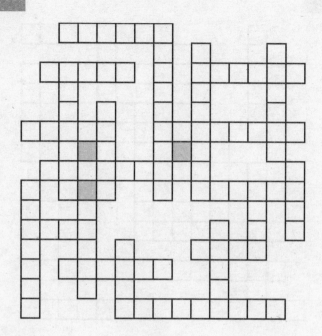

4 letters
BALK
FOUL
HITS
TEAM
WALK

5 letters
BASES
GLOVE
PLATE
STEAL
THROW

6 letters
DOUBLE
INNING
STRIKE
TRIPLE
UMPIRE

7 letters
HOME RUN
INFIELD

8 letters
OUTFIELD
SPITBALL

9 letters
CURVE BALL
GRAND SLAM
SHORTSTOP

Light Work

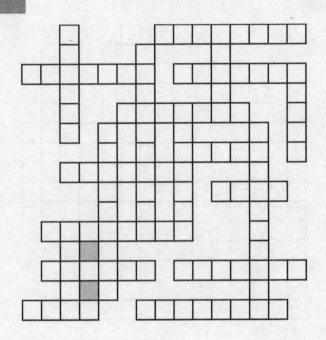

4 letters
AIRY
DAWN

5 letters
AFIRE
AGLOW
BLAZE
GLARE

6 letters
BRIGHT
GLANCE

7 letters
BEAMING
GLISTEN
GLITTER
SPARKLE
SUNRISE
TWINKLE

8 letters
DAYBREAK
ILLUMINE
RADIANCE

9 letters
BRILLIANT

10 letters
REFLECTION
REFRACTION

Stimulating

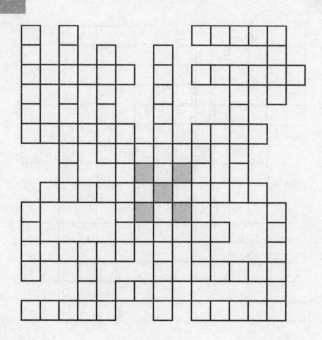

4 letters
GOAD
KICK
SPUR
URGE
WHET

5 letters
CHEER
IMPEL
RENEW
SHAKE
TEMPT

6 letters
AROUSE
AWAKEN
FOMENT
INCITE
INDUCE
KINDLE
PERK UP
PROMPT
REVIVE
STIR UP
WHIP UP

7 letters
ACTUATE
INFLAME
PROVOKE

8 letters
STIMULUS

9 letters
ENCOURAGE

Astronomical

4 letters
MARS
MOON
SUNS

5 letters
COMET
EARTH
EPOCH
ORBIT
ORION
PHASE
PLUTO
VENUS

6 letters
EUROPA
SATURN

7 letters
ECLIPSE
EQUINOX
NEPTUNE

8 letters
ASTEROID
PLEIADES
RED GIANT

9 letters
RED PLANET

11 letters
HELIOSPHERE

13 letters
ALPHA
   CENTAURI

'E' Words

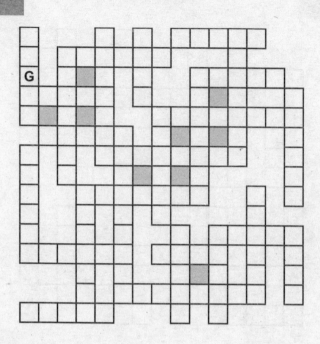

4 letters
ELKS
EMIR
ERGO

5 letters
EAGLE
EDGED
ELDER
EMBER
ERGOT
ERROR
ETUDE

EWERS
EXIST

6 letters
EDUCED
EMPIRE
ENDIVE
EQUALS
ESPIED
EXPORT

7 letters
EERIEST

ELEMENT
ENVIOUS
EPISTLE
EXTRACT
EYELASH

8 letters
ECHELONS
ELEPHANT
ESTEEMED

9 letters
ELSEWHERE

Fruit Machine

4 letters
BARS
SLOT

5 letters
BELLS
LEVER
NUDGE
PLUMS

6 letters
ARCADE
DOUBLE
LIGHTS
ORANGE
PAYOUT
REPEAT
SOUNDS
WINDOW

7 letters
BUTTONS
COLLECT
CREDITS
MACHINE
SEASIDE
WINNING

8 letters
CHERRIES
EXCHANGE
FEATURES

Football Match

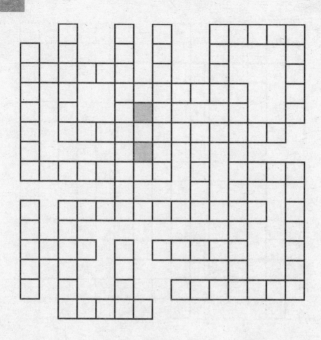

4 letters
AWAY
DRAW
GAME
TURF

5 letters
FLAGS
GOALS
PITCH
SIDES
STRIP
TEAMS

6 letters
CROWDS
GROUND
STANDS

7 letters
OFFSIDE
SCARVES
SEND OFF
WHISTLE

8 letters
CHANTING
SHOOTING

10 letters
POSSESSION

11 letters
FLOODLIGHTS
SPONSORSHIP

12 letters
DRESSING
  ROOM

Indoor Rooms

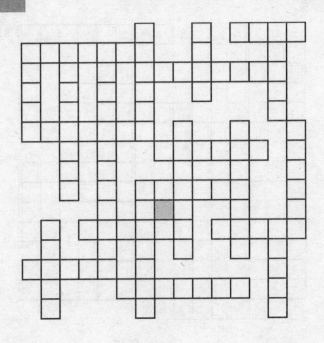

4 letters
HALL
LOFT

5 letters
ATTIC
CABIN
CRYPT
FOYER
PORCH
STUDY

6 letters
CELLAR
LOUNGE
STUDIO
TOILET
VESTRY

7 letters
ATELIER
BEDROOM
CANTEEN
CUBICLE

LIBRARY
NURSERY

8 letters
BATHROOM
SCULLERY

12 letters
CONSER-
VATORY

Creepy-Crawlies

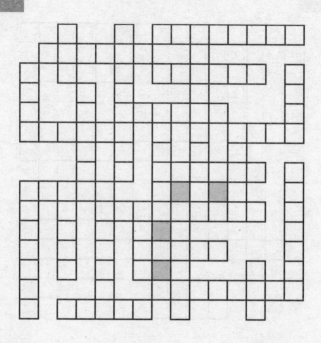

3 letters
BEE
DOR

4 letters
COXA
EGGS
FLEA
MITE

5 letters
APHID
CRAWL
IMAGO

SWARM
THRIP

6 letters
BEDBUG
BITING
EARWIG
HORNET
SCARAB
SPIDER
TARSUS
WEEVIL

7 letters
EELWORM
ITCHING
ODONATA

8 letters
FIREBRAT
MOSQUITO
WIREWORM

9 letters
DAMSELFLY

10 letters
SPRINGTAIL

Buzzwords

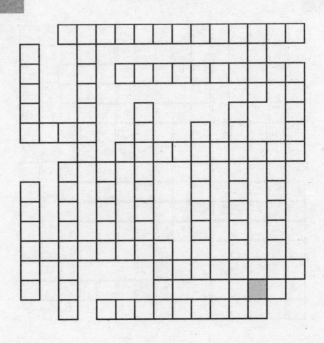

4 letters
B-TO-B
COOL
SPAM

5 letters
BUY-IN
ME PLC
SURGE

6 letters
WIN-WIN

7 letters
UPSKILL

8 letters
CYCLOSIS
DOWNLOAD
LEVERAGE
LOGOWEAR
PARADIGM
WELLNESS

9 letters
FRAMEWORK

10 letters
ACTIONABLE
GRASS ROOTS

11 letters
STAKEHOLDER

13 letters
OUTSIDE THE
BOX

Cities of England

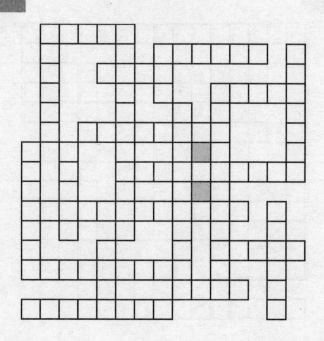

3 letters
ELY

4 letters
BATH
HULL
YORK

5 letters
LEEDS
RIPON
TRURO
WELLS

6 letters
DURHAM
EXETER
LONDON

7 letters
BRISTOL
IPSWICH

8 letters
BRIGHTON
ST ALBANS

9 letters
LANCASTER

10 letters
CANTERBURY
PORTSMOUTH

11 letters
SOUTHAMPTON
WESTMINSTER

12 letters
STOKE-ON-
TRENT

Beauty Parlour

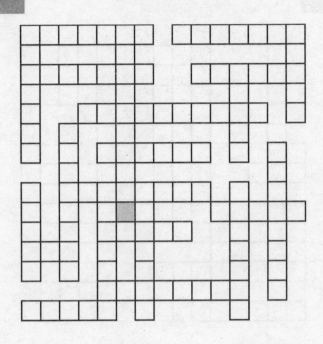

3 letters
GEL

5 letters
CREAM
CURLS
IMAGE
RINSE
ROUGE
SALON

6 letters
FACIAL
MIRROR

7 letters
BRUSHES
MASCARA
MUDPACK
PERFUME
ROLLERS
STYLIST
TINTING

8 letters
CLEANSER
LIPSTICK
MANICURE
NAIL FILE

9 letters
COSMETICS

10 letters
EMERY BOARD

Bible Characters

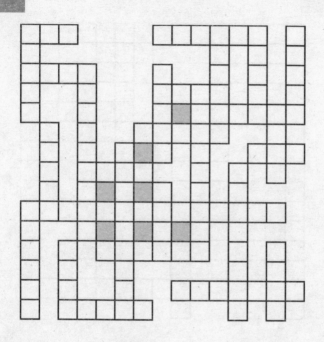

3 letters
HAM
JOB

4 letters
ADAM
AHAB
AMOS
CAIN
ESAU
PAUL
RUTH

5 letters
AARON
JACOB
JESSE
JONAH
LABAN
SARAH
URIAH

6 letters
HANNAH
JOANNA
NABOTH
NATHAN
THOMAS

7 letters
LAZARUS

8 letters
HEZEKIAH

9 letters
BATHSHEBA
NICODEMUS
THADDAEUS

14 letters
NEBUCHAD-
NEZZAR

Ice Cream Flavours

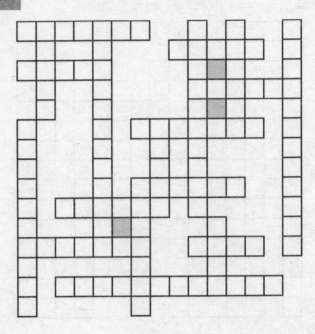

4 letters
KIWI
LIME

5 letters
HONEY
LEMON
MANGO
PEACH

6 letters
CHERRY
COFFEE

PEANUT
TOFFEE

7 letters
APRICOT
CARAMEL
PRALINE
SHERBET

10 letters
CAPPUCCINO
REDCURRANT

12 letters
CLOTTED
  CREAM
FOREST FRUITS
RUM AND
  RAISIN

Court of Law

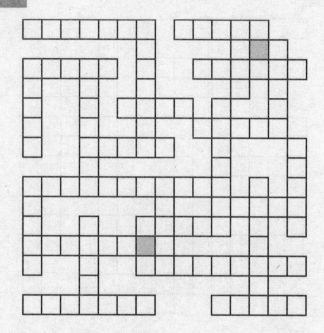

4 letters
GOWN
JURY

5 letters
BENCH
BIBLE
COURT
FALSE
FRAUD
JUDGE
LEGAL
ORDER

PENAL
QUASH
SWEAR
TRIAL
TRUTH

6 letters
APPEAL
LAWFUL

7 letters
BAILIFF
DEFENCE

JUSTICE
STATUTE
SUMMONS
WITNESS

9 letters
PLAINTIFF

11 letters
PROSECUTION

Russia

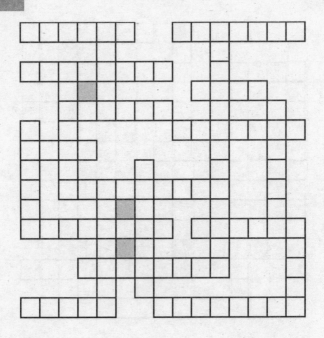

4 letters
MARX
OMSK

5 letters
LENIN
URALS
VOLGA

6 letters
MOSCOW
ROSTOV

SUZDAL
THE GUM

7 letters
FABERGE
IRKUTSK
KARA SEA
KREMLIN
SIBERIA
THE DUMA

8 letters
RASPUTIN
SAKHALIN
TUNGUSKA
WHITE SEA

9 letters
ASTRAKHAN

13 letters
KOLA
  PENINSULA

Coal Mining

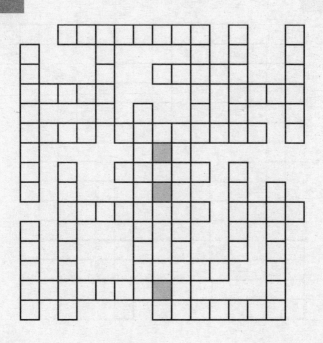

4 letters
ADIT
CAGE
FUEL

5 letters
ALARM
BENCH
DUSTY
SEAMS
SHAFT

UNION
VEINS

6 letters
RESCUE
SAFETY
SHIFTS

7 letters
CANDLES
LIGNITE
METHANE

8 letters
ACCIDENT
COALFACE
COLLIERY
DISASTER
RESERVES

10 letters
ANTHRACITE
BITUMINOUS

Bones of the Body

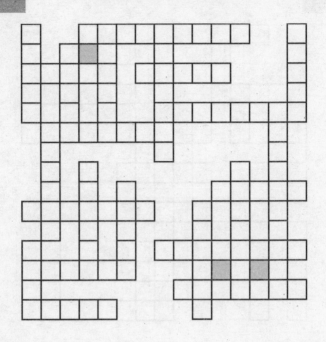

4 letters
ULNA

5 letters
ANKLE
ANVIL
FEMUR
ILIUM
SHINS
SPINE
TALUS
TIBIA

6 letters
CARPAL
FIBULA
HAMATE
LUNATE
PELVIS

7 letters
HIPBONE
KNEECAP
MALLEUS
PATELLA
TARSALS

8 letters
CAPITATE
VERTEBRA

9 letters
CHEEKBONE

10 letters
TRIQUETRAL

Ships' Names

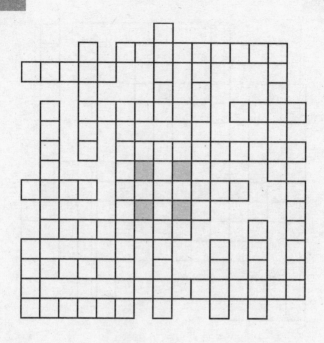

4 letters
ARGO
FRAM
HOOD
WOLF

5 letters
CAIRO
ESSEX
PINTA

6 letters
BOUNTY
EREBUS
FRANCE
ORIANA

7 letters
ARCADIA
BELFAST
TIRPITZ
VESTRIS

8 letters
SAVANNAH

9 letters
AUSTRALIS
BRITANNIA
DISCOVERY
LUSITANIA
NORMANDIE

10 letters
SANTA MARIA

Dances

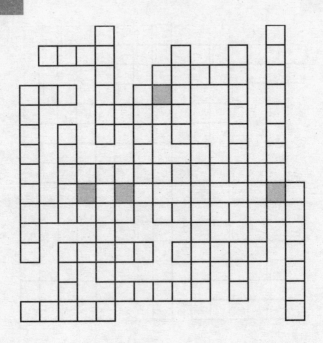

3 letters
BOP
JIG

4 letters
JIVE
REEL

5 letters
LIMBO
MAMBO
POLKA
RUMBA
SAMBA

SHAKE
TANGO
TWIST
WALTZ

6 letters
BOOGIE
MINUET
SHIMMY
VELETA

7 letters
FOXTROT
MAZURKA

8 letters
FANDANGO
FLAMENCO
HORNPIPE

9 letters
JITTERBUG

12 letters
MASHED
  POTATO

Gases

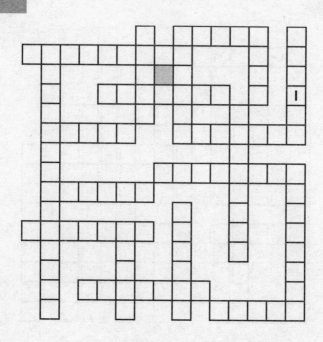

4 letters
NEON

5 letters
ARGON
HALON
OZONE
RADON
XENON

6 letters
BUTANE
HELIUM
IODINE
OXYGEN

7 letters
BROMINE
COAL GAS
METHANE
PROPANE

8 letters
CHLORINE
HYDROGEN
NITROGEN

9 letters
ACETYLENE

14 letters
CARBON
  MONOXIDE

British Cathedrals

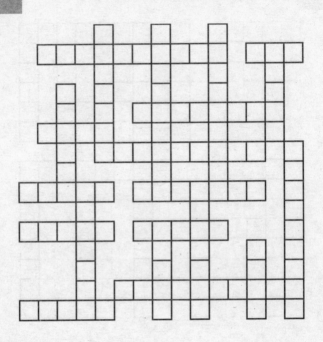

3 letters
ELY

4 letters
BATH
PEEL

5 letters
DERBY
ELGIN
LEEDS
RIPON

TRURO
WELLS

6 letters
EXETER

7 letters
ARUNDEL
BRISTOL
NORWICH
ST PAUL'S

8 letters
HEREFORD

9 letters
GUILDFORD
SHEFFIELD
SOUTHWELL
WORCESTER

10 letters
GLOUCESTER
PORTSMOUTH

Juggling

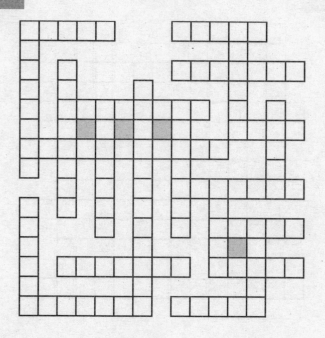

4 letters
SHOW

5 letters
BALLS
CATCH
HANDS
HOOPS
POISE
RINGS
STAGE
THROW

6 letters
MAKE-UP
PLATES

7 letters
BALANCE
CIRCLES
CONTROL
PASSING
RECOVER
ROUTINE

8 letters
ACCURACY
PRACTISE
SKITTLES

11 letters
ENTERTAINER

12 letters
BREATHTAKING

Brave Words

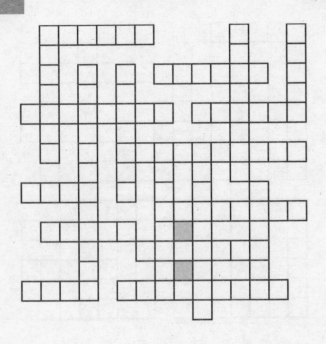

4 letters
BOLD
GAME

5 letters
HARDY
MANLY

6 letters
FEISTY
GRITTY
HEROIC

METTLE

7 letters
GALLANT
STOICAL
VALIANT

8 letters
FEARLESS
SPIRITED
UNAFRAID
VALOROUS

9 letters
AUDACIOUS
UNDAUNTED

10 letters
COURAGEOUS

12 letters
STOUT-
 HEARTED

F1 Grand Prix Winners

4 letters
HILL
HUNT
ICKX
MOSS
PACE

5 letters
ALESI
JONES
LAUDA
RINDT
SENNA

6 letters
ALONSO
ARNOUX
ASCARI
GETHIN
GURNEY
TAMBAY

7 letters
BRABHAM
IRELAND
MANSELL
TARUFFI

8 letters
HAMILTON
RATHMANN
VON TRIPS

9 letters
RAIKKONEN

10 letters
FITTIPALDI

Orchestra Conductors

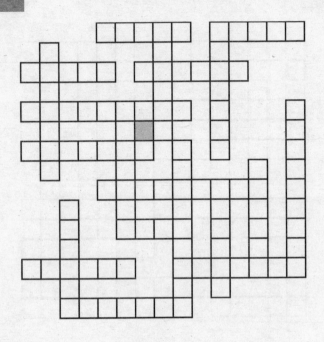

4 letters
MUTI

5 letters
DANON
KEMPE
MOTTL

6 letters
ABBADO
ANCERL
KRAUSS

LEVINE
PREVIN
RATTLE

7 letters
BEECHAM
KARAJAN
MONTEUX
ORMANDY
SALONEN
SARGENT

9 letters
BARENBOIM
CHALABALA
MRAVINSKY
TENNSTEDT

Body Language

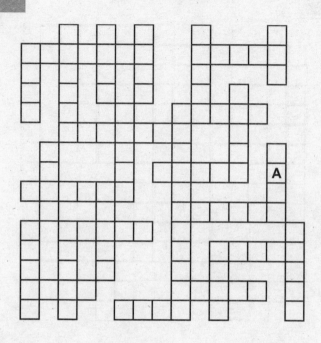

3 letters
CRY

4 letters
BEND
GAZE
GRIN
MOPE
POUT
WAVE
WINK
YAWN

5 letters
BLINK
BLUSH
COWER
DROOP
FROWN
GLARE
LAUGH
POINT
SCOWL
SMILE
STOOP
STRUT
TOUCH

6 letters
CRINGE
FIDDLE
FIDGET

7 letters
GRIMACE
TREMBLE

11 letters
GESTICULATE

Craters of the Moon

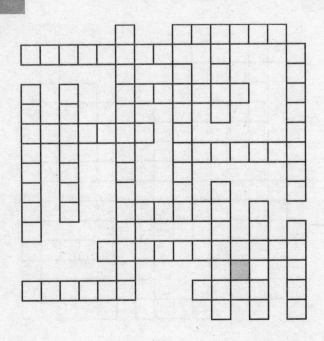

4 letters
VEGA

5 letters
NOBEL
TYCHO

6 letters
APOLLO
DARWIN
JENNER
PASCAL

7 letters
AGRIPPA
CLAVIUS
KOROLEV
LEBEDEV
MARCONI

8 letters
AMUNDSEN
EINSTEIN
HERSCHEL
HUMBOLDT

11 letters
TSIOLKOVSKY

14 letters
BELLINGS-
HAUSEN

Lord of the Rings

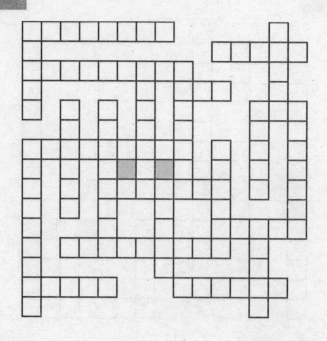

3 letters
ELF
ORC

5 letters
DWARF
EOMER
EOWYN
MERRY
MORIA
ROHAN
SHIRE
TROLL

6 letters
GAFFER
GOLLUM
WIZARD

7 letters
EREGION
FARAMIR
GANDALF
LOBELIA

8 letters
MERIADOC
RADAGAST

9 letters
BUTTERBUR
GALADRIEL
GOLDBERRY
RIVENDELL

Gulfs

4 letters
ADEN
OMAN
RIGA
SIAM
SUEZ

5 letters
GENOA
IZMIR
MOLOS
PARIA

6 letters
AEGINA
ALASKA
GONAVE
MEGARA
PANAMA
PATRAS
VENICE

7 letters
ANTALYA
TARANTO
TRIESTE

8 letters
SALONIKA
THAILAND

9 letters
VENEZUELA

13 letters
SAINT
    LAWRENCE

'F' Words

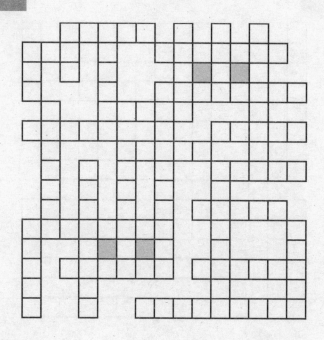

3 letters
FEZ
FIX
FOE

4 letters
FINE

5 letters
FABLE
FAKIR
FELON
FETID
FIFTH

FLINT
FLOOR
FRESH
FUDGE
FUZZY

6 letters
FEWEST
FLAYED
FLUFFY

7 letters
FATIGUE
FERTILE

FURTHER

8 letters
FIDELITY
FOREHEAD
FRECKLES
FREEZING
FUGITIVE

9 letters
FREESTYLE

10 letters
FORTHRIGHT

Car Manufacturers

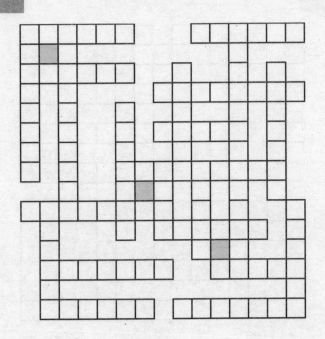

4 letters
FORD

5 letters
HONDA
ISUZU
RILEY

6 letters
DAEWOO
HOLDEN
JAGUAR
MORGAN

NISSAN
SINGER
SUZUKI
TOYOTA

7 letters
DAIMLER
FERRARI
PEUGEOT
RENAULT

8 letters
CHRYSLER

MASERATI
WOLSELEY

9 letters
ALFA ROMEO

10 letters
RANGE ROVER

13 letters
GENERAL
 MOTORS

British Statesmen

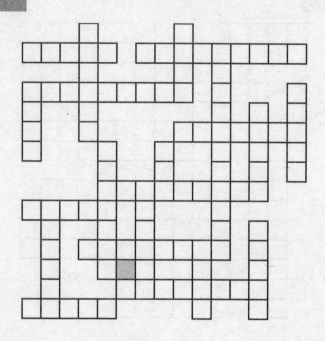

3 letters
PYM

4 letters
COOK
HURD
OWEN

5 letters
BEVIN
BROWN
CABLE

CLEGG
HAGUE
HEATH

6 letters
ATTLEE
CLARKE
WILSON

7 letters
CAMERON
OSBORNE

8 letters
MORRISON
PERCEVAL

9 letters
CHURCHILL
CROSSLAND
MACMILLAN

11 letters
CHAMBERLAIN

Mighty Meaty

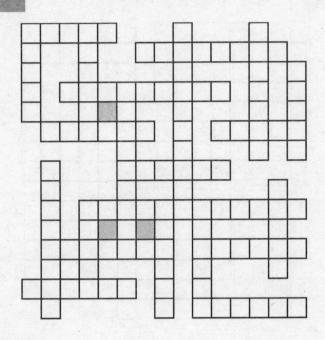

5 letters
BACON
BRAWN
GIGOT
LIVER
SKIRT
TRIPE

6 letters
FILLET
FLITCH
GAMMON
HOT DOG

OXTAIL
RAGOUT
SALAMI
TONGUE

7 letters
BRISKET
MEAT PIE

8 letters
MEATBALL
SAUSAGES

9 letters
BEEFSTEAK
HAMBURGER

10 letters
JUGGED HARE

12 letters
SHEPHERDS PIE

Puppets

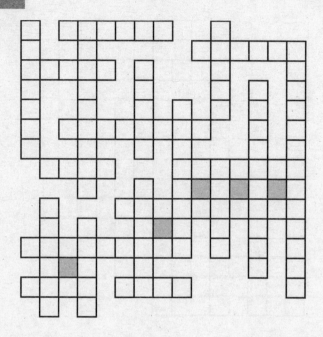

4 letters
BERT
ELMO
JUDY

5 letters
GONZO
MITCH
PERKY
SOOTY
TEDDY

6 letters
GROVER
KERMIT
PARKER
VIRGIL

7 letters
BIG BIRD
DR TEETH

8 letters
LAMB CHOP
LOOBY LOO

9 letters
ANDY PANDY
TOPO GIGIO

10 letters
BILL AND BEN
FOZZIE BEAR

13 letters
THE WOODEN-
TOPS

Diamonds

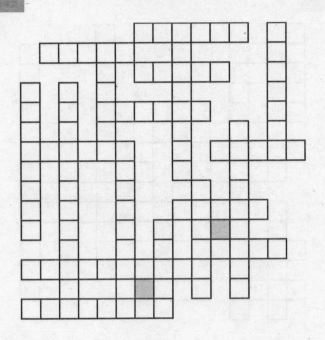

5 letters
CROWN
CULET
FACET
JEWEL
RINGS
TIARA

6 letters
CARATS
CUTTER
GIRDLE

MINING
WEIGHT

7 letters
SPARKLE

8 letters
BRACELET
FLAWLESS
NECKLACE

9 letters
CENTENARY
SOLITAIRE

10 letters
BRILLIANCE

12 letters
STAR OF
AFRICA

Dogs

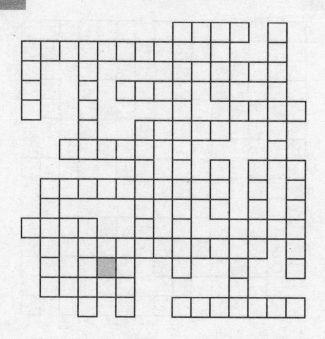

3 letters
VET

4 letters
BITE
BOWL
COAT
COMB
LEAD
PACK
TOYS
WALK

5 letters
BOXER
BRUSH
FETCH
HUSKY
LEASH
WHELP

6 letters
LAPDOG
MUZZLE
SALUKI
SHOUGH

7 letters
POINTER
SHIH TZU
WHIPPET

8 letters
COMMANDS

10 letters
ROTTWEILER
SCHIPPERKE

11 letters
SKYE TERRIER

Internet

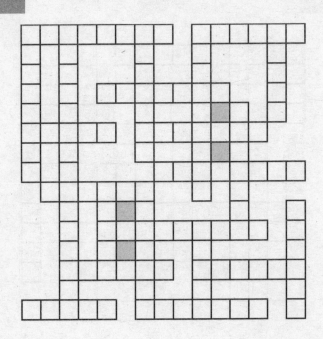

5 letters
CACHE
CLICK
MODEM
TITLE
VIRUS

6 letters
DOMAIN
FRAMES
ROUTER

SOURCE
TELNET

7 letters
BROWSER
FORWARD
GATEWAY
REFRESH
SPYWARE
SURFING

8 letters
FIREWALL
PASSWORD
PROTOCOL

9 letters
DIRECTORY
SHAREWARE

15 letters
SERVICE
  PROVIDER

Fictional Towns and Cities

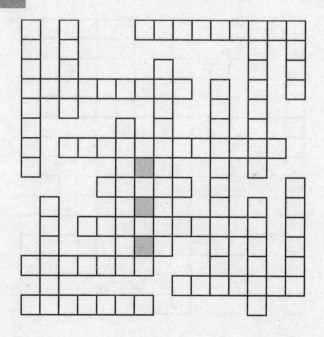

4 letters
KLOW

5 letters
FALME
QUIRM

6 letters
CYMRIL
KITEZH
XANADU

7 letters
BUGTOWN
CARCOSA
MIDWICH

8 letters
AMBRIDGE
ATLANTIS
STEPFORD

9 letters
PARLAINTH
SOUTH PARK

10 letters
GOTHAM CITY
ST MARY MEAD

11 letters
SPRINGFIELD

12 letters
CASTERBRIDGE

Autumn

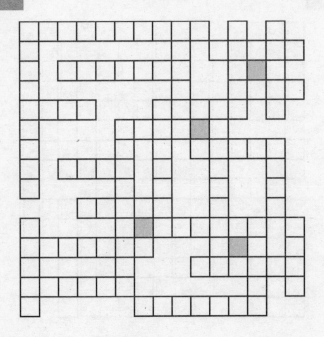

4 letters
COOL
FALL
HATS
MIST
PODS
RAIN

5 letters
ACORN
CROPS
FOGGY
FRUIT

SCARF
SEEDS
WINDY
YIELD

6 letters
APPLES
ASTERS
GLOOMY
GOLDEN

7 letters
OCTOBER
ORCHARD
ROSEHIP
STORING

9 letters
DECIDUOUS
HALLOWE'EN
MUSHROOMS

10 letters
MICHAELMAS

Books of the Bible

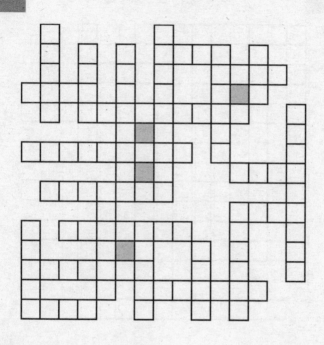

3 letters
JOB

4 letters
ACTS
AMOS
JOEL
JOHN
JUDE
LUKE
MARK
RUTH

5 letters
HOSEA
NAHUM
TITUS

6 letters
ESTHER
JUDGES
SAMUEL

7 letters
EZEKIEL
GENESIS

HEBREWS
MATTHEW

8 letters
PROVERBS

9 letters
GALATIANS
LEVITICUS
ZECHARIAH
ZEPHANIAH

GOLD and GOLDEN

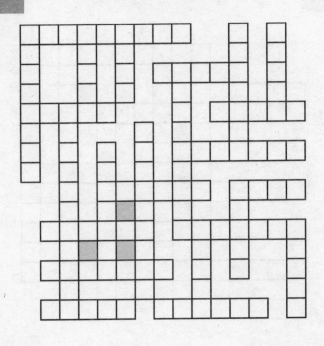

4 letters
GLOW
HAIR

5 letters
APPLE
ASTER
CHAIN
EAGLE
GIRLS
GOOSE
MEDAL

STARS
SYRUP

6 letters
FLEECE
ORIOLE
THREAD

7 letters
BUTTONS
EARRING
HAMSTER

PENDANT
SECTION

8 letters
PHEASANT

9 letters
HANDSHAKE
PARACHUTE
RETRIEVER

11 letters
ANNIVERSARY

Bitter Words

4 letters
SOUR
TART

5 letters
ACRID
ANGRY
CRUEL
HARSH
TANGY

6 letters
FIERCE
SEVERE

7 letters
HOSTILE
PUNGENT

8 letters
SPITEFUL
VENOMOUS
VINEGARY

9 letters
INDIGNANT
MERCILESS

10 letters
ASTRINGENT
BEGRUDGING
VINDICTIVE

11 letters
DISGRUNTLED

Tennis

3 letters
ACE
LET
LOB
NET
OUT
SET
WIN

4 letters
GAME
LAWN
LINE
SEED
SHOT

5 letters
FAULT
NADAL
SLICE
SMASH

6 letters
HEWITT
SAFINA
THIRTY
VOLLEY

7 letters
FIFTEEN
TENSION
TOPSPIN

8 letters
LJUBICIC
OPPONENT
WILD CARD

9 letters
CLIJSTERS

10 letters
EXHIBITION

190 Fungi

3 letters
CEP

5 letters
ENOKI
GILLS
OVOLO
RUSTS
SHELF
SMUTS
STIPE
VOLVA

6 letters
BOLETI
BUTTON
INK-CAP
MOULDS
OYSTER

7 letters
ANNULUS
CRESTED
FLAT CAP
PORCINO

8 letters
BROWN CAP
ST GEORGE

9 letters
FAIRY RING
LION'S MANE

Bills and Bens

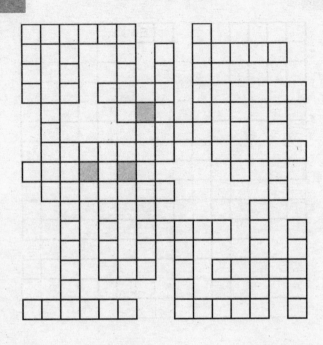

3 letters
HEE
HUR

4 letters
CODY
MOOR
SHAW
TIDY

5 letters
ALDER
COHEN
ELTON

GATES
GREEN
HALEY
HICKS
NEVIS
SANDS
WYMAN

6 letters
BAILEY
CASTLE
COTTON
LAWERS
MORRIS

ROGERS
WATERS

7 letters
SHERMAN
TRAVERS
VORLICH

8 letters
TREACHER

9 letters
REHNQUIST

'G' Words

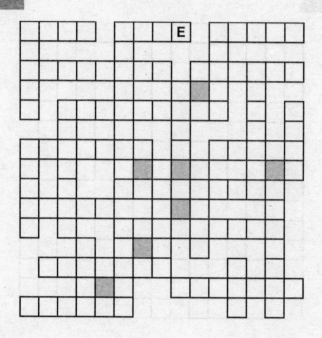

3 letters
GUM

4 letters
GAME
GIFT
GILL
GLUE
GNAT

5 letters
GEARS
GELID
GIGOT

GLARE
GLEAM
GNOME
GORGE
GUSTY

6 letters
GAGGLE
GANTRY
GREEDY

7 letters
GAINSAY
GALLEON

GENUINE
GNAWING
GRAPHIC
GRAPPLE

8 letters
GRUESOME

9 letters
GABERDINE
GARDENING
GLOWERING
GUERRILLA

Cruising

3 letters
AFT
SUN

4 letters
CREW
DOCK
PORT
SHIP

5 letters
AT SEA
CABIN
DECKS

OCEAN
SHORE

6 letters
AEGEAN
ANCHOR
FJORDS
SINGER
VOYAGE

7 letters
BATHING
BUNTING
CABARET

HOLIDAY
SEASICK

8 letters
ATLANTIC
DUTY-FREE

9 letters
DISEMBARK
STARBOARD

13 letters
MEDITER-
RANEAN

Control

3 letters
RUN

4 letters
CURB

5 letters
CHECK
DRIVE
GUIDE
PILOT
STEER

6 letters
ASSURE
HANDLE
MANAGE
MASTER
REIN IN

7 letters
COUNTER
INHIBIT
PRESIDE
REPRESS
SEE TO IT
TRAMMEL

8 letters
RESTRICT
SUPPRESS

9 letters
ASCERTAIN

15 letters
WEAR THE
TROUSERS

Bobs

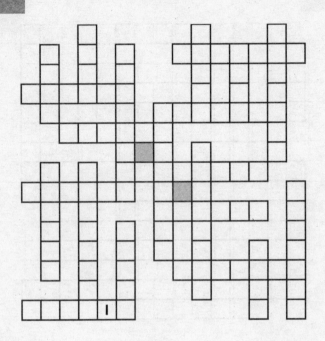

4 letters
HOPE
MOOG
SHAW
WEIR

5 letters
DYLAN
HAWKE

6 letters
DE NIRO

HARRIS
LAXTON
MARLEY
MARTIN
POWELL

7 letters
HOLNESS
KENNEDY
LINDSAY
MCELWEE
PAISLEY

8 letters
CHARLTON
MATTHIAS
MORTIMER
URQUHART
WILLIAMS

Scottish Lochs

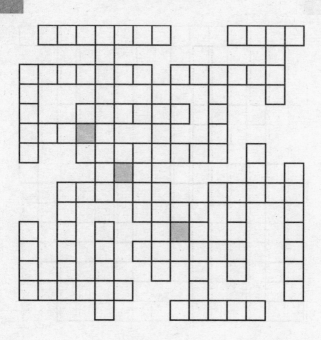

3 letters
EIL
EWE

4 letters
BUIE
GILP
GOIL
LONG
NESS
RYAN

5 letters
DUICH
ETIVE
FLEET
HUORN
LEVEN
NEVIS
SWEEN

6 letters
CARRON
CRERAN
CRINAN
EYNORT

LINNHE
RIDDON
SUNART

7 letters
ERIBOLL
SCAVAIG
STRIVEN

8 letters
GAIRLOCH

9 letters
BRACADALE

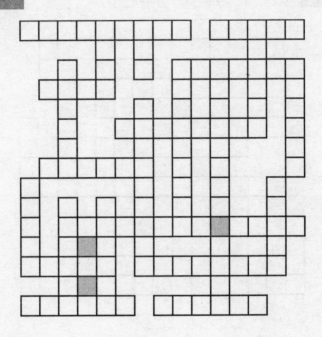

Herbal Remedies

3 letters
RUE

4 letters
ARUM
BALM
DOCK
MINT

5 letters
BASIL
ORRIS

SENNA
TANSY

6 letters
ARNICA
BORAGE
CATNIP
GARLIC
GINKGO
NETTLE
PEPPER
SORREL

7 letters
SAFFRON

8 letters
ALOE VERA
FEVERFEW
RED POPPY
SELF-HEAL

9 letters
CRANBERRY
RED CLOVER
SUNFLOWER

Paper Types

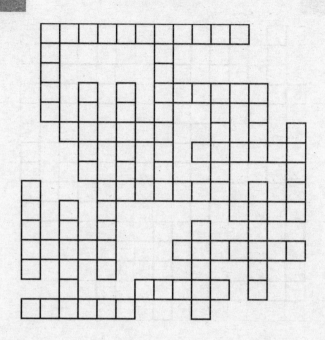

4 letters
NEWS
WALL

5 letters
BROWN
CREPE
GRAPH
GREEN
LEGAL
LINEN

WAXED
WHITE

6 letters
BAKING
CARBON
FILTER
LITMUS
MANILA
TISSUE
TOILET
VELLUM

7 letters
TRACING
WRITING

9 letters
PARCHMENT

11 letters
GREASEPROOF

Cartoon Characters

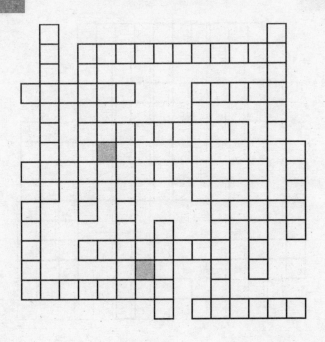

5 letters
BAMBI
DUMBO
FELIX
GOOFY
JERRY

6 letters
BOO BOO
DROOPY
MOWGLI

POPEYE
SNOOPY

7 letters
THUMPER

8 letters
GEPPETTO
YOGI BEAR

9 letters
BETTY BOOP
BUGS BUNNY
PINOCCHIO
TWEETY PIE

11 letters
BART SIMPSON

13 letters
WINNIE-THE-POOH

Battle Field

4 letters
GAZA
JUNO
NILE
RUHR

5 letters
BETWA
MALTA
MARNE
PATAY

6 letters
ARMADA
BASTIA
CANNAE
NASEBY
SADOWA

7 letters
MARENGO

8 letters
ARDENNES

ATLANTIC
CORAL SEA
TENERIFE

9 letters
LEXINGTON
MANZIKERT

14 letters
AL KASIR AL
KEBIR
CONSTAN-
TINOPLE

Dentistry

4 letters
BITE
GUMS
ORAL
ROOT

5 letters
BRACE
CHAIR
FLOSS
MOUTH
NURSE

PLATE
TEETH
ULCER

6 letters
MOLARS
TARTAR

7 letters
AMALGAM
DENTINE

8 letters
BRUSHING
CLEANING
DRILLING
FILLINGS
INCISORS

9 letters
HYGIENIST

12 letters
ORTHODONTICS

Cattle Grid

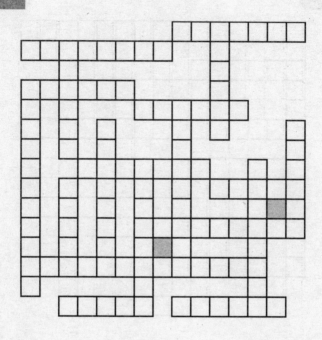

5 letters
DEVON
LUING
WHITE

6 letters
CARACU
DEXTER
DURHAM
HERENS
JERSEY
KURGAN

7 letters
BRAHMAN
RED POLL

8 letters
ALDERNEY
HEREFORD
HOLSTEIN
LIMOUSIN

9 letters
ROMAGNOLA
SHORTHORN

11 letters
CHILLINGHAM

13 letters
ABERDEEN
ANGUS

Six-letter Words

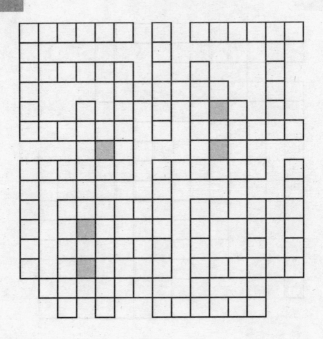

ABSENT	IMPAIR	NEARLY
ACCORD	JAGUAR	PLOVER
ADVERB	JESTER	REVOKE
ALASKA	KIPPER	STOOGE
COMICS	LIMPET	STRAIN
CRAVEN	MARTYR	TAMPER
CURLED	MATRIX	THANKS
DINNER	MOMENT	VOTIVE
EXPORT	MONKEY	ZEALOT
	NATURE	

Very Volcanic

3 letters
ASH
GAS

4 letters
ETNA
LAKI
LAVA
PIPE
TAAL
VENT

5 letters
ASAMA
CRUST
FLANK
HEKLA
LAHAR
MAGMA
PASTO
SMOKE
STEAM

6 letters
ACTIVE
PLATES
PUMICE

SHIELD
TACANA

7 letters
CONDUIT
CREVICE
FISSURE

8 letters
COTOPAXI
VESUVIUS

11 letters
PYROCLASTIC

Watch the Weight

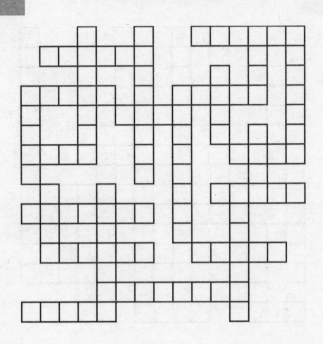

4 letters

BEAR

BULK

KILO

LIFT

LOAD

MASS

TROY

5 letters

FORCE

HEAVY

HEFTY

OUNCE

POUND

STONE

6 letters

BURDEN

SCALES

STRAIN

7 letters

BALANCE

BALLAST

GRAVITY

SUPPORT

TONNAGE

8 letters

CRUSHING

PRESSURE

UNWIELDY

3 letters
POE

4 letters
KING
POPE

5 letters
ELIOT
HOMER
JAMES
JOYCE

MILNE
STOWE
SWIFT
TWAIN
WILDE

6 letters
ALCOTT
BARRIE
CLARKE
MORTON
SEWELL

7 letters
CHAUCER
CHEKHOV
DICKENS
MITFORD

8 letters
ATKINSON
CHRISTIE
MITCHELL

At the Museum

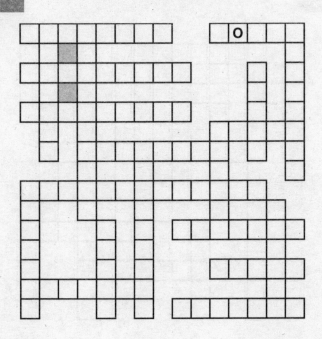

5 letters
BONES
CASES
MUMMY
ROMAN
TUDOR

6 letters
ARMOUR
RELICS

7 letters
ANCIENT
DISPLAY
HISTORY
POTTERY
RECORDS

8 letters
BROCHURE
SOUVENIR
TREASURE

9 letters
ANTIQUITY
ARTEFACTS
SCULPTURE

10 letters
COLLECTION

13 letters
DEMON-
STRATION

Committees

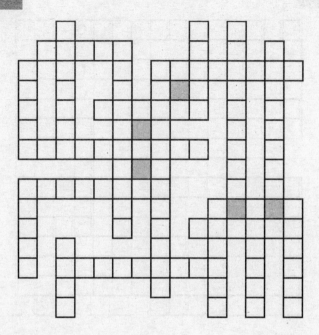

4 letters
TEAM

5 letters
BOARD
FORUM
PANEL
SYNOD

6 letters
CAUCUS
QUORUM

SELECT
SENATE
VESTRY

7 letters
COUNCIL

8 letters
CONGRESS
PLANNING
WORKSHOP

9 letters
EXECUTIVE
TASK FORCE

10 letters
DELEGATION
DEPUTATION

12 letters
WORKING
PARTY

Better and Better

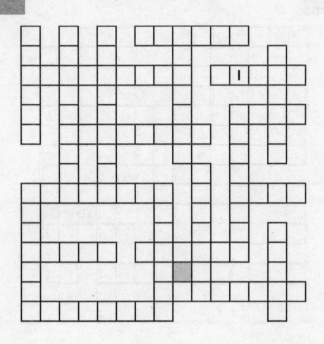

4 letters
HALE
WELL

5 letters
CURED
FINER
NICER

6 letters
BIGGER
FITTER

HEALED
NEATER

7 letters
GREATER
REVISED
SOUNDER
SWEETER

8 letters
ENHANCED
ENRICHED

RESTORED
SUPERIOR
WORTHIER

9 letters
A CUT ABOVE
HEALTHIER
TOUCHED UP

Catch!

3 letters
BAG
NAB
NET

4 letters
GRAB
GRIP
HOLD
HOOK
STOP

5 letters
GRASP
SEIZE

6 letters
ARREST
CLUTCH
COLLAR
CORNER
ENMESH
ENTRAP
HANG ON
SNAP UP
SNATCH

7 letters
CAPTURE
ENSNARE
ROUND UP

8 letters
ENTANGLE
OVERTAKE

9 letters
LATCH ON TO

'H' Words

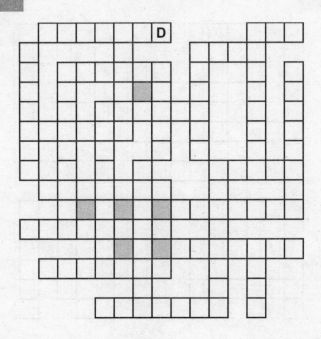

3 letters
HEX

4 letters
HEMP
HI-FI

5 letters
HASTE
HEDGE

6 letters
HEADER
HEARTH
HEBREW
HIATUS
HORSES

7 letters
HALIBUT
HATEFUL
HEATHEN
HIDEOUS
HITCHED

HOLIDAY
HUNCHED

8 letters
HABITUAL
HEDONIST
HIBISCUS
HIGHNESS
HISPANIC

9 letters
HILARIOUS
HURRICANE

Ceremonies

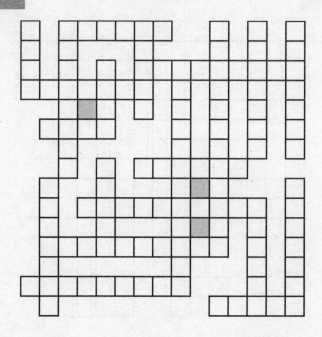

4 letters
MASS
RITE
WAKE

5 letters
AMRIT
DOSEH
TANGI

6 letters
BURIAL

MAUNDY
NIPTER

7 letters
MATSURI
OPENING
PAGEANT
SERVICE
WEDDING

8 letters
MARRIAGE

9 letters
INDUCTION
SACRAMENT

10 letters
DEDICATION
INITIATION

12 letters
CONFIRMATION
INAUGURATION

Fancy Dress Costumes

3 letters
CAT
NUN

4 letters
WASP

5 letters
CLOWN
GHOST
HIPPY
NURSE

ROBOT
SANTA
VICAR
WITCH

6 letters
DOCTOR
PIRATE
TURKEY

7 letters
ALADDIN

CAVEMAN
GORILLA
MR SPOCK

8 letters
PRINCESS
SKELETON

9 letters
CLEOPATRA
HENRY VIII
POLICEMAN

Snakes

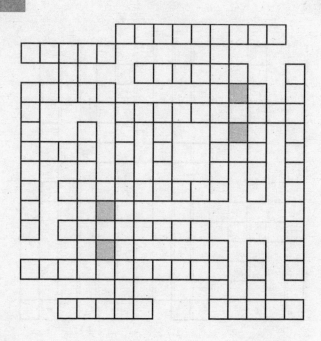

3 letters
ASP
BOA

4 letters
HABU
LORA
WUTU

5 letters
ADDER
COBRA

KRAIT
RACER
URUTU

6 letters
PYTHON
TAIPAN

8 letters
JARARACA
KEELBACK
RAT SNAKE

9 letters
CANEBRAKE
HOOP SNAKE
LANCEHEAD

10 letters
GRASS SNAKE

11 letters
FIERCE SNAKE
GOPHER SNAKE
JARARACUSSU

Parliament

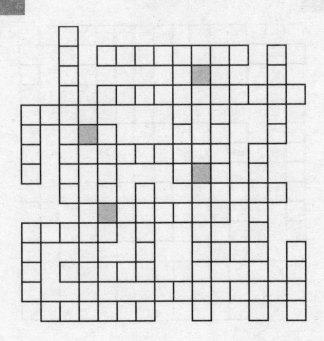

4 letters
MACE
SEAT
TORY
VETO
WARD
WHIP

5 letters
COUNT
LOBBY
LORDS

PARTY
VOTES

6 letters
DEBATE
MOTION
SPEECH

7 letters
COMMONS
SPEAKER

8 letters
MINISTER
WOOLSACK

9 letters
AMENDMENT
CANDIDATE
COALITION
MANIFESTO

11 letters
WHITE PAPERS

Exciting Times

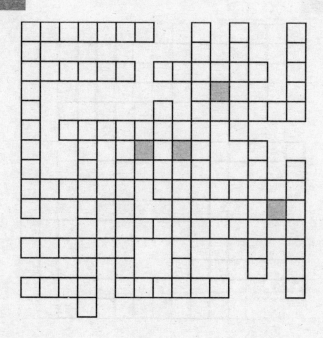

4 letters
WHET

5 letters
SHAKE
TENSE
UPSET

6 letters
AFLAME
CHARGE
FOMENT

IGNITE
THRILL
TINGLE
TURN ON

7 letters
AGITATE
ENLIVEN
INCITED
KEYED UP

8 letters
ENERGISE
VEHEMENT

9 letters
EBULLIENT
PALPITATE

10 letters
EXHILARATE
INTOXICATE
INVIGORATE

Cats

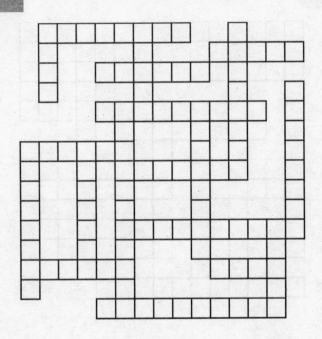

4 letters
MANX
THAI

5 letters
ASIAN
KORAT
TABBY

6 letters
BIRMAN
BOMBAY

LAPERM

7 letters
BURMESE
PERSIAN

8 letters
BALINESE
BURMILLA
KARELIAN
MUNCHKIN
SIBERIAN

9 letters
PETERBALD

10 letters
ABYSSINIAN
TURKISH VAN

11 letters
EGYPTIAN MAU

Large-scale

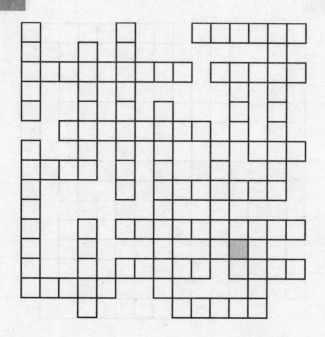

3 letters
BIG

4 letters
EPIC
HUGE
VAST

5 letters
AMPLE
BROAD
BULKY

GIANT
GREAT
HEAVY
HEFTY

6 letters
BUMPER
COSMIC

7 letters
IMMENSE
MASSIVE

8 letters
ENORMOUS
WHOPPING

9 letters
EXTENSIVE
MONSTROUS
PROMINENT

10 letters
MONOLITHIC
MONUMENTAL

Safari Park

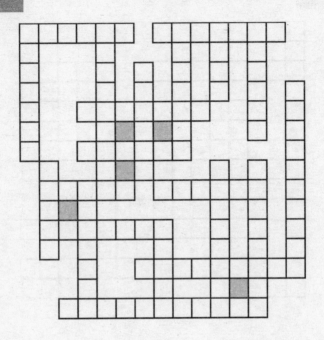

4 letters
LYNX

5 letters
ELAND
LIONS
LLAMA

6 letters
BABOON
GUIDES
MONKEY

TIGERS
WAPITI

7 letters
ANIMALS
HABITAT
MEERKAT
NATURAL
OSTRICH
WALLABY

8 letters
VISITORS
WILDLIFE

9 letters
CARNIVORE
EDUCATION

10 letters
VULNERABLE

11 letters
CHIMPANZEES

Classical Musicians

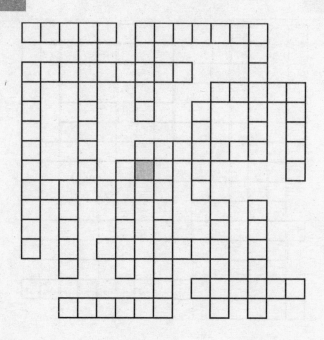

5 letters
BRAIN
BREAM
DU PRE
GOULD
SOLTI
STERN

6 letters
CASALS
GILELS
MAISKY

MUTTER
PREVIN

7 letters
BEECHAM
GLENNIE
KARAJAN
MENUHIN

8 letters
OISTRAKH

9 letters
ASHKENAZY
BERNSTEIN
TENNSTEDT

10 letters
BARBIROLLI

Behind Bars

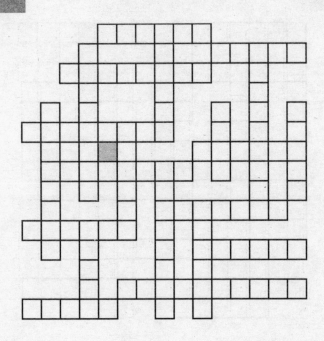

4 letters
BARS

5 letters
BLOCK
LOCKS
PENAL
WALLS

6 letters
APPEAL
DOCTOR

ESCAPE
PRISON
REMAND
ROBBER
WARDEN

7 letters
NEWGATE

8 letters
ENFORCED
EXERCISE

GOVERNOR
INTERRED
PORRIDGE
SENTENCE

9 letters
LIGHTS OUT

10 letters
RECREATION

Emergency Treatment

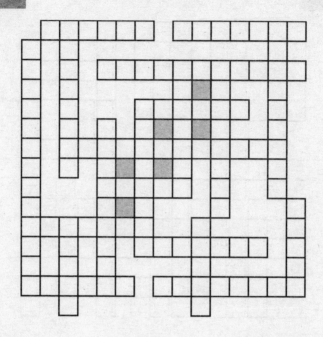

5 letters
GAUZE
PILLS
SALVE
SLING

6 letters
IODINE
NEEDLE
SPLINT

7 letters
ASPIRIN
CODEINE
SUTURES
TABLETS

8 letters
EYE PATCH
INHALANT
PENKNIFE
TINCTURE

9 letters
EMOLLIENT
SUNSCREEN

11 letters
PARACETAMOL

12 letters
COUGH
  MIXTURE

13 letters
SMELLING
  SALTS

'I' Words

4 letters
IBIS

5 letters
ICENI
ICING
IDIOM
ILIAC
IMPEL
INANE
INURE
IRISH

6 letters
IBERIA
IDLING
IMPAIR
INCISE
IRISES

7 letters
ISOLATE
ISRAELI
ITALIAN

8 letters
IDEALISE
INIQUITY
INJURIES
INTERIOR

10 letters
INEPTITUDE

11 letters
IMPERTINENT

12 letters
IMPLANTATION

Monsters

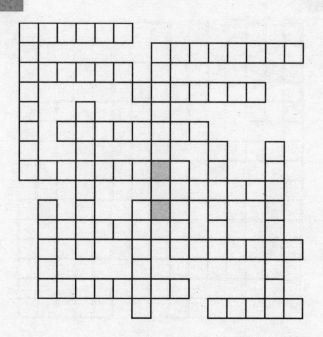

5 letters
HYDRA
MACRA
SMAUG

6 letters
BALROG
FASOLT
KRAKEN
NAZGUL
SHELOB

7 letters
AGGEDOR
CYCLOPS
FENDAHL
GRETTIR

8 letters
GODZILLA
KING KONG
MINOTAUR
SHOGGOTH

SLEIPNIR
THE THING

9 letters
DESTROYER

Scottish Islands

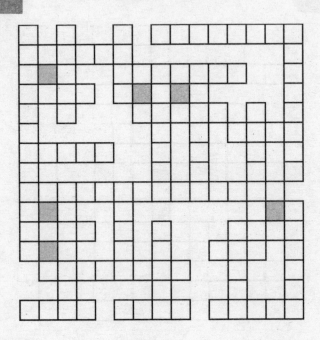

3 letters
HOY

4 letters
EDAY
FARA
NOSS
SKYE
UYEA
WIAY
YELL

5 letters
ARRAN
FOULA

FUDAY
ISLAY
SCARP
TAHAY
TORSA

6 letters
ROUSAY
VACSAY

7 letters
ERISKAY
INCHFAD
KERRERA
WESTRAY

8 letters
GRUINARD
HELLISAY
INCHCOLM
MINGULAY

12 letters
PRIEST ISLAND

14 letters
LEWIS AND
HARRIS

Greek Islands

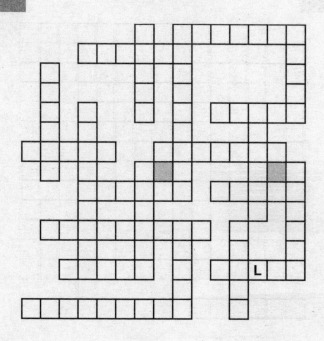

5 letters
CHIOS
CORFU
CRETE
KASOS
MILOS
NAXOS
PAROS
SAMOS
TINOS

6 letters
AEGINA
ANDROS
LEMNOS
LESBOS
RHODES
SKYROS

7 letters
KYTHNOS
THASSOS

9 letters
KARPATHOS
KEFALONIA
SANTORINI
ZAKINTHOS

Anatomy Lesson

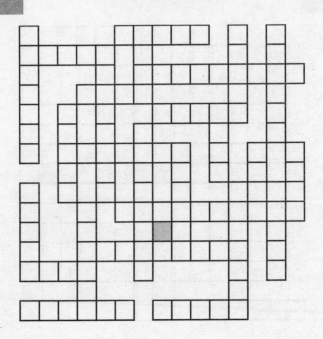

4 letters
FOOT
KNEE
NECK
NOSE
SKIN
SOLE
TOES

5 letters
FEMUR
HEELS
LIVER
LUNGS

PORES
SKULL
TEETH
VEINS

6 letters
FINGER
JOINTS
KIDNEY
LARYNX

7 letters
MIDRIFF
STOMACH

THYROID

8 letters
SHOULDER
WINDPIPE

9 letters
DIAPHRAGM
EPIDERMIS

10 letters
EPIGLOTTIS

Aromatherapy

4 letters
PINE
ROSE

5 letters
BASIL
ELEMI
MANGO
MYRRH
PEONY
THYME

6 letters
ALMOND
GINGER
MIMOSA
NUTMEG

7 letters
BAY LEAF
FREESIA

8 letters
BLUEBELL
CARDAMOM

GERANIUM
MARJORAM
ROSEMARY

9 letters
AMBERGRIS
LEMON BALM

13 letters
SAMARKAND
MUSK

Bend It

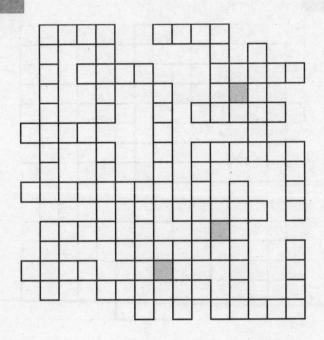

4 letters
ARCH
CURL
FLEX
KINK
LEAN
LOOP
SWAY
TURN
WARP
WIND

5 letters
CROOK
ELBOW
EXERT
KNEEL
LOWER
MOULD
STOOP

6 letters
BUCKLE
DEFORM
SUBMIT

SWERVE
ZIGZAG

7 letters
CONTORT
DEFLECT
DIVERGE

8 letters
PERSUADE

9 letters
CONVOLUTE

Cocktails

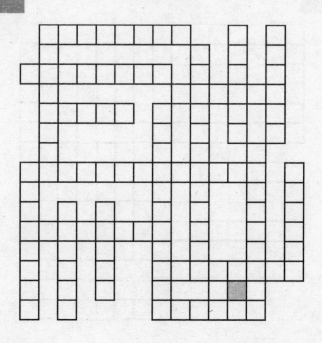

3 letters
KIR

RICKEY
ROB ROY

9 letters
WHITE LADY

5 letters
BRONX
JULEP

8 letters
ACAPULCO
MOONWALK
PARADISE
PINK LADY
SAKETINI
SNOWBALL

11 letters
GRASSHOPPER

6 letters
BATIDA
MAI TAI
MOJITO
PANAMA

12 letters
BLACK RUSSIAN

13 letters
PLANTER'S
PUNCH

Get Your Tickets

3 letters
BUS

4 letters
RAIL
TOLL

5 letters
COACH
DANCE
FERRY
MATCH

PLANE
TRAIN

6 letters
CINEMA
CIRCUS
MUSEUM
RAFFLE

7 letters
CONCERT
GALLERY
LIBRARY

THEATRE
TOMBOLA

8 letters
ENTRANCE
EUROSTAR

9 letters
ADMISSION

11 letters
STATELY HOME

Alloys and Metals

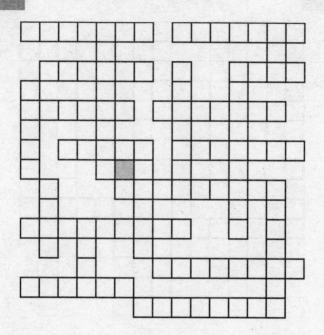

3 letters
TIN

4 letters
GOLD
LEAD
ZINC

5 letters
BRASS
INVAR

6 letters
BRONZE
NICKEL
SILVER
SOLDER

7 letters
AMALGAM
BABBITT
INCONEL
MERCURY

RHODIUM
WOLFRAM

8 letters
CARBOLOY
GUNMETAL
TITANIUM

9 letters
ALUMINIUM
MANGANESE
ZIRCONIUM

Ancient Egypt

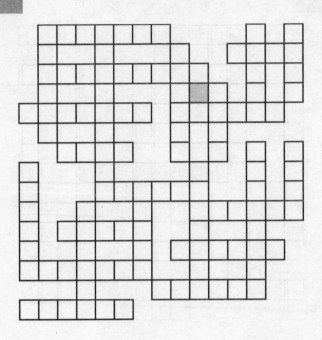

4 letters
EDFU
GIZA
GOLD
ISIS
NILE

5 letters
ASYUT
MUMMY
TOMBS

6 letters
ABUSIR
BAKARE
HAWARA
KARNAK
NUBIAN
OSIRIS
PRIEST
SCARAB
SLAVES
TEMPLE

7 letters
EL-LISHT
RAMESES
SHADOOF
USHABTI

8 letters
PYRAMIDS

9 letters
AMENHOTEP
DYNASTIES

Clock Work

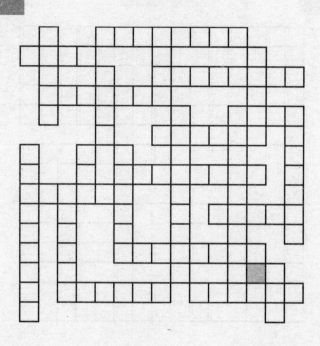

3 letters
KEY
OAK

4 letters
DESK
DIAL
FACE
WALL

5 letters
HANDS
TABLE
WATER

6 letters
BRONZE
CHIMES
CUCKOO
MANTEL
SPRING
WINDER

7 letters
DIGITAL
KITCHEN

8 letters
ELECTRIC
FLYWHEEL
LONGCASE
ROSEWOOD

9 letters
MECHANISM
TIMEPIECE

10 letters
DECORATION

Grape Varieties

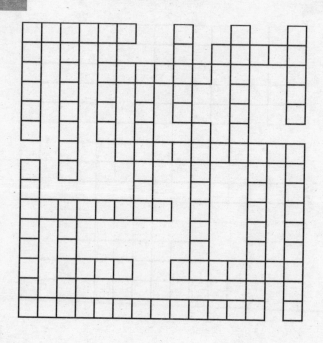

4 letters
BUAL

5 letters
FIANO
GAMAY
VIURA

6 letters
MALBEC
MERLOT
MUSCAT

OPTIMA
TANNAT

7 letters
CORVINA
PICPOUL

8 letters
ALBARINO
MUSCADET
NEBBIOLO
RIESLING

SEMILLON

9 letters
ASSYRTIKO
COLOMBARD

10 letters
VIDAL BLANC

13 letters
TOCAI
FRIULANO

All About Horses

3 letters
BIT

4 letters
COLT
FOAL
MANE
PONY

5 letters
FILLY
MARES
MOUNT

NEIGH
PINTO
REINS
SHIRE

6 letters
BRONCO
EQUINE
HUNTER
WHINNY

7 letters
PADDOCK

8 letters
BLINKERS
DRESSAGE
PALOMINO
SKEWBALD
STIRRUPS
TROTTING
YEARLING

10 letters
CLYDESDALE

Sculpting Materials

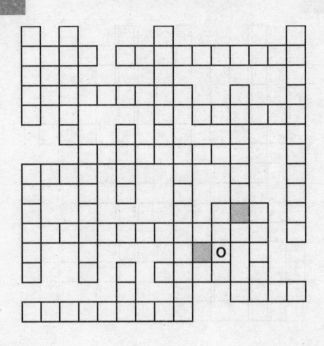

3 letters
JET

4 letters
CLAY
COAL
GOLD
IRON
LEAD
WOOD

5 letters
GLASS
METAL

6 letters
BASALT
BRONZE
COPPER
MARBLE

7 letters
GRANITE
PLASTER

9 letters
LIMESTONE
PIPESTONE

PORCELAIN
SOAPSTONE

10 letters
TERRACOTTA

11 letters
PAPIER MACHE

13 letters
PORTLAND
STONE

Dictators and Despots

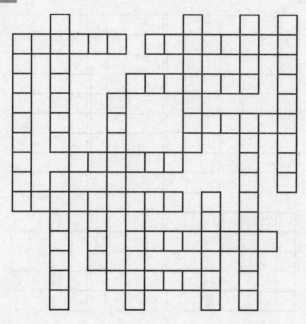

4 letters
SHWE
TITO

6 letters
CASTRO
FRANCO
MARCOS
MUGABE
POL POT
SADDAM
STALIN

7 letters
ARAP MOI
BOKASSA
QADDAFI
SUHARTO

8 letters
DUVALIER
KHOMEINI

9 letters
CEAUSESCU
KIM JONG IL
MILOSEVIC

10 letters
LUKASHENKO

Archery Contest

3 letters
YEW

4 letters
HOLD
MARK
NOCK
PILE
SHOT

5 letters
BELLY
BUTTS

LOOSE
NOTCH
PLATE
SIGHT
SPINE

6 letters
AIMING
FLIGHT
TARGET
TILLER
TORQUE

7 letters
CLICKER
FEATHER
RED RING

8 letters
ARBALEST
FLETCHER
LAUNCHER
STACKING

10 letters
STABILISER

Astrology

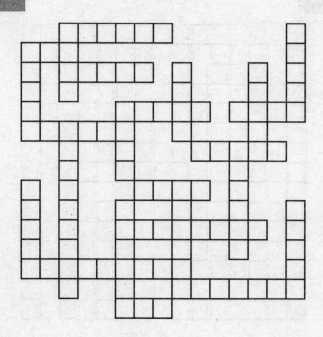

3 letters
LEO
RAM

4 letters
BULL
CRAB
CUSP
FIRE
GOAT

5 letters
ARIES
CHART
EARTH
HOUSE
LIBRA
VIRGO
WATER
WHEEL

6 letters
ARCHER
CANCER

GEMINI
SCALES
TAURUS

7 letters
SCORPIO

8 letters
AQUARIUS

9 letters
CAPRICORN
HOROSCOPE

A Lot of Sauce

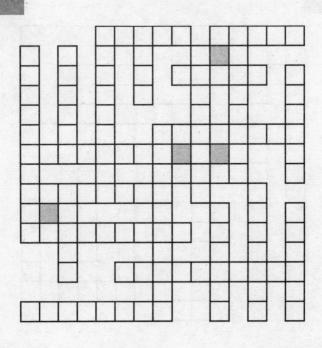

4 letters
PLUM

5 letters
AIOLI
APPLE
CAPER
CURRY
GRAVY

6 letters
CHEESE

GARLIC
MORNAY
TOMATO

7 letters
TABASCO

8 letters
AU GRATIN
AU POIVRE
BARBECUE
BECHAMEL

MUSHROOM
PERI-PERI

9 letters
A LA GREQUE
CARBONARA

10 letters
ARRABBIATA
BLANQUETTE
PUTTANESCA

Cakes

5 letters
ICING
LARDY
LAYER
MOCHA
POUND

6 letters
CARROT
CHEESE
CHERRY
DUNDEE

ECCLES
MARBLE
ORANGE
SCONES

7 letters
CURRANT
FILLING
MIXTURE

8 letters
DOUGHNUT
MACAROON
MARZIPAN

9 letters
CHRISTMAS

11 letters
LEMON
  SPONGE

243 Baby Words

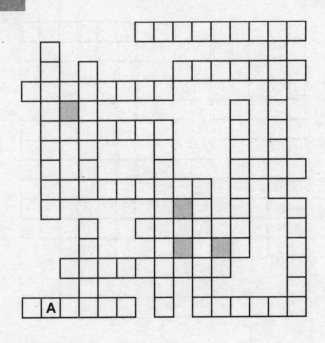

4 letters
SCAN

5 letters
BIRTH

6 letters
DOCTOR
FATHER
LABOUR
MOTHER

7 letters
LAYETTE
MIDWIFE
NATURAL
NEWBORN

8 letters
DELIVERY
FIRST CRY

9 letters
ANTENATAL
CAESAREAN
HEARTBEAT
PREGNANCY
PREMATURE

10 letters
NINE MONTHS

'J' Words

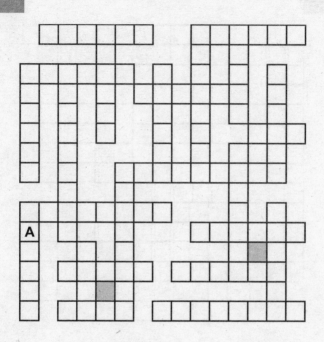

3 letters
JIB

4 letters
JEST
JOVE

5 letters
JADED
JOKER

6 letters
JAILOR
JAMJAR
JARGON
JASPER
JEJUNE
JINXES
JOINER
JOKING
JOTTER
JUDAIC
JUJUBE
JUMBLE

7 letters
JIBBING

8 letters
JAMBOREE
JINGOISM
JODHPURS
JUICIEST

9 letters
JABBERING
JOCKEYING

Inventors

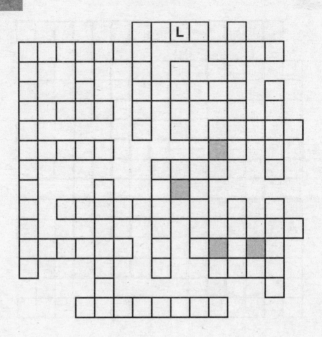

4 letters
BELL
BENZ
BIRO
COLT
FORD
TULL
WATT

5 letters
DYSON
MORSE

NOBEL
TESLA
VOLTA

6 letters
BENDIX
BRUNEL
DIESEL
EDISON
FULTON
SCHICK

7 letters
CARLSON
MARCONI
WHITTLE

8 letters
BIRDSEYE
FRANKLIN

12 letters
WESTING-
HOUSE

Inventions

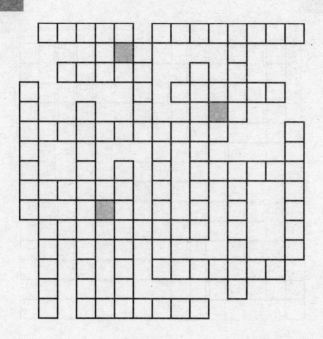

3 letters
CAR

5 letters
CLOCK
LASER
MODEM
TORCH
WHEEL

6 letters
CAMERA
CEMENT
DYNAMO

7 letters
BATTERY
COMPASS
MATCHES
PLASTIC
TORPEDO

8 letters
ATOM BOMB
HOLOGRAM
LINOLEUM

9 letters
METRONOME
TELESCOPE

11 letters
COMPACT DISC
RAZOR BLADES

Armed Forces

4 letters
ARMY
GUNS
NAVY
TANK

5 letters
BERET
FLEET
MEDAL
RANKS
SHIPS

6 letters
COMBAT
ENSIGN
SAILOR
STOKER
VESSEL

7 letters
ADMIRAL
ARSENAL
GENERAL
MARINES

MISSION
OFFICER

8 letters
AIR FORCE
ENGINEER

9 letters
BRIGADIER

10 letters
OPERATIONS

King Arthur

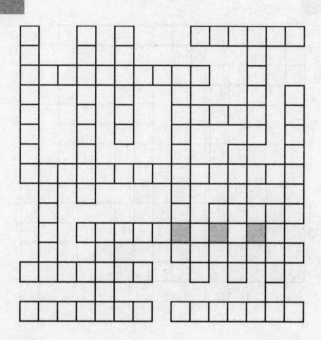

3 letters
KAY

5 letters
BORIS
LUCAN
NIMUE
UTHER

6 letters
ARTHUR
AVALON
ISOLDE

LIONEL
MERLIN

7 letters
CAMELOT
DAGONET
KNIGHTS
LAMORAK
MORDRED
PELLEUS

8 letters
LANCELOT
PERCIVAL

9 letters
PENDRAGON

10 letters
ROUND TABLE

15 letters
LA COTE MALE
   TAILE

Escape Plan

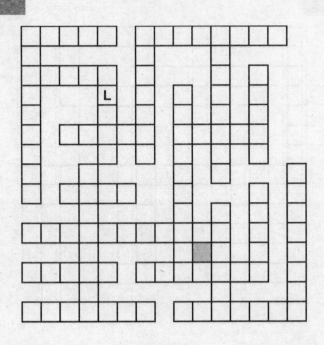

4 letters
JUMP

5 letters
AVOID
BREAK
DODGE
ELOPE
ELUDE
EVADE
LEG IT
SKIVE

6 letters
DEFECT

7 letters
BAIL OUT
GET AWAY
RETREAT
SCARPER

8 letters
SIDESTEP
SLIP AWAY

SNEAK OFF
TURN TAIL

9 letters
SKEDADDLE

10 letters
PLAY TRUANT

11 letters
FRENCH LEAVE

English Cricketers

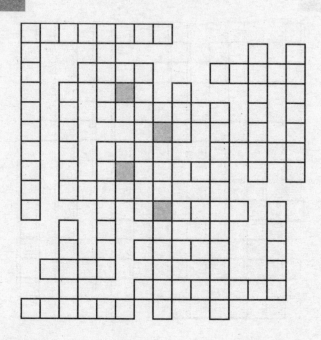

3 letters
KEY
MAY

4 letters
CORK
LAMB
LOCK
SNOW

5 letters
ADAMS
EVANS
GOWER

GRACE
KNOTT
LEWIS
SMALL
SMITH

6 letters
DEXTER
HUTTON
RADLEY

7 letters
CADDICK
DENNESS

STEWART
VAUGHAN

8 letters
BREARLEY
FLETCHER
RICHARDS

10 letters
RAMPRAKASH

11 letters
TRESCOTHICK

Animal Farm

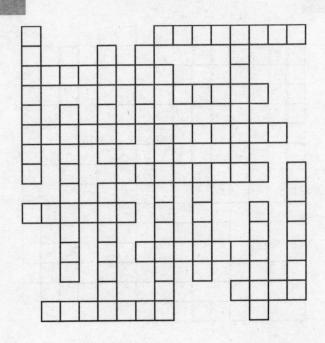

4 letters
DOGS
PIGS

5 letters
BOXER

6 letters
CLOVER
HUMANS
JESSIE

MOLLIE
MURIEL

7 letters
ANIMALS
COWSHED
MINIMUS
MR JONES
PINKEYE

8 letters
BENJAMIN
BLUEBELL
NAPOLEON
SNOWBALL
WINDMILL

9 letters
MR WHYMPER

10 letters
PINCHFIELD

A Few Friendly Words

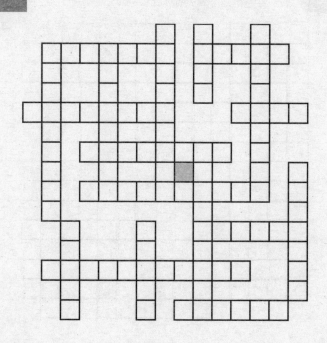

4 letters
ALLY
CHUM

5 letters
BUDDY
CRONY
LOVER

6 letters
COHORT
PEN PAL

7 letters
BROTHER
COMRADE

8 letters
FAMILIAR
PLAYMATE
ROOMMATE

9 letters
ASSOCIATE
BEDFELLOW

COLLEAGUE
NEIGHBOUR

10 letters
WELL-WISHER

11 letters
CONFEDERATE

Charleses

4 letters
BYRD
LAMB
LANE

5 letters
BROWN
CHASE
DAVID
PEACE
PRICE
SHEEN

6 letters
DINGLE
GRODIN
SMIRKE
TOWNES

7 letters
CHESTER
HAUGHEY
PARNELL
PENROSE
REISNER

RICHTER
WINDSOR

8 letters
DE GAULLE
NICHOLAS
PASARELL

9 letters
MACARTHUR

Beekeeping

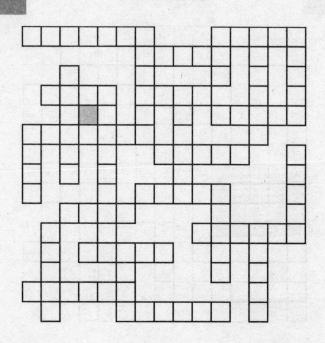

3 letters
WAX

4 letters
COMB
EGGS
FOOD
PUPA
VEIL

5 letters
CELLS
DRONE

FRAME
LARVA
MITES
NESTS
QUEEN
SMOKE
SWARM
TREES
WINGS

6 letters
COLONY
FLYING

GARDEN
GLOVES
INSECT
NECTAR
SOCIAL

7 letters
FLOWERS
HUMMING

9 letters
BEEKEEPER

Amuse Yourself

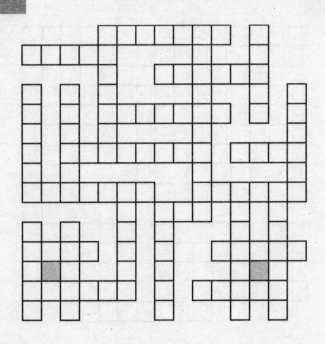

3 letters
FUN

4 letters
GAME
PLAY

5 letters
CHARM
CHEER
LAUGH
MIRTH

SMILE
SPORT

6 letters
ENGAGE
FROLIC
LIVELY
OCCUPY
PLEASE
REGALE
THRILL
TICKLE

7 letters
COMICAL
DELIGHT
DISPORT
ENLIVEN
GLADDEN
PASTIME

8 letters
INTEREST

10 letters
RECREATION

Deserts

4 letters
GOBI
THAR

5 letters
KAVIR
MONTE
NAMIB
ORDOS

6 letters
GIBSON

JUDEAN
LIBYAN
MOJAVE
NUBIAN
SAHARA
SYRIAN
TANAMI

7 letters
AL-DAHNA
SECHURA
SONORAN

9 letters
BLEDOWSKA
LA GUAJIRA

10 letters
AUSTRALIAN
PATAGONIAN
STRZELECKI

In the Theatre

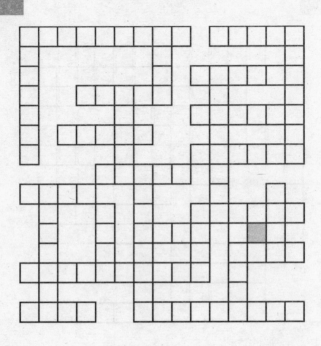

4 letters
CALL
CAST
DECK
GRID
GRIP
LEFT
LEGS
PLOT

5 letters
AD-LIB
ARENA

BOARD
CABLE
LINES

6 letters
ANCHOR
DIMMER
PLACES
STROBE
TRACKS

7 letters
BORDERS

DRESSER
REVOLVE

8 letters
BLOCKING
INTERVAL

9 letters
DOWNSTAGE
GREEN ROOM

10 letters
BLACK LIGHT

Deep, Very Deep

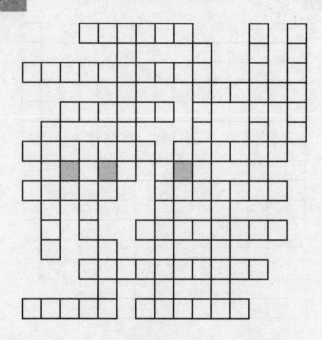

4 letters
BASS

5 letters
ABYSS
GRAVE
VIVID

6 letters
ARDENT
ASTUTE
CANYON

GAPING
SEVERE
STRONG

7 letters
EARNEST
FERVENT
INTENSE
LEARNED

8 letters
PROFOUND
RESONANT
SONOROUS
VIGOROUS

9 letters
CAVERNOUS

10 letters
FATHOMLESS
PASSIONATE

Ports of the World

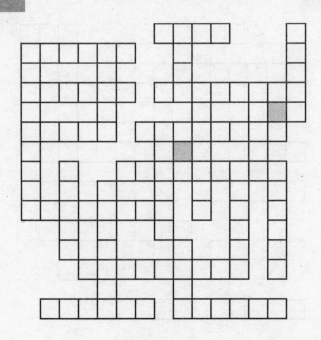

4 letters
ACRE
COBH
HULL

5 letters
AQABA
CADIZ
GENOA
HAIFA
OSAKA

6 letters
BERGEN
BILBAO
DIEPPE
DURBAN
LISBON
MUMBAI
OSTEND

7 letters
ANTWERP
ESBJERG

8 letters
KINGSTON
PORT SAID
SHANGHAI

9 letters
DUBROVNIK
ROTTERDAM
ZEEBRUGGE

Airports of the World

5 letters
LOGAN

6 letters
CHANGI
HANEDA
LINATE
NARITA
NEWARK

7 letters
ARLANDA
ATLANTA
BANGKOK
BARAJAS
BEIJING
GATWICK
MIRABEL
ORLANDO

8 letters
CIAMPINO
HEATHROW
MCCARRAN

9 letters
LA GUARDIA
SKY HARBOR

10 letters
LOS ANGELES

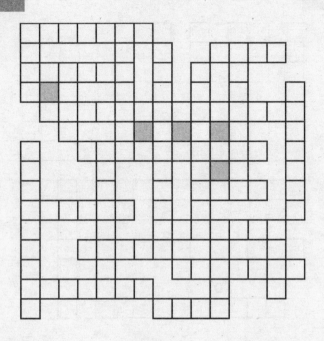

4 letters
CARE
HELP
SALE
SHOP
TACT
TEAM

5 letters
FOCUS
PHONE

6 letters
LISTEN

RIGHTS

7 letters
CONCERN
PRODUCT
RAPPORT
RESPECT
SERVICE
SUCCESS

8 letters
EXTERNAL
ONE-TO-ONE

9 letters
AWARENESS
OWNERSHIP

10 letters
MONITORING

11 letters
COMPETITORS

14 letters
CORRES-
PONDENCE

Indian Towns and Cities

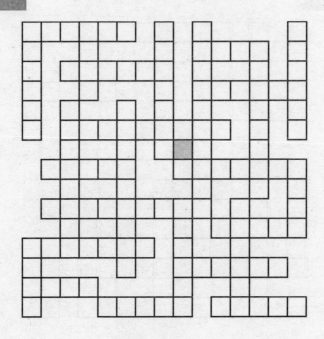

4 letters
AGRA
AMLI
DHAR
OBRA
PUNE

5 letters
ERODE
KOCHI
PATNA
SURAT

6 letters
GUNTUR
INDORE
JAIPUR
KANPUR
MEERUT
NAGPUR
NASHIK
RAJKOT

7 letters
CHENNAI
DHANBAD

KOLKATA

8 letters
AMRITSAR
VADODARA

9 letters
ALLAHABAD
BANGALORE
FARIDABAD

10 letters
COIMBATORE

Plane Thinking

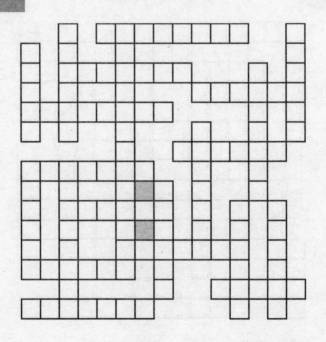

5 letters
PITCH
RADAR

REFUEL
SUKHOI
WHEELS

8 letters
CONCORDE
ELEVATOR
FUSELAGE

6 letters
ENGINE
FOXBAT
HANGAR
INTAKE
JAGUAR
NIMROD
PYLONS

7 letters
GRUMMAN
LANDING
PHANTOM
STEWARD
TORNADO
TUPOLEV

13 letters
UNDER-
CARRIAGE

Photography

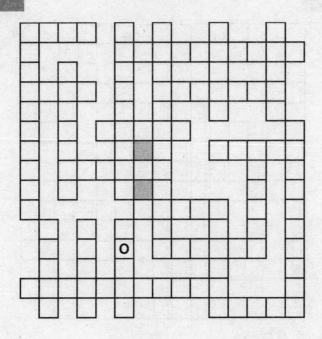

4 letters
BLUR
BULB

5 letters
DODGE
FIXER
F-STOP
MODEL
PRISM
SHOTS
SNAPS
TINTS
TONER

6 letters
CAMERA
REWIND
SLIDES
TRIPOD

7 letters
SUBJECT
TEXTURE

9 letters
DEVELOPER

10 letters
BOX BROWNIE
EXHIBITION
SPOTLIGHTS

11 letters
PERSPECTIVE

12 letters
PHOTO-
GRAPHER

'K' Words

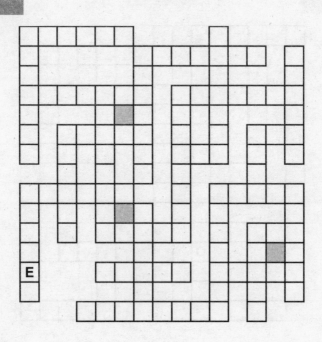

E

3 letters
KEG
KIP
KIT

4 letters
KELP

5 letters
KAPOK
KHAKI
KNAVE
KNIFE

KOALA
KRILL

6 letters
KANSAS
KARATE
KAYAKS
KEENLY
KILLER
KIMONO
KIPPER

7 letters
KASHMIR
KEELING
KICKING
KIDDING
KISSING
KNOCKED
KNUCKLE

8 letters
KEYSTONE
KNAPSACK
KRAKATOA

Ancient Civilisations

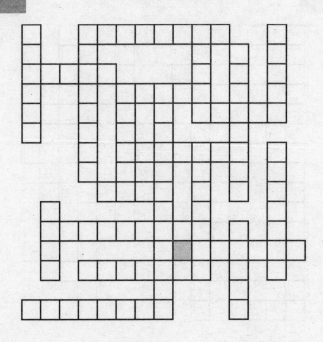

4 letters
INCA
ZHOU

5 letters
AZTEC
CELTS
MAYAN
MEDES
MOCHE
ROMAN

6 letters
ARATTA
JIROFT
MINOAN

7 letters
HITTITE
MINAEAN
OTTOMAN
PERSIAN

8 letters
ARAMAEAN
ASSYRIAN
HELLENIC
SUMERIAN

9 letters
HIMYARITE

12 letters
CARTHAGINIAN

Children

3 letters
BOY
KID
LAD
SON
TOT

4 letters
BABY
GIRL
LASS
WEAN

5 letters
CHILD
MINOR
PUPIL
YOUTH

6 letters
CHERUB
HOYDEN
INFANT
NIPPER
SHAVER

7 letters
BAMBINO
TODDLER

8 letters
DAUGHTER
JUVENILE
TEENAGER

9 letters
OFFSPRING
YOUNGSTER

Fonts and Typefaces

4 letters
VIVA

5 letters
ARIAL
BAUER
BIRCH
FLAMA
NUEVA
RAVIE

6 letters
CHEVIN
FUTURA
LUCIDA
MYRIAD
OPTIMA
TAHOMA

7 letters
ARNO PRO
COURIER

8 letters
HUMANIST
PERPETUA
WEBDINGS

9 letters
EUROSTILE
TREBUCHET

10 letters
CONSTANTIA

11 letters
BASKERVILLE

Monopoly Board

3 letters
DOG
RED

4 letters
BLUE
IRON
JAIL
PINK
RENT

5 letters
BOARD

BROWN
GREEN
HOTEL
RULES

6 letters
PIECES
STRAND
TOP HAT
YELLOW

7 letters
ADVANCE

ANNUITY
PLAYERS

8 letters
BIRTHDAY

9 letters
BOW STREET
INCOME TAX
RACING CAR

10 letters
EUSTON ROAD

Seven-letter Words

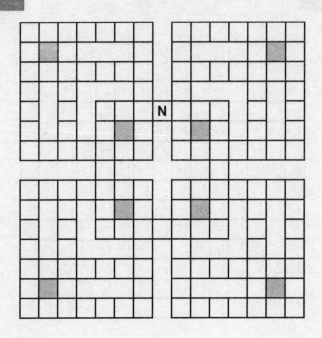

ARRIVED	KETCHUP	SEAWEED
COMMENT	NEAREST	SIGNALS
DROPPED	OBSERVE	SUPPOSE
EMPEROR	OCTOBER	SWEATER
ENDLESS	PATCHES	TIPPING
FAILURE	PIRATES	TOUGHEN
GROWN-UP	PLANNED	TRAFFIC
GUITARS	PROUDLY	TROUBLE
KEEPERS	RETIRES	URANIUM
	SCENERY	

Mobile Phone

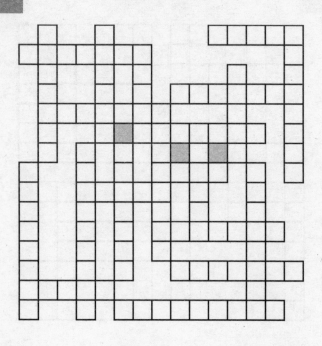

4 letters
GPRS

5 letters
ALARM
GAMES
SKINS
SMART
TOP-UP

6 letters
CAR KIT
SIGNAL

7 letters
DIGITAL
HEADSET
KEY LOCK
NETWORK
SIM CARD
SPEAKER

STANDBY
TEXTING

8 letters
PEAK TIME
RINGTONE
VIBRATOR
WIRELESS

9 letters
DIRECTORY
MESSAGING

Animal Stars

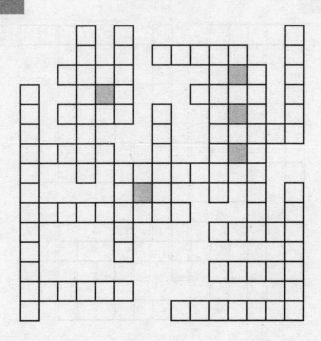

4 letters
BABE
FURY
MR ED

5 letters
BENJI
BUDDY
COMET
HOOCH
PETEY

TRAMP
WILLY

6 letters
LASSIE
MURRAY
NUNZIO

7 letters
FLIPPER
TRIGGER

8 letters
CHAMPION
HERCULES
WISHBONE

9 letters
GENTLE BEN
OLD YELLER

12 letters
LANCELOT LINK

Fictional Sleuths

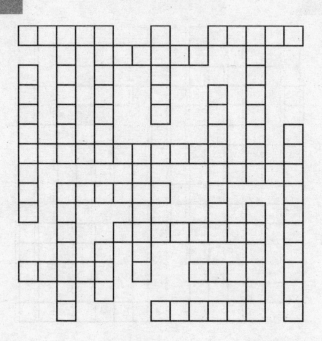

3 letters
ZEN

4 letters
CHAN

5 letters
LACEY
MORSE
REBUS
REGAN
SGT HO

6 letters
CAGNEY
HAZELL
MANNIX
QUINCY

7 letters
BIGGLES
LAIDLAW
MAIGRET
SHANNON

8 letters
CALLAHAN
CLOUSEAU
CROCKETT
IRONSIDE

10 letters
SHOESTRING

11 letters
ARSENE LUPIN

Mountains

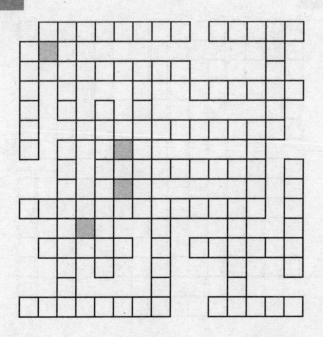

5 letters
ADAMS
CENIS
HEKLA
JANNU
KAMET

6 letters
ARARAT
CARMEL
GONGGA
MAKALU

NUPTSE
TALUNG
VINSON

8 letters
CHANGTSE
MCKINLEY
RUSHMORE

9 letters
ACONCAGUA
ANNAPURNA

BROAD PEAK
KAMBACHEN

11 letters
MACHU PICCHU

13 letters
KANGCHEN-
JUNGA

Speech, Speech

4 letters
BLAB
RANT
TALK

5 letters
ARGUE
ORATE
PLEAD
QUOTE
STATE
UTTER
VOICE

6 letters
DEBATE
GABBLE
GOSSIP
PREACH
REMARK
REPEAT
SPEECH

7 letters
CHATTER
ITERATE
NARRATE
PROTEST

8 letters
CONVERSE
PROCLAIM

9 letters
REPRESENT

11 letters
INTERROGATE

Music Lesson

4 letters
BEAT

5 letters
BREVE
MINIM
PITCH
SHARP
SUITE
TEMPO
WALTZ

6 letters
BRIDGE
QUAVER
RUBATO
SCALES
STAVES

7 letters
POSTURE
TWO-STEP

8 letters
BASS CLEF
DOMINANT
PLECTRUM
PRACTICE

9 letters
SOFT PEDAL

11 letters
BROKEN
  CHORD

Funfair Fun

3 letters
FUN

4 letters
KIDS
MAZE
SHOW

5 letters
DARTS
GASPS
MUSIC
RIDES
SLIDE
SPEED

6 letters
CROWDS
HOOP-LA
PRIZES
SMELLS
SOUNDS
SWINGS

7 letters
COCONUT
MIRRORS
WALTZER

8 letters
CARAVANS
ICE CREAM

10 letters
CANDY FLOSS
ROUNDABOUT

13 letters
FORTUNE-
TELLER

Architecture

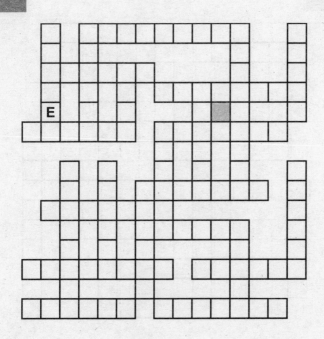

4 letters
ARCH

5 letters
NICHE
TORUS

6 letters
CORBEL
CUPOLA
FINIAL
FLECHE

IMPOST
LANCET
LINTEL
NORMAN
PILLAR
PLINTH
SCREEN
SOFFIT

7 letters
CAPITAL
PORTICO

TRANSOM
TREFOIL

8 letters
EGYPTIAN
GARGOYLE
TRIGLYPH

9 letters
NEOLITHIC
STANCHION

Sweet…

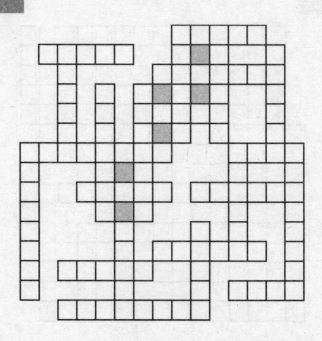

4 letters
CORN
PEAS

5 letters
BASIL
BRIAR
CIDER
HEART
MEATS
TOOTH
WATER

6 letters
BREADS
CHERRY
CLOVER
ORANGE
PEPPER
SHERRY
VIOLET

7 letters
REVENGE
SCENTED
WILLIAM

8 letters
CHESTNUT
NOTHINGS
SMELLING
SOUNDING

Fifth of November

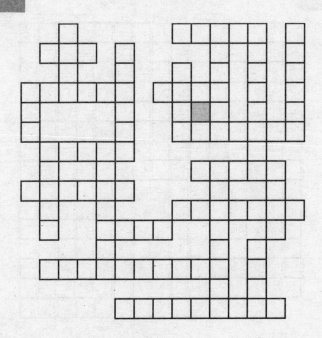

3 letters
BOX
GUY

4 letters
BURN
FUSE
PLOT
SOAR
SOUP
WOOD

5 letters
FIFTH
FLAME
MASKS
SCARF

6 letters
BANGER
EFFIGY
FAWKES
SPARKS
WARMTH

7 letters
CHINESE
DISPLAY
TREASON

8 letters
CHILDREN
SPARKLER

9 letters
CHESTNUTS

10 letters
STAND CLEAR

A Lot of Anger

3 letters
IRK
VEX

4 letters
FITS
FURY
MIFF
RILE

5 letters
ANNOY
GET AT

PIQUE
ROUSE

6 letters
ENRAGE
FRENZY
FURORE
NEEDLE
NETTLE
RATTLE
SPLEEN
TEMPER
WIND UP

7 letters
QUARREL
RANCOUR
TANTRUM

8 letters
EMBITTER

9 letters
AGGRAVATE

10 letters
ANTAGONISE
EXASPERATE

Do You Have the Ability?

5 letters
FORTE
MEANS
MIGHT
POWER
SKILL
TOUCH

6 letters
ENERGY
GENIUS

TALENT
VIGOUR

7 letters
FACULTY
KNOW-HOW
MASTERY

8 letters
APTITUDE
CAPACITY

DEFTNESS
STRENGTH

9 letters
EXPERTISE

10 letters
CLEVERNESS
COMPETENCE

Hold It

4 letters
BELT
KNOT
LINK
NAIL
ROPE
TACK
VICE

5 letters
CHAIN
CLASP

CLEAT
RIVET
SCREW
STRAP

6 letters
STRING
VELCRO
ZIPPER

8 letters
CABLE TIE
FASTENER
SHOELACE

9 letters
SELLOTAPE
SUPERGLUE

10 letters
NUT AND BOLT
PARCEL TAPE

Printworks

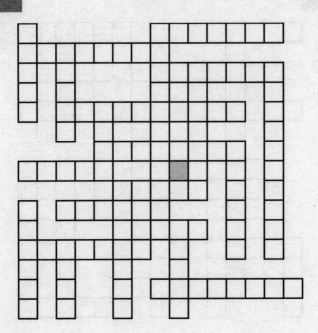

4 letters
MARK
PAGE
TEXT

5 letters
IMAGE
LITHO
PLATE
PRESS
SPIRO
TINTS

6 letters
FORMAT
OZALID
STAPLE

7 letters
ARTWORK
COLOURS
IMPRESS
OUTLINE
PROCESS

8 letters
GRAPHICS
INTAGLIO
PRINT RUN

10 letters
SILKSCREEN
TYPESETTER

11 letters
COPPERPLATE

Transport

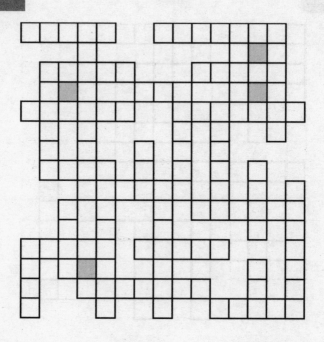

3 letters
BUS
CAR
VAN

4 letters
BOAT
FOOT
SHIP
SKIS

5 letters
COACH
HORSE

KAYAK
SEDAN
SLOOP
TRAIN
YACHT

6 letters
ARMADA
BANGER
GLIDER
JALOPY
LAUNCH
SKATES
SLEIGH

7 letters
CORACLE
LIGHTER
MINICAB
PASSAGE
TRAILER

8 letters
PASSPORT

9 letters
HYDROFOIL

'L' Words

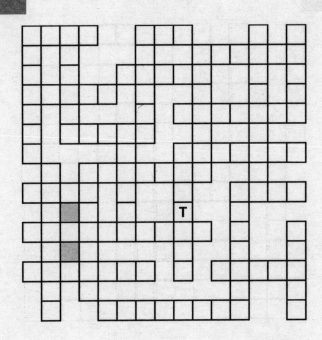

3 letters
LEY

4 letters
LILY
LIME
LYNX

5 letters
LATCH
LAYER
LEAFY
LOWLY
LUCKY

LYING

6 letters
LABOUR
LAXITY
LINTEL
LOUDLY

7 letters
LAGGING
LAPLAND
LASTING
LENDING
LIBERAL

LICKING
LIONESS
LOTTERY
LYRICAL

8 letters
LIFELIKE
LOCALITY

9 letters
LIABILITY

10 letters
LEADERSHIP

Yorkshire

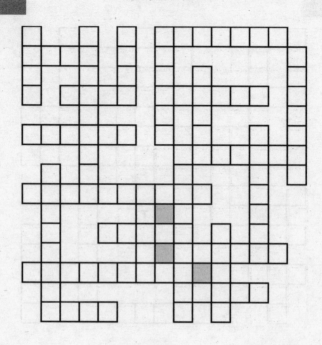

4 letters
AIRE
DOVE
KYLE
OUSE
POOL

5 letters
DALES
FILEY
HAWES
LEEDS
SWALE

6 letters
DEARNE
MALHAM
SETTLE
TOWTON

7 letters
DERWENT
HAWORTH
LEYBURN
SKIPTON

8 letters
HAREWOOD

9 letters
BOSTON SPA
DENBY DALE
PEN-Y-GHENT

10 letters
EAST RIDING

The Environment

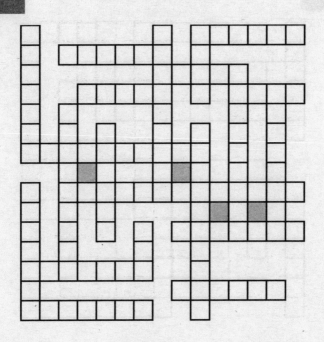

3 letters
CFC

4 letters
COAL
SMOG

5 letters
FLOOD
OZONE

6 letters
BAMBOO

EL NINO
ENERGY
SEWAGE

7 letters
COMPOST
LOGGING
ORGANIC
TSUNAMI
WARMING

8 letters
ACID RAIN

9 letters
BLEACHING
ECOSYSTEM
FOOD CHAIN

10 letters
GREENPEACE
VEGETARIAN

13 letters
CARBON
NEUTRAL

Orienteering

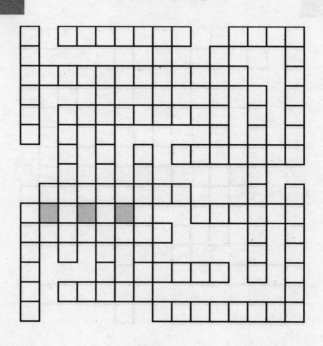

4 letters
MAPS

5 letters
ROUTE
SCALE
TREES

6 letters
CIRCLE
EFFORT
FINISH
FOREST

7 letters
COMPASS
FITNESS
SYMBOLS
WHISTLE

8 letters
CONTOURS
FORM LINE
MOUNTAIN
NAVIGATE
TRAINERS

9 letters
CHALLENGE

10 letters
DIRECTIONS

12 letters
REGISTRATION
STARTING LINE

Genealogy

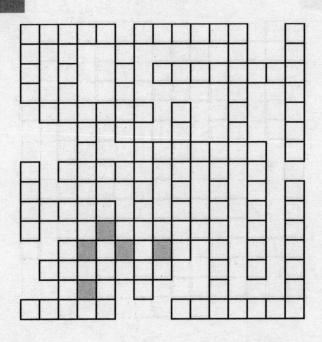

4 letters
BABY
SONS
WIFE
WILL

5 letters
BANNS
BIBLE
BIRTH
DEATH
DEEDS
WIDOW

6 letters
CHARTS
PARENT
PARISH

7 letters
ANCIENT
DIVORCE
HISTORY
HUSBAND
LIBRARY
RECORDS

SIBLING
SURNAME

8 letters
ARCHIVES
REGISTER
RESEARCH

9 letters
RELATIVES

Ancient Writers

4 letters
LIVY
OVID

5 letters
AESOP
HOMER
MOSES

6 letters
CICERO
HESIOD
HORACE
LUCIAN
PINDAR
SAPPHO
SENECA
VIRGIL

7 letters
TACITUS

8 letters
CATULLUS
SOCRATES

9 letters
ARISTOTLE
EURIPEDES
SOPHOCLES

12 letters
ARISTOPHANES

Breeds of Sheep

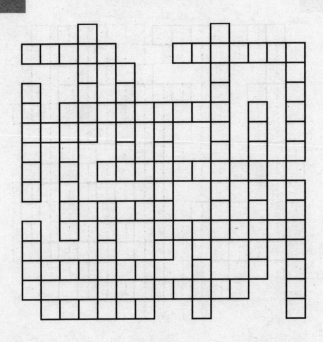

4 letters
DALA
SOAY

5 letters
JACOB
LLEYN
TEXEL

6 letters
ARCOTT
AWASSI
BELTEX

DORPER
MASHAM
MERINO
ROMNEY

7 letters
KARAMAN
LINCOLN
RYELAND
VENDEEN

8 letters
COTENTIN
HERDWICK

9 letters
FUGLESTAD
KERRY HILL

10 letters
BORDERDALE

11 letters
WENSLEYDALE

Hiking Gear

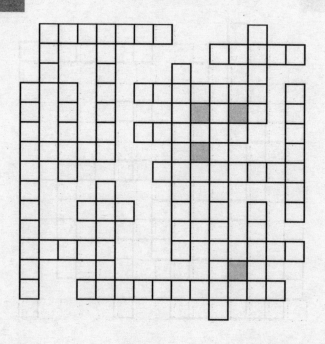

3 letters
HAT
MAP
RUG

5 letters
BOOTS
KNIFE
PHONE
SCARF
SOCKS
TORCH
WATER

6 letters
CAMERA
GLOVES

7 letters
BLANKET
COMPASS
MATCHES
WHISTLE

8 letters
RUCKSACK

10 letters
BINOCULARS

11 letters
FIRST-AID KIT
VACUUM FLASK

12 letters
TREKKING POLE

UK Prime Ministers

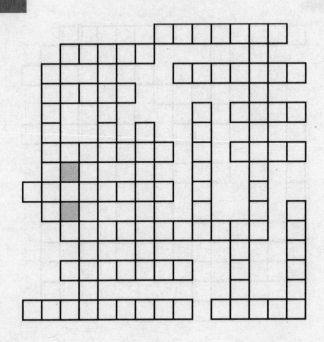

4 letters
EDEN
PEEL

5 letters
BLAIR
BROWN
HEATH
MAJOR

6 letters
ATTLEE
WILSON

7 letters
ASQUITH
BALDWIN
BALFOUR
CAMERON
WALPOLE

8 letters
BONAR LAW
PERCEVAL
THATCHER

9 letters
GLADSTONE
MACDONALD

11 letters
DOUGLAS-
HOME
LLOYD GEORGE

Scottish Tartans

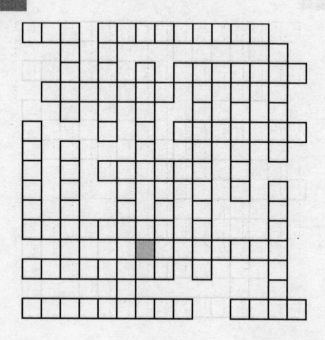

3 letters
GOW

4 letters
KERR

5 letters
WYLIE

6 letters
GORDON
HUNTER
RAMSAY

STUART
TAYLOR
WILSON

7 letters
AINSLIE
BRAEMAR
BRANDON
CAMERON
JACKSON
KENNEDY
OGILVIE

8 letters
SINCLAIR
TURNBULL
URQUHART

9 letters
MACARTHUR
ROBERTSON

11 letters
ABERCROMBIE

Lakes

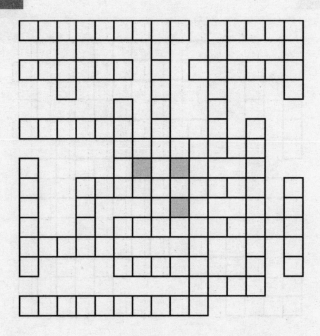

4 letters
CHAD
COMO
ERIE
EYRE

5 letters
GARDA
HURON
ONEGA
PATOS
TAHOE

6 letters
BAIKAL
CRATER
GENEVA
LADOGA

7 letters
TURKANA

8 letters
TITICACA

9 letters
CONSTANCE
GREAT SALT
MARACAIBO

10 letters
CASPIAN SEA
GREAT SLAVE
WINDERMERE

11 letters
LOCH KATRINE

Circus Fun

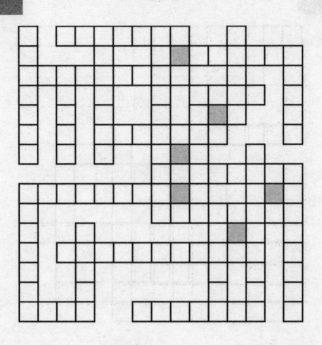

4 letters
DOGS
TENT

5 letters
FUNNY
LIONS
SEALS
STARS

6 letters
PONIES
STUNTS

7 letters
ACROBAT
ARTISTE
CARAVAN
COMMAND
POPCORN
TICKETS
TRAPEZE

8 letters
CHILDREN
ELEPHANT
ICE CREAM

MOTOR CAR

9 letters
MENAGERIE
POLAR BEAR

10 letters
TRAMPOLINE

11 letters
PERFORMANCE

Bang!

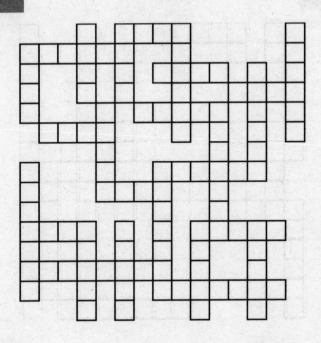

4 letters
BASH
BEAT
BLOW
CLAP
LICK
PEAL
RING
SHOT
SLAM

5 letters
CLANG
CLOUT
CLUNK
CRACK
CRASH
KNOCK
THUMP

6 letters
CRUNCH
RATTLE

STRIKE
THRASH
WALLOP

7 letters
CLATTER
EXPLODE
RESOUND
THUNDER

8 letters
DETONATE

Art Work

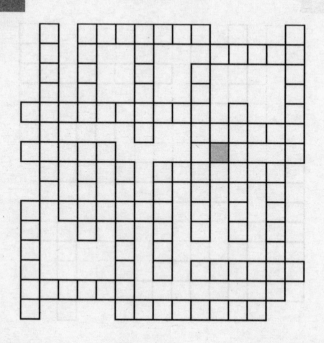

5 letters
BATIK
EASEL
LINES
PAPER

6 letters
CRAYON
DESIGN
ENAMEL
MIXING
PENCIL

SHADOW
SKETCH

7 letters
BRUSHES
CARTOON
ETCHING
PALETTE
PROFILE

8 letters
GRAPHICS
PAINTING

9 letters
ENGRAVING
MODELLING

10 letters
BACKGROUND

300   Hard as Can Be

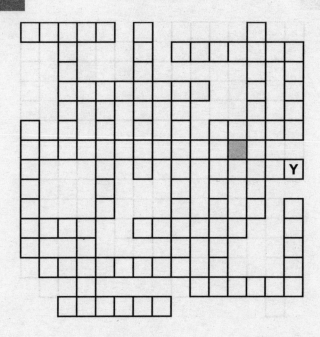

4 letters
NUMB

5 letters
BRAVE
RIGID
ROCKY
SOLID
STONY
STOUT

6 letters
FLINTY
SEVERE
STEELY

7 letters
CALLOUS
DIAMOND
GRANITE
ONEROUS

8 letters
EXACTING

INTREPID
RIGOROUS

9 letters
RESISTANT

10 letters
COURAGEOUS
UNYIELDING

11 letters
INSENSITIVE

'M' Words

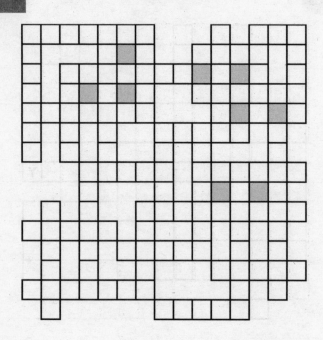

3 letters
MUM

4 letters
MESA

5 letters
MAFIA
MAMMA
MARCH
MASON
MAUVE
MAYBE
MEATY

MONEY
MORSE
MOUTH
MURRE
MUSTY

6 letters
MEDIUM
MEMORY
MIMICS
MOHAIR

7 letters
MAMMOTH

MAXIMUM
MIASMIC
MISERLY
MIXTURE
MYCOSIS
MYSTIFY

8 letters
MACHISMO
MOISTURE

9 letters
MARQUETRY
MELODIOUS

Pizza

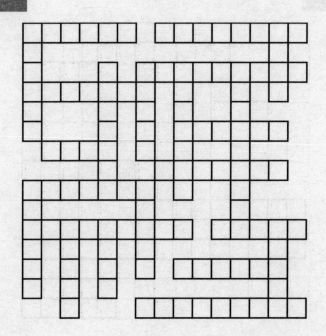

4 letters
CORN
OVEN
TUNA

5 letters
BACON
CRUST
DOUGH
HERBS
SPICY

6 letters
CHEESE
GARLIC
OLIVES
ONIONS
PRAWNS

7 letters
CHICKEN
DEEP PAN
OREGANO

PEPPERS
SAUSAGE

8 letters
BBQ SAUCE

9 letters
ANCHOVIES
DICED PORK
PEPPERONI
PINEAPPLE

Tropical Fish

4 letters
CORY

5 letters
DANIO
GUPPY
JULIE
OSCAR
PLECO

6 letters
BICHIR
DISCUS

7 letters
RASBORA
RED PACU
SEVERUM

8 letters
ROSY BARB

9 letters
ANGELFISH
FLYING FOX
GREEN SCAT
HARLEQUIN

10 letters
RED PIRANHA

12 letters
PARADISE FISH

14 letters
SIAMESE
 FIGHTER

What's Your Aim?

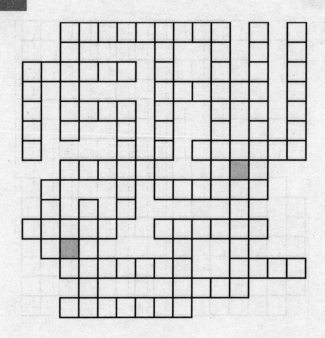

4 letters
GOAL
HOPE
MARK
VIEW

5 letters
DRIFT
LEVEL
SIGHT
TRAIN

6 letters
ASPIRE
COURSE
DESIGN
DESIRE
DIRECT
LINE UP
MOTIVE
SCHEME
STRIVE

7 letters
ATTEMPT
BEARING
MISSION
PROPOSE

9 letters
DETERMINE
ENDEAVOUR
OBJECTIVE

Sculptors

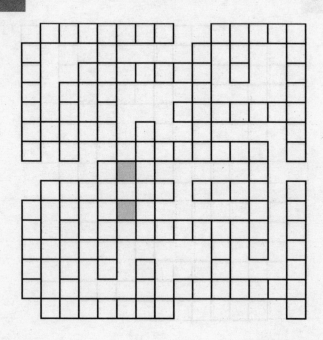

3 letters
LEE
PYE

4 letters
LONG
SWAN
TODD

5 letters
BLOYE
KEMPF
MOORE

RODIN

6 letters
CALDER
DEACON
HANSON
PISANO
STUART
WELDON

7 letters
ALGARDI
BERGIER

DA VINCI
EPSTEIN
GORMLEY
LACOMBE
PIGALLE
WILDING
ZADKINE

8 letters
HEPWORTH

9 letters
DONATELLO

Lovely Chocolate

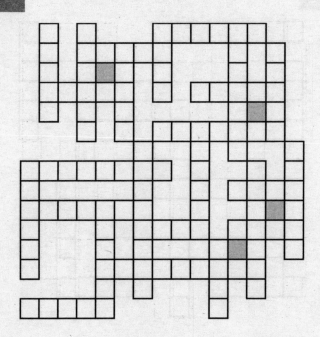

4 letters	PLAIN	7 letters
BARS	SAUCE	BISCUIT
CAKE	SWEET	CARAMEL
DARK		LIQUEUR
MILK	**6 letters**	TRUFFLE
RICH	BITTER	
	DOUBLE	8 letters
5 letters	ECLAIR	BEVERAGE
CANDY	FONDUE	BROWNIES
CHIPS	KISSES	
COCOA	SMOOTH	9 letters
FUDGE		DIGESTIVE

Capital Cities of Africa

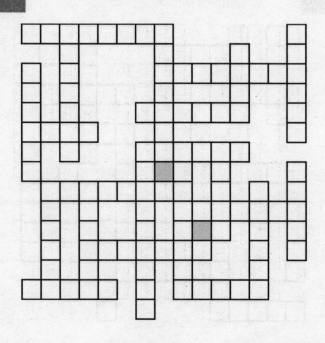

4 letters
JUBA
LOME

5 letters
ABUJA
CAIRO
RABAT
TUNIS

6 letters
BANJUL

DODOMA
HARARE
LUANDA
LUSAKA
MAPUTO
NIAMEY

7 letters
ALGIERS
KAMPALA
NAIROBI
TRIPOLI

8 letters
LILONGWE
MONROVIA
PRETORIA
WINDHOEK

9 letters
MOGADISHU

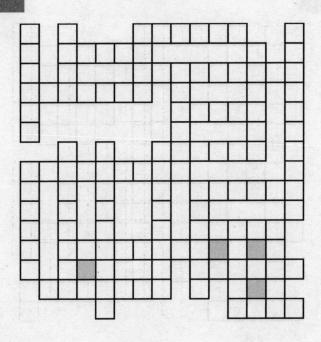

4 letters
DISK
PERL
USER

5 letters
BUILD
ROBOT
SLAVE
STACK
TOOLS

6 letters
BACK-UP
EDITOR
LAPTOP
PACKET
PASCAL
REBOOT
SCREEN
SCROLL
SERVER

7 letters
STORAGE
VIRTUAL

8 letters
ETHERNET
LANGUAGE
NETSCAPE

9 letters
DIRECTORY
REPLICATE
RETRIEVAL

10 letters
EXECUTABLE

Art Media

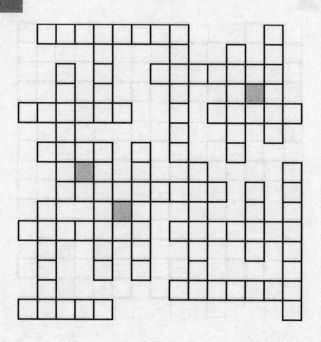

4 letters
DAUB
OILS

5 letters
BATIK
GLAZE
TINGE

6 letters
MOSAIC
PASTEL
PENCIL
RELIEF

7 letters
CARTOON
GILDING
GOUACHE
GRAPHIC
LACQUER

SHADING
TEMPERA
TRACERY
VARNISH

8 letters
ABSTRACT
CHARCOAL

9 letters
GRADATION

Bright

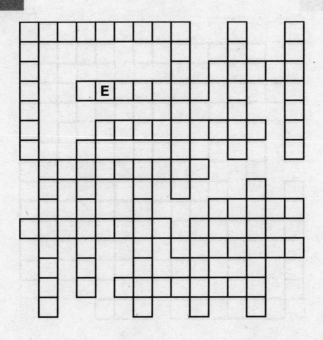

5 letters
FIERY
SUNNY
VIVID

7 letters
BEAMING
BLAZING
INTENSE
RADIANT

SHINING
SILVERY

8 letters
DAZZLING
LUMINOUS
LUSTROUS
PELLUCID
SPLENDID

9 letters
BRILLIANT
EFFULGENT
SPARKLING
TWINKLING

London Areas

3 letters
BOW
KEW

4 letters
SOHO

5 letters
ACTON
BRENT

6 letters
BALHAM
BARNET

EALING
EUSTON
PUTNEY

7 letters
CHELSEA
DULWICH
HAMPTON
LAMBETH
STEPNEY

8 letters
BROMPTON

9 letters
DOCKLANDS

10 letters
SHOREDITCH
TWICKENHAM
WANDSWORTH

11 letters
ROTHERHITHE
WALTHAMSTOW

Space Vehicles

4 letters
LUNA
VEGA
ZOND

5 letters
ARIEL
ORION

6 letters
APOLLO
GIOTTO

SELENE
VENERA
VIKING
VOSTOK

7 letters
MARINER
PIONEER
TELSTAR
VOYAGER

8 letters
ATLANTIS
SAKIGAKE
STARDUST
SURVEYOR

9 letters
DISCOVERY
ENDEAVOUR

Take a Flight

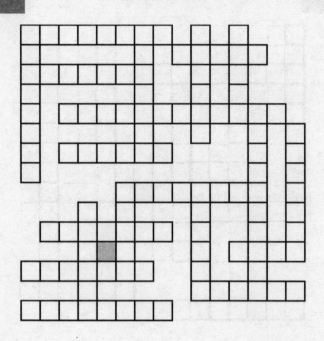

4 letters
GATE

5 letters
AISLE
CABIN
PILOT

6 letters
BRIDGE
LOCKER
PILLOW

SAFETY
WINDOW

7 letters
BAGGAGE
CHECK-IN
LANDING
TICKETS
TROLLEY

8 letters
BOARDING
PASSPORT
SEAT BELT
SECURITY

10 letters
AIR STEWARD

12 letters
IN-FLIGHT MEAL

'N' Words

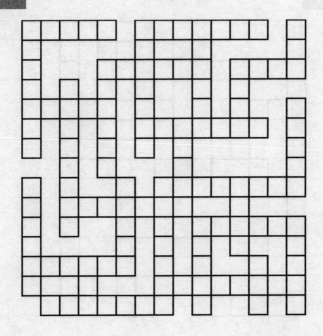

3 letters
NEW
NIP
NUT

4 letters
NEAR
NEXT
NOAH

5 letters
NACRE
NAILS

NINTH
NOISE
NOUNS
NOVEL
NURSE

6 letters
NEEDLE
NIACIN
NOGGIN
NUANCE
NUTMEG
NYLONS

7 letters
NAGGING
NAPPING
NATURAL
NETTING
NEWNESS
NOMINEE
NUNNERY

8 letters
NEATNESS
NIGGLING
NORTHERN

Clear Enough

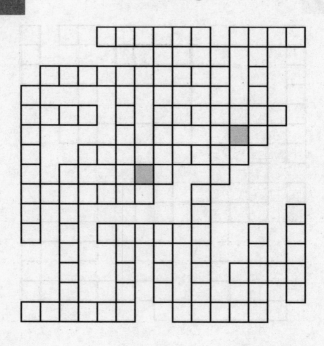

4 letters
FAIR
OPEN
PURE
SURE

5 letters
CLEAN
LIGHT
PLAIN
SHARP

6 letters
GLASSY
LIMPID
PATENT
PURGED

7 letters
CERTAIN
CRYSTAL
EVIDENT
REFINED
UNMIXED

8 letters
DISTINCT
PELLUCID
SPOTLESS

9 letters
CLARIFIED

10 letters
IMMACULATE

Many Michaels

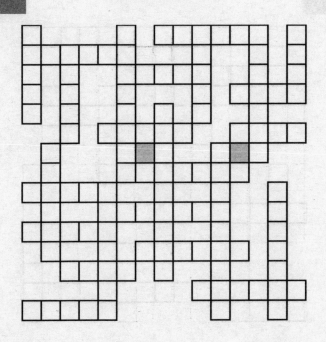

4 letters
REID
TODD
VICK
YORK

5 letters
ASPEL
CHANG
JONES
MOORE
MYERS
PALIN

STICH
WELCH

6 letters
DOLENZ
HAMMER
HOWARD
KEATON
ROONEY

7 letters
DENISON
DOUGLAS

ELPHICK
MEACHER
NESMITH

8 letters
CRAWFORD

9 letters
PARKINSON
TROUGHTON

Talking Turkey

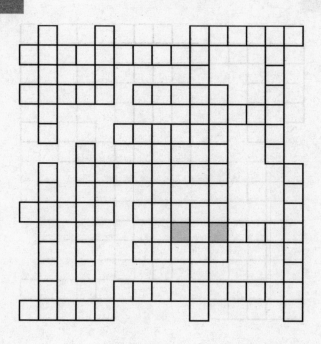

4 letters
RAKI
TROY

5 letters
BAYAR
BURSA
HATAY
INONU
KONYA
MUTLU
PAMUK

6 letters
KEBABS
LEVENT
MASLAK
MERSIN
YILMAZ

7 letters
ANTALYA
ATATURK
CITADEL
VAN GOLU

8 letters
ANATOLIA
BESIKTAS
ISTANBUL

10 letters
CAPPADOCIA
FENERBAHCE

Varieties of Pear

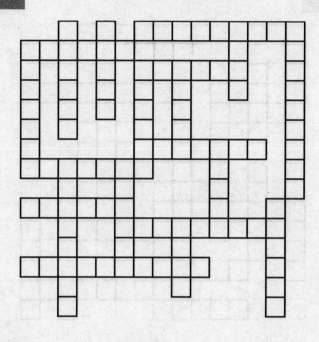

4 letters
BETH
SACK

5 letters
ANJOU
ROCHA
THORN

6 letters
BEACON
BRANDY

CLARET
COMICE
LULLAM
PARROT
TUMPER

7 letters
CLUSTER
MAGNATE
PACKHAM

8 letters
GOLDINGS

9 letters
BROWN BESS
PARSONAGE
SAINT REMY

10 letters
CONFERENCE

The Romans

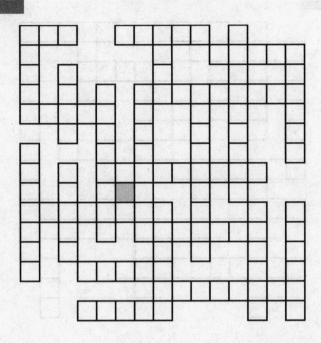

3 letters
LAW

4 letters
NERO
TOGA

5 letters
EAGLE
FORUM
LATIN
NERVA
REMUS

TITUS
VILLA

6 letters
CAESAR
MOSAIC
PROBUS
SENECA

7 letters
BACCHUS
SENATOR

8 letters
CALIGULA
CLAUDIUS
COMMODUS
PANTHEON

9 letters
APPIAN WAY
CATACOMBS
COLOSSEUM
HADRIANUS

Wedding Anniversaries

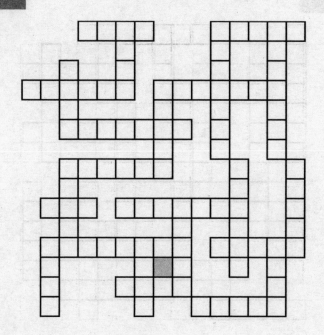

3 letters
TIN

4 letters
GOLD
IRON
LACE
RUBY
SILK
WOOD
WOOL

5 letters
CHINA
CORAL
IVORY
LINEN
PAPER
PEARL
STEEL

6 letters
BRONZE
COTTON

SILVER

7 letters
CRYSTAL
DIAMOND
EMERALD
LEATHER
POTTERY

8 letters
SAPPHIRE

Eating Out

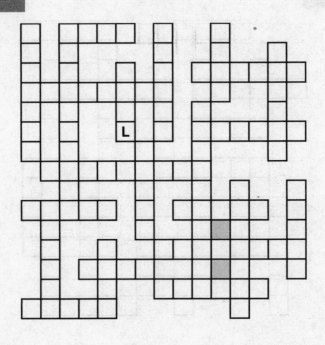

4 letters
BILL
FISH
MEAL
MEAT
MENU

5 letters
GLASS
GRILL
PARTY
SEATS
SWEET

6 letters
DINERS
DINNER
DRINKS
EATERY
NAPKIN
WAITER

7 letters
CUTLERY
STARTER

8 letters
LUNCHEON
WAITRESS

9 letters
BRASSERIE

10 letters
MAIN COURSE
VEGETARIAN

Build a House

4 letters
COWL
HALL
LATH
LOFT
SITE

5 letters
ATTIC
GLASS
LEDGE
LEVEL
SILLS

STRUT
TILES

6 letters
ALCOVE
CAVITY
CEMENT
DRAINS
FLOORS
JOISTS
STAIRS

7 letters
FOREMAN

8 letters
CORRIDOR
DECORATE
MOULDING

9 letters
ARCHITECT

11 letters
ELECTRICITY

People in Uniform

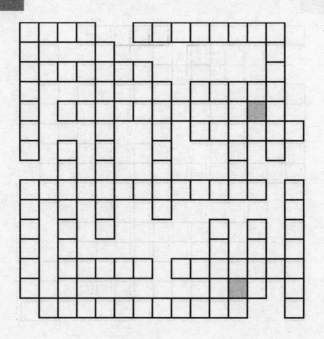

4 letters
CHEF
MAID

5 letters
GUARD
NURSE
PILOT

6 letters
AIRMAN
PORTER
SAILOR

7 letters
CAPTAIN
CLEANER
DENTIST
MIDWIFE
POSTMAN
SOLDIER
SURGEON

8 letters
WAITRESS

9 letters
ZOOKEEPER

10 letters
AIR STEWARD

11 letters
TRAIN DRIVER

13 letters
SHOP
ASSISTANT

Satellites and Asteroids

4 letters
EROS
MOON
PUCK
RHEA

5 letters
MIMAS

6 letters
DEIMOS
EUROPA
OBERON
PALLAS
PHOBOS
PORTIA
SAPPHO
TETHYS
TRITON

7 letters
ASTRAEA
CALYPSO
HIMALIA
IAPETUS
MIRANDA
TITANIA

8 letters
AMALTHEA
HYPERION

Hairstyles

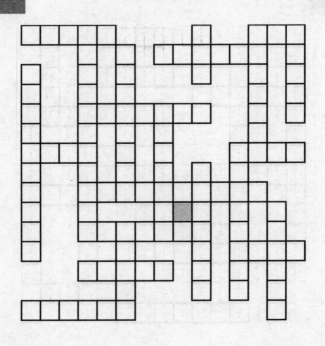

3 letters
BOB
BUN

4 letters
AFRO
CROP
PERM

5 letters
BANGS
PLAIT
QUIFF

WEAVE

6 letters
CURLED
MULLET
POUFFE

7 letters
BEEHIVE
CHIGNON
CREWCUT
PIGTAIL
TOPKNOT

8 letters
PONYTAIL
UNDERCUT

10 letters
BACK-COMBED
EXTENSIONS

11 letters
FRENCH PLEAT

Collector's Corner

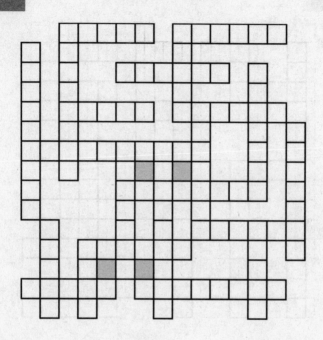

4 letters
MUGS

5 letters
BOOKS
COINS
DOLLS
FLAGS
MOTHS
VASES

6 letters
CAMEOS
COMICS
MEDALS
SILVER
SPOONS

7 letters
CANDLES
PISTOLS
POTTERY
RECORDS

8 letters
BEER-MATS
CARTOONS
PICTURES

9 letters
PORCELAIN
POSTCARDS

10 letters
AUTOGRAPHS

All Electric

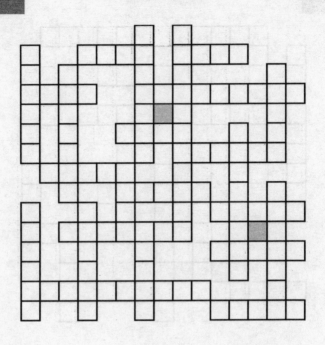

4 letters
GRID
LIVE
PLUG
ROSE
SPUR

5 letters
CABLE
EARTH
PLATE
POWER
UNITS

WATTS
WIRES

6 letters
AMPERE
SLEEVE
SWITCH
TUBING

7 letters
ADAPTOR
CURRENT
DUCTING
NEUTRAL

8 letters
TERMINAL

9 letters
PHOTOCELL

10 letters
CONNECTION

11 letters
FLUORESCENT

Move

4 letters
JUMP
TREK

5 letters
BOUND
BUDGE
CRAWL
CREEP
SHIFT
STEAL
SURGE
TRAMP

6 letters
BOUNCE
LUMBER
RAMBLE
SCURRY
SHIMMY
STREAK
TIPTOE
TRUDGE

7 letters
CASCADE
JOURNEY
MEANDER
SAUNTER
SCUTTLE
STUMBLE
TRAIPSE

Tunnels

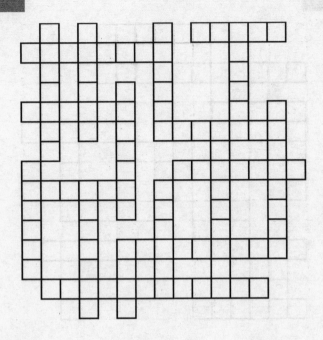

4 letters
HIGO

5 letters
ROKKO

6 letters
ENASAN
FREJUS
FRUDAL
HARUNA
IIYAMA

KAKUTO
SEIKAN

7 letters
CHANNEL
SIMPLON
SOMPORT
TAIHANG
VEREINA

8 letters
HEX RIVER
STRENGEN

9 letters
HSUEHSHAN
PLABUTSCH

12 letters
ZHONG-
NANSHAN

Varieties of Apple

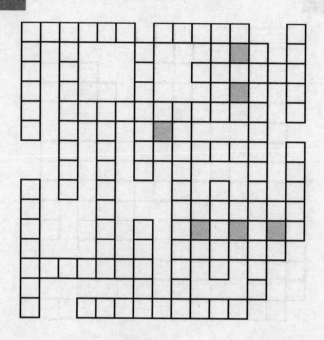

5 letters
AKANE
BRINA
CAMEO
PIXIE
SONYA
TOPAZ

6 letters
BAILEY
ELSTAR
EMPIRE
HAWAII

7 letters
CRISPIN
EPICURE
MONARCH
SPARTAN
WINESAP

9 letters
LIMELIGHT
ROYAL GALA
SWEETANGO

11 letters
SPITZENBERG
TOLMAN SWEET

13 letters
LAXTON'S
  SUPERB

African Tribes

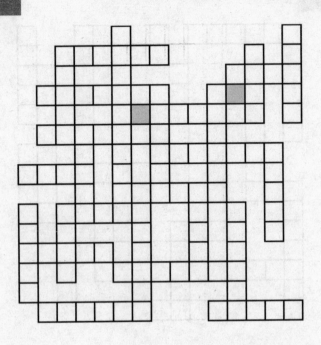

4 letters
BETE
FANG
MERU
YAKO

5 letters
AFARS
BASSA
DINKA
GANDA

HAUSA
MASAI
PYGMY
SHONA
SOTHO

6 letters
ANGONI
BASUTO
IBIBIO
KIKUYU
LUMBWA

SOMALI
TSONGA

7 letters
ASHANTI
BERBERS
SAMBURU
TURKANA
WATUTSI

10 letters
HOTTENTOTS

Medical Matters

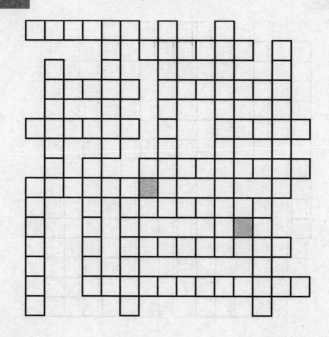

5 letters
LOCUM
TESTS

6 letters
ASTHMA
ATAXIA
CORNEA
MYOPIA
SEPSIS

7 letters
ABDOMEN
ABSCESS
CHECK-UP
GLOTTIS
INSULIN
ROSEOLA

8 letters
BOTULISM
FRACTURE

9 letters
OPERATION
PULMONARY

10 letters
TOURNIQUET

12 letters
PRESCRIPTION
RECEPTIONIST

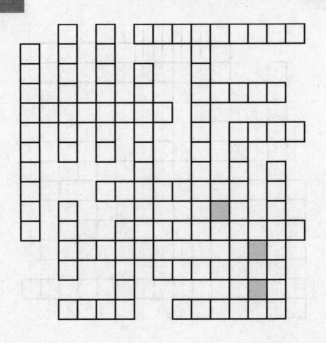

4 letters
FIFE
OBOE
TUBA

5 letters
BUGLE
FLUTE
KAZOO

6 letters
CORNET

7 letters
BASSOON
HAUTBOY
PICCOLO

8 letters
CLARINET
POST HORN
TROMBONE

9 letters
EUPHONIUM

10 letters
FLUGELHORN
FRENCH HORN
MOUTH ORGAN
TIN WHISTLE

11 letters
HECKELPHONE

Robin Hood

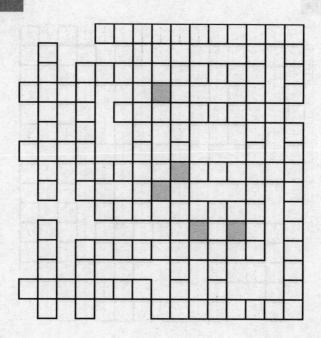

4 letters
HERO
MYTH
POOR
TALE

5 letters
ARROW
TAXES

6 letters
RAIDER
TARGET

7 letters
CONTEST
POVERTY
ROMANCE
SHERIFF

8 letters
MERRY MEN
SHERWOOD

9 letters
GISBOURNE
ROBIN HOOD

10 letters
LANDOWNERS
LITTLE JOHN
MAID MARIAN
PRINCE JOHN

11 letters
WILL SCARLET

12 letters
LINCOLN
   GREEN

Pacific Islands

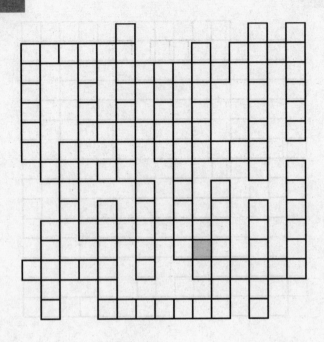

4 letters
FIJI
GUAM

5 letters
DUCIE
FLINT
LANAI
PALAU
SERAM
SUMBA

6 letters
BIKINI
CANTON
EASTER
JARVIS
KODIAK
MIDWAY
NASSAU
NECKER
TAIWAN
VOSTOK

7 letters
KANDAVU
MAUPITI
TAHAUTA
VANUATU

8 letters
JOHNSTON
PITCAIRN
PUKAPUKA

Foot Work

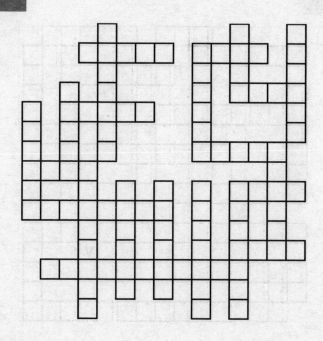

4 letters
ARCH
BARE
CORN
HEEL
SOLE
TOES

5 letters
ANKLE
DIGIT

NAILS
TALUS

6 letters
BUNION
CUBOID
HALLUX
INSTEP
TARSAL
TENDON

7 letters
BLISTER
HOPPING
WALKING

8 letters
PEDICURE
SKIPPING

11 letters
CHIROPODIST

'O' Words

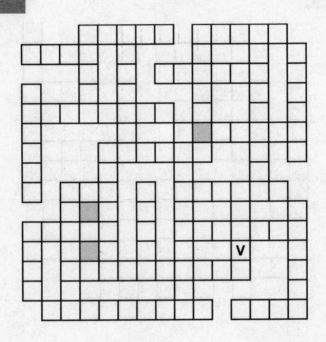

3 letters	OTTER	OKAYING
ODD	OXIDE	OMINOUS
	OZONE	OMNIBUS

4 letters
OVAL
OWNS — **6 letters** — **8 letters**
OYEZ — OBLONG — OFFERING
— OBTUSE
— OGLING — **9 letters**
5 letters — OOZING — OPERATION
OATHS — OSIRIS — OSTEOPATH
OFTEN — OWLISH
OLDIE — — **10 letters**
OLIVE — **7 letters** — ONCOLOGIST
ORION — ODDMENT — OSTENSIBLE

Shakespearean Characters

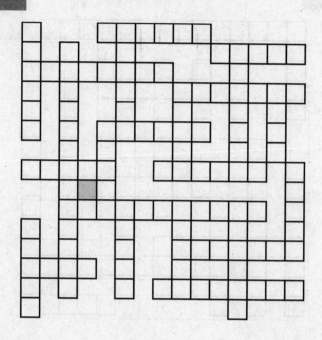

4 letters
IAGO
PUCK

5 letters
ARIEL
BELCH
CUPID
EDGAR
EGEUS
FLUTE
ROMEO
SNARE

6 letters
ALONSO
BOTTOM
EMILIA
HAMLET
OBERON
TYBALT

7 letters
ANTONIO
LEONTES
MACBETH

8 letters
MERCUTIO
ROSALIND

11 letters
ROSENCRANTZ

13 letters
FRIAR
LAWRENCE

IFs and BUTs

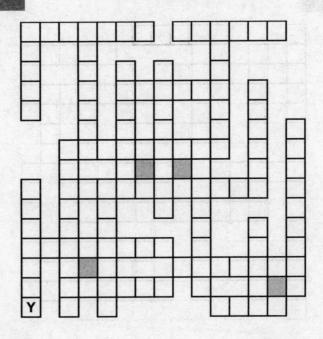

4 letters
WIFE

5 letters
KNIFE
QUIFF

6 letters
ADRIFT
DEBUTS
EIFFEL
STRIFE

7 letters
AIRLIFT
AMPLIFY
BAILIFF
BEATIFY
BUTCHER
HALIBUT
KIBBUTZ

8 letters
DRIFTERS
LIFELESS
REBUTTAL

9 letters
MAKESHIFT
TERRIFIED
TRIBUTARY

11 letters
REATTRIBUTE

All Alone

4 letters
SOLO

5 letters
QUIET

6 letters
LONELY
REMOTE
UNIQUE

7 letters
DISTANT
RETIRED
UNAIDED
UNLOVED

8 letters
DESERTED
ISOLATED
LONESOME
MAROONED
SOLITUDE

STRANDED
UNWANTED

9 letters
SEPARATED

10 letters
UNATTENDED

13 letters
COMPANION-
LESS

Nautical Terms

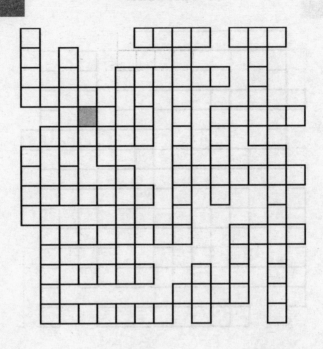

3 letters
AFT
SOS

4 letters
BOAT
BOWS
CREW
MESS
PORT
PROW
SHIP
YAWL

5 letters
PILOT
STACK
STERN
WINGS

6 letters
ABOARD
BRIDGE
DAVITS
FUNNEL
LADDER

7 letters
DOCKING
STEWARD
TURBINE

8 letters
BINNACLE
POOP DECK

9 letters
ANCHORAGE

11 letters
WEATHER DECK

Weapons Store

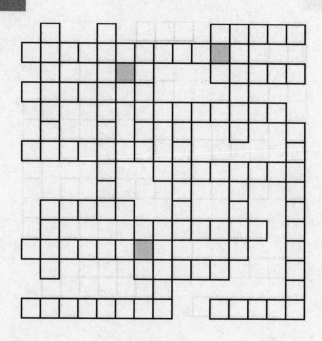

4 letters
SCUD

5 letters
ARROW
H-BOMB
LANCE
RIFLE
SABRE
SPEAR
SWORD

6 letters
AIRGUN
BULLET
EXOCET

7 letters
ASSEGAI
BAYONET
BAZOOKA
TEAR GAS
TORPEDO

8 letters
CATAPULT
CROSSBOW
DYNAMITE

10 letters
BOWIE KNIFE
MACHINE GUN
SIDEWINDER

Stars

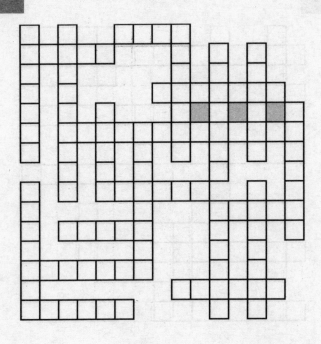

4 letters
VEGA

5 letters
ATLAS
MERAK
MIZAR
SPICA

6 letters
ALTAIR
CASTOR
MIMOSA

POLLUX
SIRIUS

7 letters
ANTARES
CANOPUS
CAPELLA
ELECTRA
MINTAKA
POLARIS
PROCYON
REGULUS

8 letters
ARCTURUS

9 letters
ALDEBARAN

13 letters
ALPHA
  CENTAURI

Haunted House

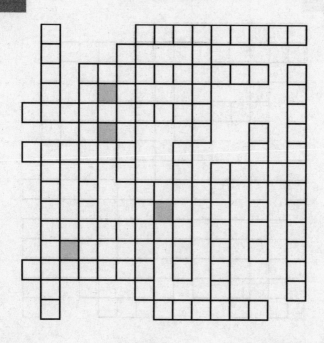

5 letters
CURSE
GHOST
SPELL

6 letters
FRIGHT
NOISES
SCARED
TERROR

7 letters
BANSHEE
SCREAMS
SPECTRE
VAMPIRE

8 letters
CLANKING
PORTRAIT

9 letters
ECTOPLASM
TURN WHITE

10 letters
ATMOSPHERE
FLASHLIGHT

11 letters
FLOORBOARDS

12 letters
THUNDER-
STORM

Fishing

4 letters
BAIT
DACE
HOOK
LURE
NEWT
PARR
TOPE
TUNA

5 letters
GUPPY
MARKS

SMACK
SMELT
WHELK

6 letters
DORSAL
HERMIT
MAGGOT

7 letters
ANCHOVY
HERRING
KEEPNET

OARFISH
TIDDLER
WHITING

8 letters
SEAHORSE

9 letters
BARRACUDA
JELLYFISH
THORNBACK

10 letters
CUTTLEFISH

Sushi

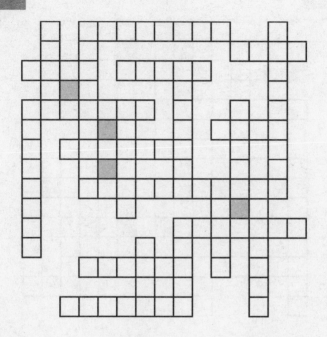

4 letters
CRAB
RICE
TOFU
TUNA

5 letters
HOCHO
IKURA
ROLLS
SQUID
UNAGI

6 letters
MAKISU
TAMAGO

7 letters
CARROTS
HALIBUT
HANGIRI
SCALLOP
SEAWEED
SHAMOJI

8 letters
CUCUMBER
SOY SAUCE

9 letters
NAREZUSHI
SEA URCHIN

11 letters
NIGIRIZUSHI

Wild Flowers

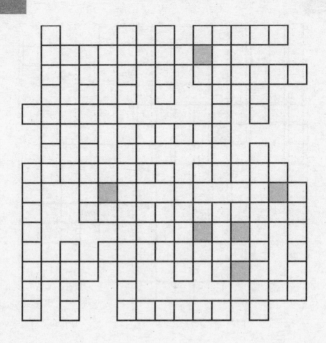

3 letters
HOP

4 letters
ARUM
HEMP
IRIS
LILY
ROSE
RUSH

5 letters
ASTER
OXLIP

POPPY
STOCK

6 letters
BRYONY
FAT HEN
NETTLE
SORREL

8 letters
ASPHODEL
DAFFODIL
PLANTAIN
PURSLANE

TOADFLAX

9 letters
DANDELION
DIAPENSIA
PIMPERNEL

10 letters
SNAPDRAGON

12 letters
LADY'S SLIPPER

Musicals

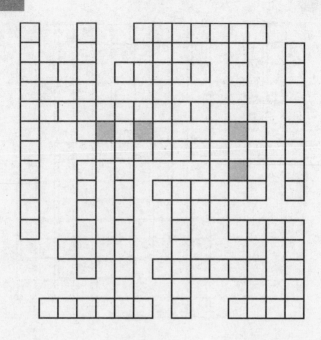

4 letters
CATS
GIGI
HAIR
NINE
RENT

5 letters
ANNIE
GYPSY
SHOUT
TOMMY

6 letters
BARNUM
GREASE
OLIVER
PIPPIN
SHOLAY
TOP HAT

7 letters
COMPANY
RAGTIME
SCROOGE

8 letters
CAROUSEL

11 letters
CRAZY FOR
  YOU
HIGH SOCIETY
MARY POPPINS

12 letters
SWEET
  CHARITY

Home Brewing

3 letters
KEG

4 letters
BEER
BUNG
CASK
HOPS
JUGS
LEES
MALT
MASH
WINE

5 letters
AROMA
CORKS
STOUT
SUGAR
WATER
WHEAT

6 letters
BUCKET
HEATER
TUBING
ULLAGE

7 letters
RACKING

8 letters
STRAINER

10 letters
STERILISER

11 letters
TEMPERATURE
THERMOMETER

Famous Pictures

4 letters
LEDA

5 letters
ALONE
DANAE
DUNES
FLORA
MOSES
PIETA

6 letters
ICARUS
IRISES

7 letters
BATHERS
ERASMUS
GIN LANE
LA BELLA

8 letters
ECCE HOMO
MONA LISA

9 letters
DONI TONDO
SHIPWRECK

10 letters
ADAM AND EVE

11 letters
CRUCIFIXION

14 letters
DANCER AT THE BAR

Books

4 letters
PLOT
READ
TEXT
TOME

5 letters
PAGES
SPINE
STORY

6 letters
AUTHOR
EDITOR
SCRIPT
SEQUEL
WRITER

7 letters
LIBRARY
MYSTERY
TRILOGY

8 letters
EPILOGUE
PROLOGUE
SUSPENSE
THRILLER

9 letters
ANTHOLOGY
BIOGRAPHY
THESAURUS

10 letters
BESTSELLER

Absolutely

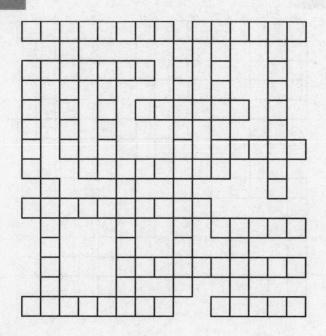

5 letters
FULLY
TOTAL
TRULY
UTTER

6 letters
ACTUAL
ENTIRE
Purely
WHOLLY

7 letters
CERTAIN
PERFECT
SUPREME

8 letters
COMPLETE
DECISIVE
DEFINITE
DESPOTIC
FARTHEST

9 letters
ARBITRARY

10 letters
AUTOCRATIC
EXHAUSTIVE

13 letters
UNCON-
DITIONAL

Racecourses

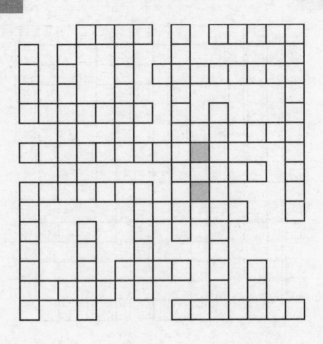

3 letters
AYR

4 letters
BATH
CORK
NAAS

5 letters
ASCOT
EPSOM
PERTH
RIPON

6 letters
EXETER
REDCAR

7 letters
AINTREE
KEMPTON
TAUNTON
TRAMORE
WEXFORD
WINDSOR

8 letters
BRIGHTON
PLUMPTON

9 letters
UTTOXETER

10 letters
HUNTINGDON

11 letters
MARKET RASEN
PUNCHESTOWN

Things to Give Up

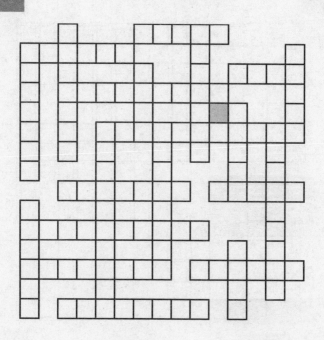

4 letters
BEER
COLA
WINE

5 letters
CAKES
CHIPS
DRUGS
LAGER

6 letters
COFFEE

SNACKS
SWEETS

7 letters
MOANING
NAGGING
PEANUTS
SMOKING

8 letters
BISCUITS
DRINKING
FLIRTING

9 letters
DOUGHNUTS
GOSSIPING

10 letters
CIGARETTES
OVEREATING

11 letters
CREDIT CARDS

The Druids

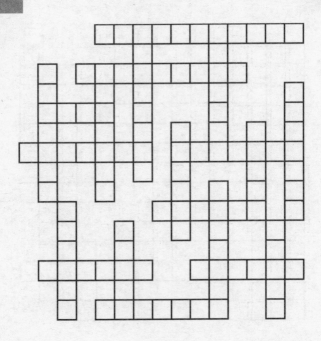

4 letters
LUGH

5 letters
CLOAK
HOLLY
MAGIC

6 letters
CELTIC
GROVES
PRIEST

TEMPLE
WISDOM

7 letters
ANCIENT
ASH WAND
BELTANE
CRYSTAL
RITUALS
SAMHAIN
STORIES
SYMBOLS

8 letters
CEREMONY

9 letters
SACRIFICE

11 letters
INCANTATION

Golfing Surnames

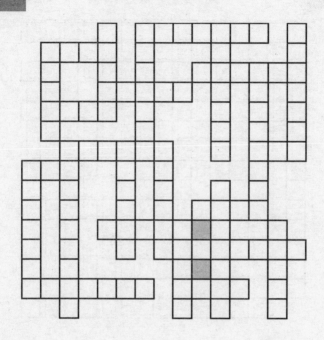

3 letters
COE
FRY

4 letters
DALY
DUKE
GINN
WEIR

5 letters
BOROS
CLARK

FURYK
PRICE
SINGH
WOODS

6 letters
GOOSEN
NELSON
NORMAN
SUTTON

7 letters
COUPLES

JANUARY
LEONARD
STADLER
STEWART
STRANGE
WADKINS

8 letters
MAHAFFEY
NICKLAUS

9 letters
GEIBERGER

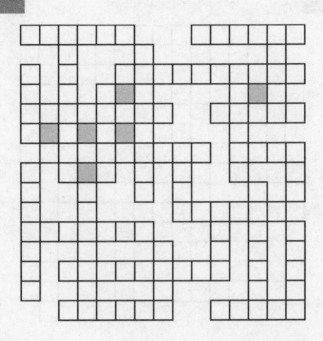

3 letters
TAN

4 letters
CUBE
HALF
PLUS
ROOT
ZERO

5 letters
DIGIT
FIFTH
SIXTH

TENTH
TOTAL

6 letters
ABACUS
DIVIDE
FACTOR
SERIES
THEORY

7 letters
AVERAGE
COMPLEX
DECIMAL

INTEGER

8 letters
ADDITION
NEGATIVE
RATIONAL

9 letters
CALCULATE
LOGARITHM

10 letters
PERCENTAGE

'P' Words

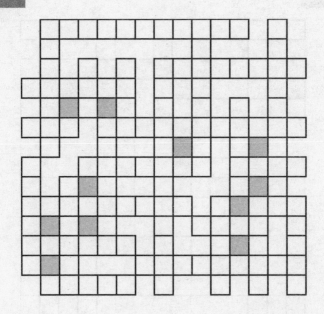

3 letters
PAY
PEP
POD

4 letters
PEEL
PERI
PUNT

5 letters
PALPS
PANSY
PERRY
PIXIE
PYLON

6 letters
PAROLE
POP-UPS
PRETTY
PYTHON

7 letters
PARABLE
PLACEBO
PYJAMAS

8 letters
PREACHER
PRESSURE

9 letters
PORBEAGLE
PORTRAITS

10 letters
PREVALENCE

11 letters
PHOTOGRAPHY
PLEASURABLE

12 letters
PERAMBU-
LATOR

Words Derived from Italian

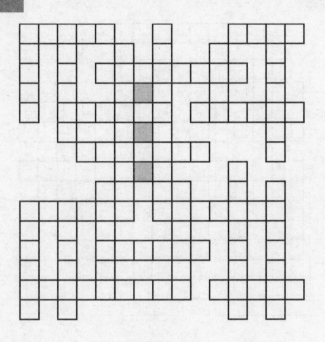

4 letters
DOME
ZERO

5 letters
DEBIT
DITTO
JEANS
VISTA

6 letters
ARCADE
FASCIA

MANAGE
MUSLIN
SALOON
SEQUIN
TARIFF
TURBAN
VIRTUE

7 letters
ARTISAN
BALCONY
INFERNO
REPLICA

8 letters
CORRIDOR
DISASTER

9 letters
GROTESQUE
PORCELAIN

10 letters
TERRACOTTA

Peter Pan

4 letters
JOHN
MARY
NANA
NIBS

5 letters
CURLY
GREEN
STORY
SWORD
WENDY

6 letters
JUNGLE
MR SMEE

7 letters
CARTOON
INDIANS
NURSERY
TOOTLES

8 letters
MERMAIDS
NARRATOR
SLIGHTLY
THE TWINS

9 letters
NEVERLAND

10 letters
TINKER BELL

Fast Food

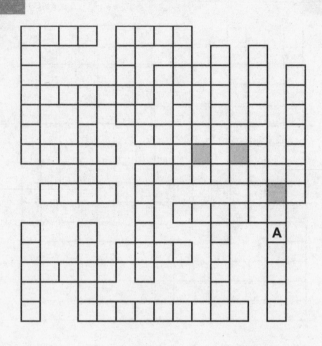

A

4 letters
BUNS
FISH
KIDS
MAYO
MENU

5 letters
COMBO
FRIED
MEALS
PARTY
SALAD

6 letters
BURGER
CARTON
SAUCES
SHAKES
TABLES

7 letters
CHICKEN
COUNTER
KETCHUP
PICKLES
PLASTIC

8 letters
HEAT LAMP

9 letters
DRIVE-THRU
FRANCHISE
SUPERSIZE

Shell Collection

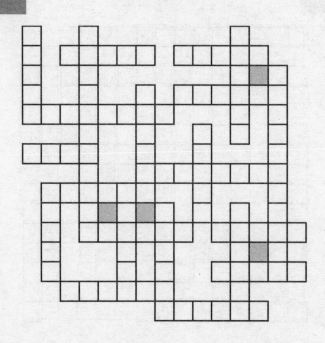

4 letters
CONE

5 letters
CONCH
MITRE
MUREX
RAZOR
SOLEN
TOOTH
WHELK

6 letters
CHITON
COCKLE
COWRIE
HELMET
MUSSEL
OYSTER
QUAHOG
TROUGH
TURBAN
WINKLE

8 letters
AMMONITE
NAUTILUS

11 letters
DINOTHERIUM
NEEDLE SHELL

Wild West USA

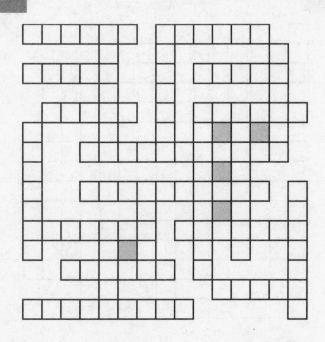

5 letters
HOWDY
LASSO
POSSE
RANCH
RODEO
SPURS

6 letters
BOUNTY
CATTLE
GAUCHO

STEERS
WAGONS

7 letters
COWPOKE
HOLSTER
MARSHAL
ROY BEAN
SAM BASS
STETSON

8 letters
GOLDRUSH

9 letters
TOMBSTONE
WYATT EARP

10 letters
HENRY STARR

11 letters
ANNIE OAKLEY

Potato Varieties

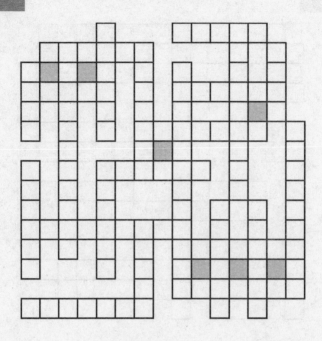

4 letters
ANYA
CARA

5 letters
AGRIA
KIKKO
WILJA

6 letters
ACCORD
COSMOS
NADINE

NICOLA
OSPREY
ROMANO
SUNSET
VERITY

7 letters
DESIREE
DUNDROD
ROBINTA
ROOSTER
RUDOLPH

9 letters
KERR'S PINK
MARIS PEER
SARPO GWYN

11 letters
CARLINGFORD

12 letters
GOLDEN
  WONDER

Ropes

3 letters
GUY

4 letters
CORD
VANG

5 letters
BRACE
CABLE
LASSO
NOOSE
WIDDY

6 letters
HOBBLE
LARIAT
RUNNER
TETHER

7 letters
BOBSTAY
CRINGLE
HALYARD
LANYARD
LASHING
MOORING

OUTHAUL
TOWROPE

8 letters
BUNTLINE
CLEW-LINE
DOCKLINE
DOWNHAUL

Composers

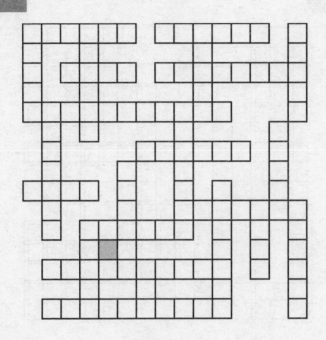

3 letters
SOR

4 letters
ARNE
BACH
WOLF

5 letters
BLISS
GLUCK
HAYDN
HOLST
VERDI

6 letters
ARNOLD
BARBER
BRAHMS
DVORAK
HANDEL
MOZART
WAGNER

7 letters
COPLAND
DEBUSSY
SMETANA
STRAUSS

8 letters
BRUCKNER

10 letters
MUSSORGSKY
SAINT-SAENS

11 letters
TCHAIKOVSKY

At Auction

3 letters
LOT

4 letters
BIDS
GOLD
JARS
LIST
VASE

5 letters
BUYER
CHEST
GOODS

GUIDE
ITEMS
PRICE
STYLE

6 letters
DEALER
ORMOLU
SILVER
STATUE

7 letters
ANTIQUE
RESERVE

SHELVES

8 letters
PURCHASE
TRANSFER

9 letters
IMITATION
PORCELAIN
SALESROOM

11 letters
MEMORABILIA

About Time

3 letters
DOT
ERA
NOW

4 letters
AGES
DAWN
GONE
IDES
JUNE
LAST
LENT
NEXT

NOON
PACE
SOON
STAY
THEN

5 letters
NIGHT

6 letters
ANNUAL
DECADE
LATTER
MINUTE

PERIOD

8 letters
DATELINE
PENDULUM
PUNCTUAL

9 letters
ERSTWHILE
METRONOME

10 letters
MILLENNIUM

Totally Tribal

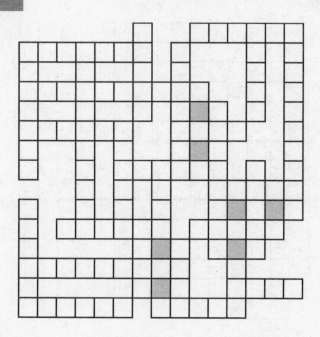

3 letters
WEA

4 letters
CREE
CROW
ERIE
INCA
MAYA

5 letters
ADENA
AZTEC
HAIDA
NAZCA

OLMEC
SIOUX

6 letters
APACHE
APINAI
ATOARA
CAYUGA
DAKOTA
SENECA
TOLTEC

7 letters
ARAUCAN
WAIMIRI
WYANDOT

8 letters
SEMINOLE

9 letters
TUSCARORA

10 letters
ALACALUFAN
ALGONQUIAN
MICCOSUKEE

Gym Workout

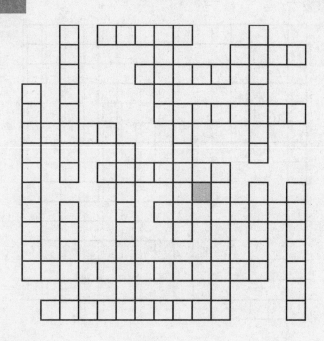

4 letters
YOGA

5 letters
BENCH
DANCE
HORSE
SAUNA
STEPS

6 letters
SHOWER

7 letters
JOGGING
MASSAGE
PILATES
WEIGHTS

8 letters
EXERCISE
LEVERAGE
PRESS-UPS
SPINNING

9 letters
WARMING UP

10 letters
INSTRUCTOR
TRAMPOLINE

13 letters
ROWING
  MACHINE

Make It Your Mission

3 letters
AIM
JOB

4 letters
DUTY
GOAL
RAID
TASK
WORK

5 letters
CHORE

FORCE
QUEST

6 letters
ERRAND
SORTIE
TARGET

7 letters
CRUSADE
EMBASSY
PURPOSE
PURSUIT

8 letters
EXERCISE
MINISTRY

10 letters
ASSIGNMENT
COMMISSION

11 letters
RAISON D'ETRE

Walk in the Woods

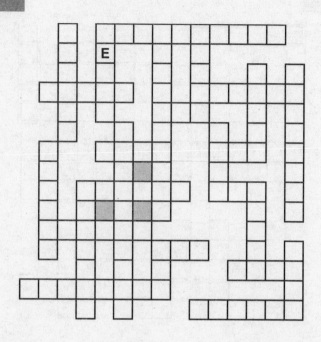

3 letters
ASH
ELM
IVY
OAK
OWL

4 letters
CROW
DEER
LOGS
PINE

5 letters
BEECH
BIRCH
FENCE
HOLLY
MAPLE

6 letters
BADGER
BEETLE
CANOPY
LEAVES
STREAM
WILLOW

7 letters
BRACKEN

8 letters
BLUEBELL
SYCAMORE

10 letters
BLACKBERRY
COW PARSLEY
WOODPECKER

Tools

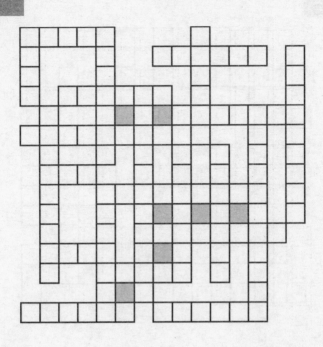

3 letters
AWL

4 letters
ADZE
RASP

5 letters
AUGER
PLANE

6 letters
CHISEL
JIGSAW

ROLLER
SHAVER
SHEARS

7 letters
CHOPPER
HACKSAW
ROTATOR
SCRAPER

8 letters
CLIPPERS

9 letters
BLOWTORCH
CORKSCREW
HANDSPIKE
SECATEURS

10 letters
KEYHOLE SAW

11 letters
ELECTRIC SAW
SCREWDRIVER

'Q' Words

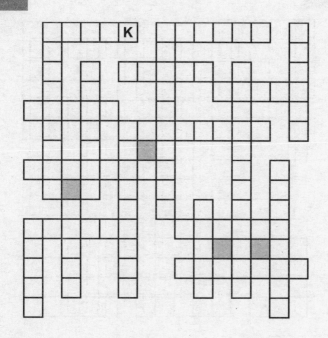

5 letters
QATAR
QUACK
QUASH
QUEEN
QUEUE
QUILT
QUOIN

6 letters
QUALMS
QUARTZ

QUENCH
QUINCE

7 letters
QUIBBLE
QUINTET

8 letters
QUAGMIRE
QUEEREST
QUELLING

9 letters
QUERULOUS
QUICKSAND

10 letters
QUADRANGLE

12 letters
QUARANTINING

The Mr Men

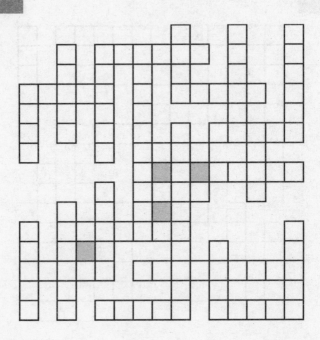

4 letters
BUMP
BUSY
LAZY
MEAN
SLOW
SNOW

5 letters
BRAVE
DIZZY
FUNNY
JELLY
MESSY

NOISY
NOSEY
SILLY
SMALL
WORRY
WRONG

6 letters
BOUNCE
CLUMSY
SKINNY
SNEEZE
UPPITY

7 letters
PERFECT

9 letters
FORGETFUL

10 letters
IMPOSSIBLE
TOPSY-TURVY

Showjumping

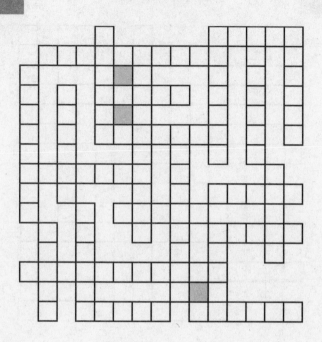

5 letters
BAULK
CLOCK
EVENT
FAULT
FENCE
POSTS
STYLE
TOUCH
TURNS

6 letters
CANTER
HEDGES
RIDERS
SADDLE
STABLE

7 letters
BARRIER
REFUSAL
ROSETTE
TRAILER

8 letters
HORSE BOX

9 letters
TIME LIMIT

10 letters
EQUESTRIAN
SQUARE OXER

11 letters
COMBINATION

Poets

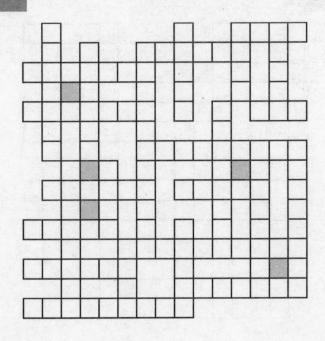

3 letters
LEE

4 letters
BEER
GRAY
GREY
MANN

5 letters
BRAUN
ENGLE
GLUCK
HULSE
PAINE

6 letters
DE SADE
MORRIS
SOUTAR
THORPE

7 letters
BECKETT
CAMERON
HERRICK
MCGOUGH

8 letters
CERAVOLO
ESHLEMAN

FLETCHER
MILLIGAN

9 letters
BRODERICK
SUTCLIFFE

10 letters
BELLINGHAM

11 letters
SHAKESPEARE

Artists

3 letters
ARP
ONO

4 letters
COLE
ETTY
GOYA
GRIS
NASH

5 letters
COROT
ERNST

MORSE
NOLAN
NOLDE
PENCZ

6 letters
BRAQUE
BUTLER
TITIAN

7 letters
BINGHAM
BOLOGNA
MURILLO

8 letters
BRUEGHEL
DRYSDALE

9 letters
ANTOLINEZ
DONATELLO
GIORGIONE

10 letters
MODIGLIANI
TINTORETTO

Cricket

4 letters
BALL
DUCK
TEST

5 letters
COVER
CROWD
MATCH
OVERS
PITCH

6 letters
CREASE
MAIDEN
NOT OUT
RETURN
UMPIRE
WICKET

7 letters
BATSMAN
FIELDER
LEG SIDE

LONG HOP
OVERARM

8 letters
BOUNDARY
DECISION
THIRD MAN
UNDERARM

Rocks and Minerals

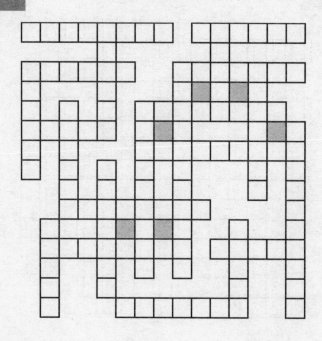

5 letters
AGATE
CHERT
FLINT
SHALE
SLATE

6 letters
BASALT
GABBRO
GYPSUM
MARBLE
SCHIST

7 letters
EPIDOTE
GRANITE
IGNEOUS
SYENITE

8 letters
DOLOMITE
GANISTER
MUDSTONE
TRACHYTE

9 letters
LIMESTONE
MALACHITE

10 letters
SERPENTINE

11 letters
SEDIMENTARY

Wine

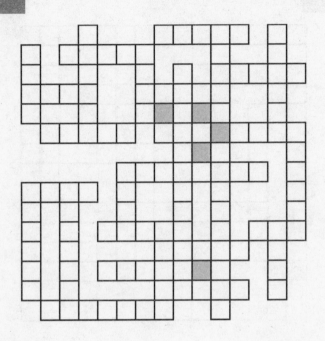

3 letters
DRY
RED

4 letters
BODY
CAVA
CORK
FINO
LEES
NAPA
ROSE

5 letters
AROMA

BLANC
KAUTZ
MACON
MEDOC
RIOJA
ROUGE
SWEET
SYRAH
TOKAY
WHITE

6 letters
ALSACE
BOTTLE
CHENIN

SHERRY

7 letters
RETSINA
VINTAGE

8 letters
BORDEAUX

9 letters
SAUVIGNON

12 letters
COTES DU
RHONE

Words Derived from Spanish

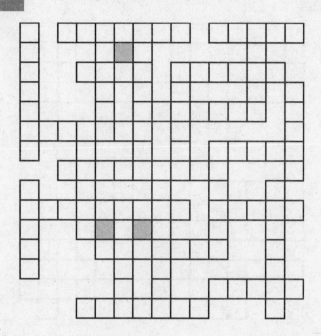

4 letters
PUMA

5 letters
ADOBE
COPRA
GUANO
PATIO
RODEO
SHACK
TILDE

6 letters
AGOUTI
ARMADA
CORRAL
IGUANA
SHERRY
TOMATO

7 letters
ABALONE
CRIMSON
CRUSADE

GALLEON
OREGANO
PIMENTO
TAPIOCA

8 letters
RENEGADE
STAMPEDE

9 letters
DESPERADO
HURRICANE

Time for Coffee

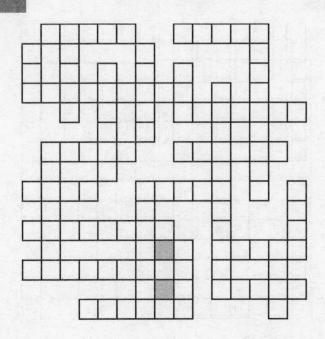

3 letters
JAR
POT

4 letters
BREW
JAVA
MILL
NOIR

5 letters
AROMA
BEANS
HOUSE

IRISH
LATTE
MOCHA
TABLE
WHITE

6 letters
FILTER
GROUND
KENYAN

7 letters
BARISTA
INSTANT
TURKISH

8 letters
ESPRESSO

9 letters
AMERICANO
MACCHIATO
RISTRETTO

11 letters
FRENCH ROAST

James Bond

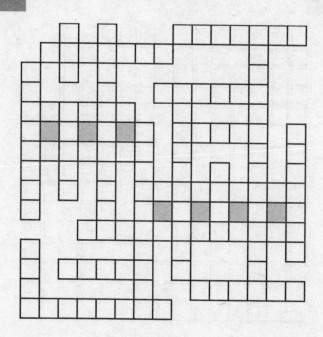

3 letters
ZAO

4 letters
DR NO
JAWS

5 letters
CHANG
GABOR
NAOMI

6 letters
MR WINT
RENARD
RUSSIA

7 letters
CAMILLE
MISCHKA
MR OSATO
QUARREL

8 letters
KERIM BEY
SAUNDERS

9 letters
DR MORTNER

10 letters
GOLDFINGER
ROGER MOORE

11 letters
TIGER TANAKA

12 letters
CASINO ROYALE

14 letters
HECTOR
GONZALES

Explorers

4 letters
COOK
DIAS

5 letters
CABOT
DRAKE
PARRY
SCOTT

6 letters
BAFFIN
BERING
CORTES
DE SOTO
HUDSON
NANSEN

7 letters
FIENNES
RALEIGH
STANLEY

8 letters
AMUNDSEN
BONPLAND
COLUMBUS
FRANKLIN

9 letters
FROBISHER
MARCO POLO

Yeoman of the Guard

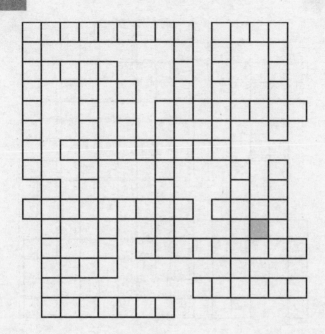

4 letters
ARMY
DUTY
HOSE
LACE
ROSE

5 letters
BOYNE
ROYAL
TOWER

6 letters
EMBLEM
ENSIGN

7 letters
DOUBLET
HALBERD
MARINES
THISTLE

8 letters
AIR FORCE
BOULOGNE
BREECHES
CEREMONY

9 letters
BODYGUARD
CROSS-BELT
DETTINGEN
SOVEREIGN

'R' Words

3 letters
RUT

4 letters
REEL
RELY

5 letters
RAJAH
REINS
RELAX
RISKY

6 letters
RAZZLE
RENTAL
RHYTHM
ROGUES
RUNNER

7 letters
RHOMBUS
ROISTER
ROLLING
ROSTRUM
RURALLY

8 letters
REQUIRED
RESEARCH
ROSEMARY
RUPTURED

9 letters
RECKONING
RENDERING
REVERENCE
RIGHTEOUS

UP Words

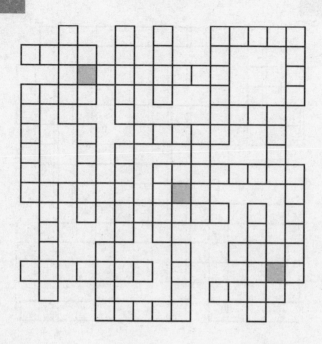

4 letters
BEAT
CAST
HELD
KEEP
RUSH
SHOT
SIDE
TAKE
TOWN
WARD
WIND

5 letters
DATED
FIELD
FRONT
GRADE
RAISE
START
THROW
TIGHT

6 letters
GROWTH
LOADED

STAGED
STAIRS
STROKE
THRUST
TURNED

7 letters
HOLSTER
SETTING

8 letters
BRINGING

Get Set

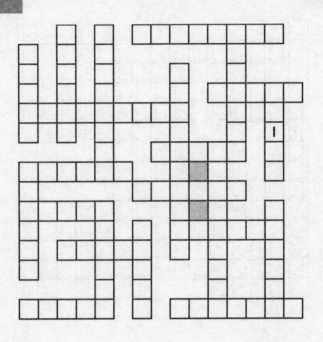

5 letters
CLOSE
DENSE
FIXED
RIGID
SOLID
STIFF
STUCK
TIGHT

6 letters
DOGGED
ROOTED
SECURE
STABLE
STEADY
STRICT
WELDED

7 letters
DECIDED
RIVETED

8 letters
ANCHORED
EMBEDDED

9 letters
INELASTIC
STEADFAST

10 letters
MOTIONLESS

Admirable Adjectives

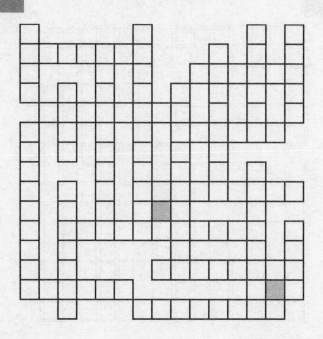

4 letters
CALM
GOOD
NICE

5 letters
LOYAL

6 letters
GENIAL
KINDLY
MODEST
TRUSTY

7 letters
AMIABLE
SHINING

8 letters
FAITHFUL
RELIABLE
TERRIFIC
TOLERANT
VIRTUOUS

9 letters
NECESSARY
SPARKLING

10 letters
ATTRACTIVE
BENEVOLENT

11 letters
INTELLIGENT
SENSATIONAL

Volcanoes

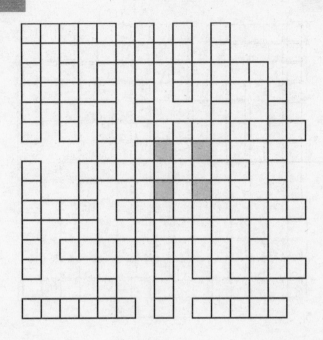

4 letters
FUJI
OAHU
RUIZ
TAAL
TOON
VOON
YEGA

5 letters
AGUNG
HARGY
HEKLA
KETOI

OPALA
PELEE
YASUR

6 letters
CHIRIP
HAKONE
KATMAI
LOLORU
RABAUL
SAJAMA
VISOKE

7 letters
FANTALE

8 letters
SABATINI

9 letters
JEFFERSON
PARICUTIN

10 letters
LONG VALLEY
SAKURAJIMA

IN and OUT

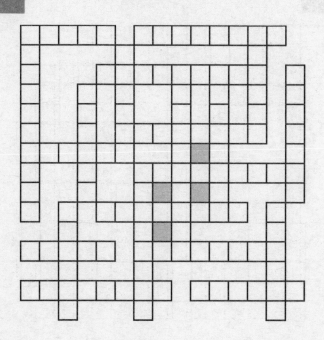

5 letters
INVAR
OUTDO

6 letters
INDEED
INGEST
INLAND
INSANE
INSECT
INVEST
OUTWIT

7 letters
INQUIRE

8 letters
INFERIOR
INSTINCT
INTEREST
OUTDOORS
OUTSTRIP
OUTVOICE
OUTWEARY

9 letters
OUTGIVING
OUTRIGGER

10 letters
INSENTIENT
OUTPATIENT

Perfume

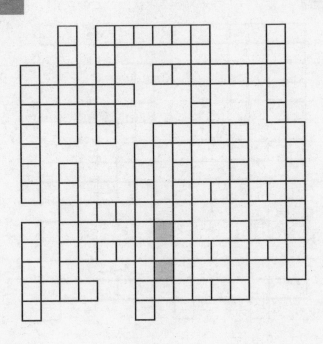

4 letters
MUSK

5 letters
AROMA
ROSES
SCENT

6 letters
CITRUS
FLORAL
FRUITY

LILIES
ORCHID
SPICES

7 letters
BOUQUET
COLOGNE
INCENSE
OAKMOSS
VIOLETS

8 letters
LAVENDER

9 letters
ORRIS ROOT
REDOLENCE
SWEETNESS

13 letters
EAU-DE-
TOILETTE

Types of Pasta

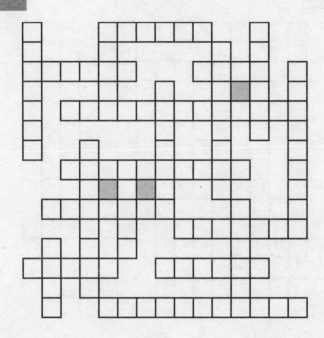

4 letters
PIPE
ZITI

5 letters
FIORI
GIGLI
PENNE

6 letters
FIDEOS
FILINI
PILLUS

STELLE
ZITONI

7 letters
FUSILLI
GEMELLI
MAFALDE
TUFFOLI

8 letters
FARFALLE
LINGUINE

9 letters
SPIRALINI

10 letters
FARFALLONE

11 letters
QUADREFIORE

13 letters
CRESTE DI
   GALLI

Spain

4 letters
VIGO

5 letters
CADIZ
IBIZA
JEREZ

6 letters
BILBAO
MADRID

MALAGA
MURCIA

7 letters
CASTILE
GRANADA
MAJORCA

8 letters
ALHAMBRA
ALICANTE
ARANJUEZ

ASTURIAS
GAZPACHO
SANTIAGO
ZARAGOZA

9 letters
CATALONIA
SANTANDER

12 letters
SIERRA NEVADA

Mountain Ranges

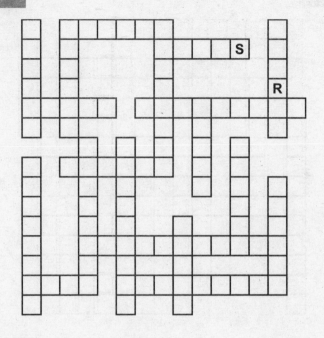

4 letters
ALPS

5 letters
ALTAI
ANDES
ATLAS
URALS

6 letters
HOGGAR
HOOSAC

MOURNE
PAMIRS
TAUNUS
TAURUS
VOSGES

8 letters
CASCADES
CAUCASUS
TIEN SHAN

9 letters
APPENINES
HIMALAYAS
KARAKORUM

11 letters
DRAKENSBERG

Dragons

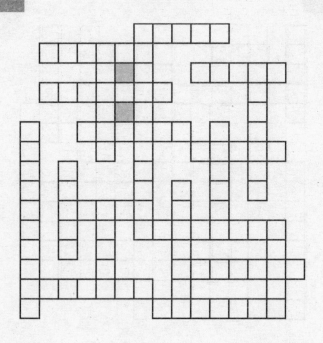

5 letters
DANNY
DRACO
DULCY
GRISU
LADON
MUSHU
WAWEL

6 letters
FAFNIR
FALKOR

SCATHA
TIAMAT

7 letters
APALALA
APOPHIS
GRIAULE
HAKURYU
NIDHOGG
NORBERT

8 letters
GLAURUNG

10 letters
MALEFICENT

11 letters
MAYLAND LONG

Calm Down

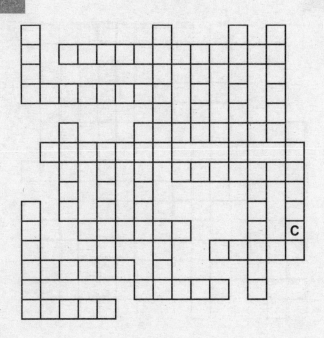

C

4 letters
CALM
HUSH

5 letters
ABATE
ALLAY
CHILL
LOWER
RELAX

6 letters
DEDUCT
PACIFY
REBATE
REDUCE
SOOTHE
TEMPER

7 letters
APPEASE
ASSUAGE
COOL OFF

QUIETEN
SLACKEN

8 letters
DECREASE
MITIGATE
MODERATE

12 letters
TRANQUILLISE

Ballets

3 letters
JOB

4 letters
AGON
JEUX

5 letters
CHOUT
MANON
RODEO

6 letters
APOLLO
BOLERO
FACADE
GAYANE
ONDINE
SYLVIA
TOY BOX

7 letters
ORPHEUS

8 letters
COPPELIA
LES NOCES
SWAN LAKE

9 letters
SPARTACUS

14 letters
SLEEPING BEAUTY

Harry Potter

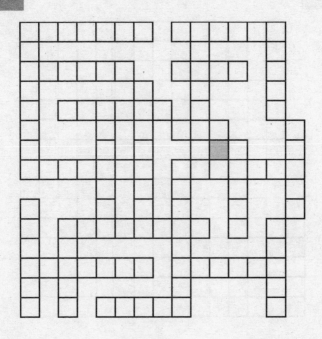

3 letters
RON

4 letters
LUNA

5 letters
AVERY
BASIL
DOBBY
DRACO
HOKEY
TONKS

6 letters
BERTIE
MUGGLE
OSWALD
TURPIN
WIZARD

7 letters
AZKABAN
MOONDEW
NEVILLE
ROWLING
SECRETS

8 letters
HOGWARTS
MR BORGIN
SEPTIMUS
SPUDMORE
VIOLETTA

'S' Words

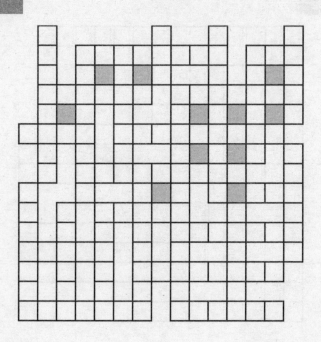

3 letters
SEW
SPA
SUM

4 letters
SIGN

5 letters
SAGGY
SHIRT
SINKS

6 letters
SAFETY
SAMOSA
SEIZED
SETTLE
SHIFTY
SIFTER
STAYED

7 letters
SADNESS
SEESAWS
SIBLING
SONATAS
STETSON

8 letters
SISTERLY
SOFTNESS
SUNSHINE
SWEETEST
SYNOPSIS

9 letters
SAILCLOTH
SENSELESS
SYMBOLISM

12 letters
SELFLESSNESS

Water, Water Everywhere

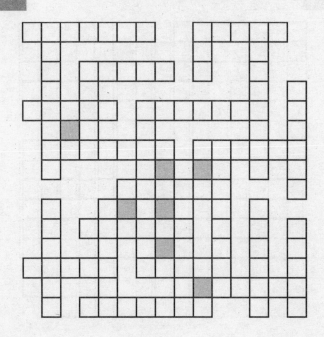

3 letters
DEW

5 letters
CRAFT
CRESS
DITCH
EAGRE
OASIS
OCEAN
RIVER
WAVES

6 letters
BARREL
DELUGE
DILUTE
GALLON
SPRING
STREAM
VAPOUR

7 letters
CASCADE
FLOWING

HYDRANT
ICE CUBE

8 letters
CATARACT
CHESTNUT
FOUNTAIN
IRRIGATE

9 letters
HYDRAULIC

Prisons

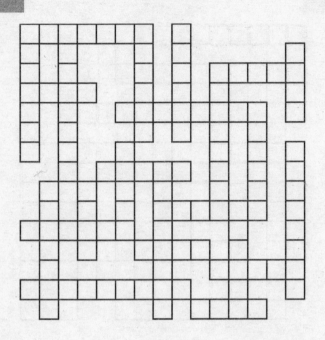

4 letters
BURE
FORD
HULL
ISIS
SEND

5 letters
GARTH
RANBY
STYAL
WOLDS

6 letters
ARMLEY
DURHAM
ELMLEY
EXETER
RISLEY
WYMOTT

7 letters
BEDFORD
BRISTOL
KIRKHAM

8 letters
DARTMOOR
DEERBOLT
DOWNVIEW
THE MOUNT
WOODHILL

9 letters
MAIDSTONE

Ladders

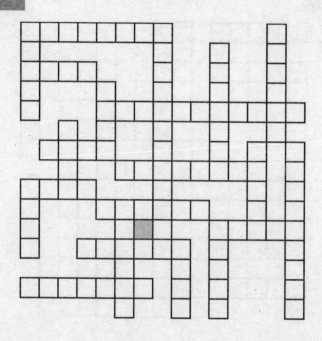

4 letters
HOOK
JACK
LOFT
ROOF
ROPE
SIDE
STEP

5 letters
PILOT
SCALE

STERN
STILE

6 letters
AERIAL
ETRIER
JACOB'S
MONKEY

7 letters
GANGWAY
ROLLING

8 letters
PLATFORM
STRAIGHT

9 letters
EXTENSION

11 letters
ARTICULATED

12 letters
MULTIPURPOSE

Roulette

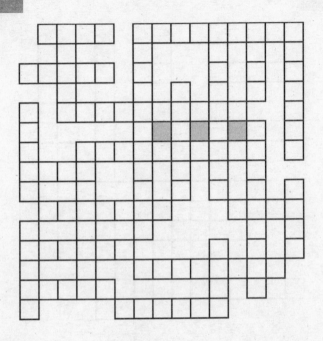

4 letters
BALL
COUP
PLAY
SPIN
TOKE
ZERO

5 letters
BLACK
HOUSE
PRESS
SLOTS
TIERS

6 letters
CHANCE
ODD BET
PARLEY

7 letters
TRIO BET
VOISINS

8 letters
FINAL BET
SPLIT BET

9 letters
RED NUMBER
SQUARE BET
STREET BET

10 letters
SIX-LINE BET
STRAIGHT UP

11 letters
SPECIAL LINE

Operas

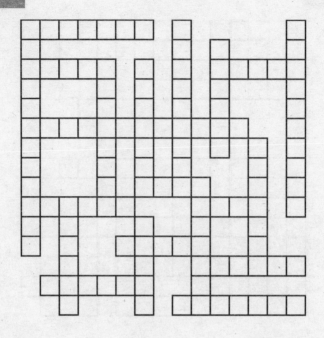

4 letters
AIDA
LULU

5 letters
MEDEE
NORMA
SERSE
THAIS

6 letters
ALCINA
CARMEN

OTELLO
SALOME
SEMELE

7 letters
ALCESTE
MACBETH
NABUCCO
RUSALKA
WERTHER

8 letters
AKHNATEN

9 letters
BILLY BUDD

10 letters
LES TROYENS

12 letters
LA
   SONNAMBULA
MANON
   LESCAUT

Christmas Time

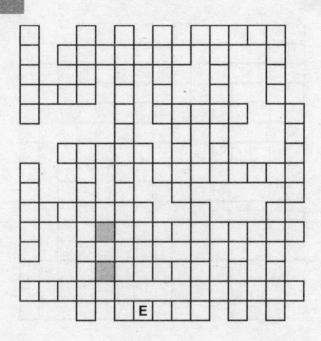

E

4 letters
BABE
HALO
HOLY
NOEL
SAGE

5 letters
ANGEL
BERRY
FAIRY
FEAST
GAMES
HYMNS
ICING

JESUS
MYRRH
PARTY
ROBIN
SANTA

6 letters
BRANDY
DONKEY
TINSEL

7 letters
GABRIEL
MESSIAH

8 letters
DECEMBER
YULETIDE

9 letters
CHESTNUTS

10 letters
PAPER CHAIN

13 letters
WRAPPING
PAPER

ME, ME, ME

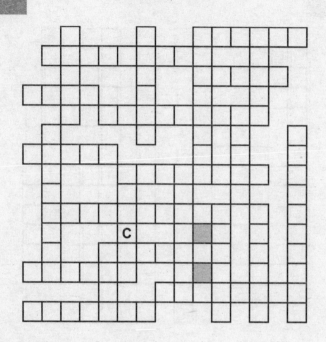

4 letters
MEND
MENU

5 letters
MEANT
MECCA
MELON
MERCY
MERIT

6 letters
MEDALS
MEDLEY
MEDUSA
MERCER
MERGER
MERMAN

7 letters
MEDIATE
MERCURY
MERMAID

8 letters
MELAMINE
MEMBRANE
MENSWEAR
MESMERIC

9 letters
MELODRAMA
MENAGERIE

10 letters
MEMORANDUM
MESOSPHERE

Bath Time

4 letters
PLUG
SINK
SOAP
SUDS

5 letters
BIDET
FLOSS
FLUSH
RAZOR

6 letters
HOT TAP
LOOFAH
MAKE-UP
MOUSSE
SPONGE

7 letters
AEROSOL
BATH MAT
BATHTUB
CABINET

CISTERN
COLOGNE
FLANNEL
SHAMPOO

9 letters
HAIRBRUSH

10 letters
TOOTHBRUSH
TOOTHPASTE

Be Quick!

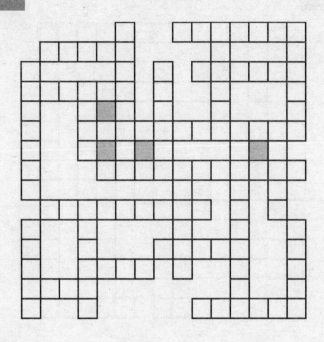

4 letters
BUSY
DEFT
SPRY

5 letters
AGILE
ALERT
FLEET
RAPID
READY

6 letters
ACTIVE
LIVELY
MOBILE
NIMBLE
PRESTO
PROMPT
RUSHED
SPEEDY

7 letters
EXPRESS
INSTANT

8 letters
METEORIC

9 letters
EXPLOSIVE

10 letters
ALACRITOUS

11 letters
ACCELERATED

12 letters
STRAIGHT
AWAY

Setting a Table

4 letters
BOWL
DISH
FORK
SALT

5 letters
BREAD
FRUIT
GLASS
KNIFE
LADLE
PLATE

SAUCE
SPOON

6 letters
NAPKIN
PEPPER
TUREEN

7 letters
FLOWERS
KETCHUP
MUSTARD

8 letters
PLACE MAT
WATER JUG

9 letters
LAZY SUSAN

10 letters
WINE BOTTLE

Feeling Adventurous

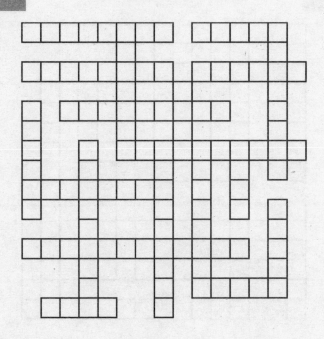

4 letters
BOLD
RASH
WILD

5 letters
BRAVE
GUTSY
RISKY

6 letters
CHANCY
HEROIC

7 letters
FOOLISH

8 letters
EVENTFUL
EXCITING
INTREPID
PERILOUS
SPORTING

9 letters
AUDACIOUS
DAREDEVIL
THRILLING

10 letters
HEADSTRONG

12 letters
ENTERPRISING

Ready

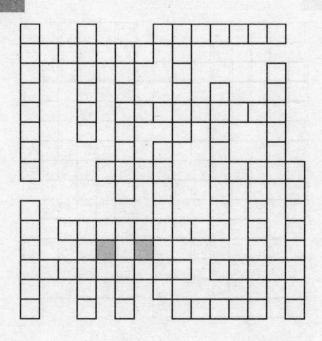

4 letters
KEEN

5 letters
ALERT
EAGER
FIXED
RAPID
SHARP

6 letters
ALL SET
BRACED
CLEVER
PROMPT

7 letters
IN ORDER
WAITING

8 letters
ARRANGED
DISPOSED
EQUIPPED
FINISHED
INCLINED
PREPARED

9 letters
COMPLETED
IMMEDIATE
ORGANISED

Double 'T'

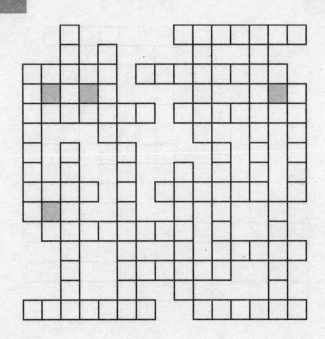

4 letters
SETT

5 letters
DITTO
MOTTO
POTTY
UTTER

6 letters
BITTEN
BOTTOM

COTTON
GHETTO
NETTLE
TATTOO

7 letters
ATTEMPT
COTTAGE
RICOTTA
TROTTER
WATTAGE
YTTRIUM

8 letters
KNITTING
LIBRETTO
MATTRESS

9 letters
JITTERBUG
MANHATTAN
PETTICOAT

Windows

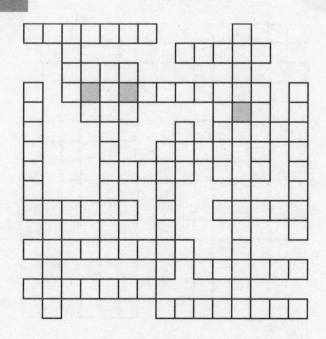

3 letters
BAY
BOW

4 letters
LOCK
PANE
SASH
SILL

5 letters
CLEAR
FRAME
GLASS

LIGHT
PUTTY
SLATS

6 letters
CASING
DORMER
OPAQUE

7 letters
DIMPLES
LOUVRED
MULLION
ROSETTE

STAINED
TRANSOM

8 letters
CASEMENT
FASTENER

9 letters
PATTERNED

10 letters
CROSSPIECE

Wake-up Call

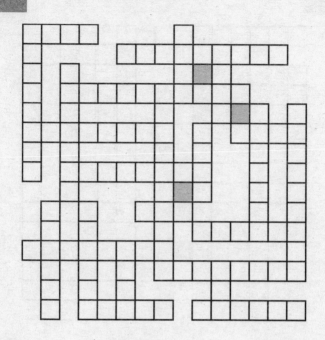

3 letters
SUN
TEA

4 letters
DAWN
DOZE
RISE
STIR
WASH
YAWN

5 letters
LIE-IN

6 letters
CEREAL
MUESLI
SHOWER
SNOOZE

7 letters
KIPPERS
STRETCH

8 letters
COCK-CROW
DAYBREAK
DRESSING

EXERCISE
PORRIDGE

9 letters
BED-MAKING
OFF TO WORK

10 letters
BLEARY-EYED
TOOTHBRUSH

Soup

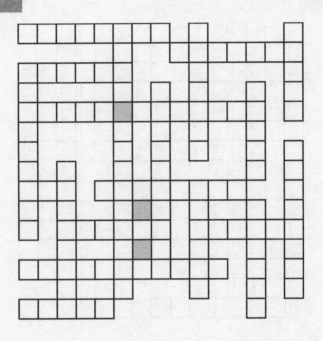

3 letters
PEA

4 letters
BEEF

5 letters
BROTH
ONION
PASTA
STOCK

6 letters
CARROT
OXTAIL
POTAGE
POTATO
TOMATO

7 letters
CHICKEN
CHOWDER
WINDSOR

8 letters
ALPHABET

BEETROOT
CONSOMME
GAZPACHO

9 letters
PEPPER POT
VEGETABLE

10 letters
MINESTRONE

11 letters
COCK-A-LEEKIE

Timber

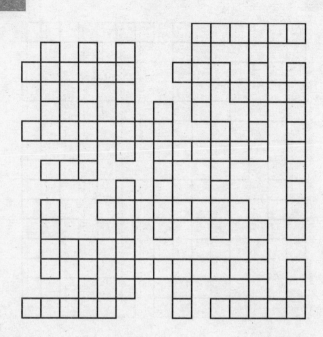

3 letters
ASH
ELM
OAK
YEW

4 letters
DEAL
PINE
TEAK

5 letters
ALDER

BALSA
BEECH
BIRCH
CEDAR
MAPLE

6 letters
BAMBOO
CHERRY
MERBAU
PARANA
SAPELE
WALNUT

7 letters
BUBINGA
CYPRESS
HEMLOCK

8 letters
CHESTNUT
MAHOGANY
ROSEWOOD

9 letters
ZEBRAWOOD

'T' Words

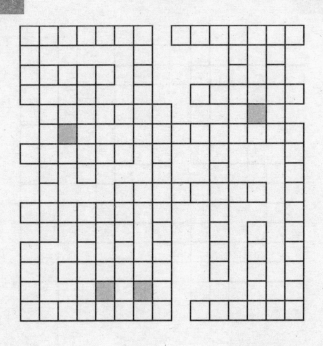

4 letters
TACT
TUTU

5 letters
TATTY
THROB

6 letters
TAHITI
TALCUM
TALLOW
TAVERN

TIPTOE
TOMATO
TREBLE
TUCKED
TYCOON
TYPIST

7 letters
TALLEST
TANGENT
TEASING
TESTATE
THYROID

8 letters
TERRAPIN
TOBOGGAN
TRIMARAN

9 letters
TREATMENT

10 letters
TEMPERANCE

11 letters
TREPIDATION

Making...

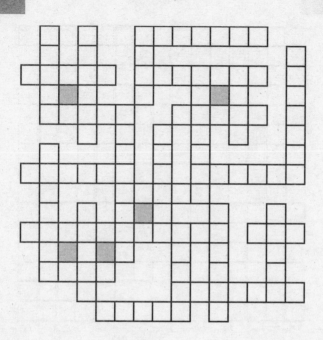

3 letters
WAY

4 letters
BOLD
OVER
SURE

5 letters
A FACE
A FUSS
FUN OF
HASTE

MERRY
MONEY
PEACE
SENSE
WAVES

6 letters
A NOISE
A POINT
AMENDS
EYES AT
TRACKS

7 letters
BELIEVE
CHANGES
FRIENDS
HEADWAY
LIGHT OF
WHOOPEE

8 letters
ENDS MEET

11 letters
UNNECESSARY

Commonwealth Countries

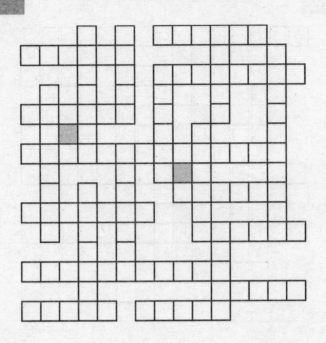

5 letters
GHANA
INDIA
KENYA
MALTA
NAURU
SAMOA

6 letters
BELIZE
CANADA
GUYANA
MALAWI

TUVALU
UGANDA
ZAMBIA

7 letters
LESOTHO
NAMIBIA
NIGERIA
VANUATU

8 letters
MALAYSIA
MALDIVES

10 letters
NEW ZEALAND

11 letters
SOUTH AFRICA

14 letters
PAPUA NEW
GUINEA

Easter

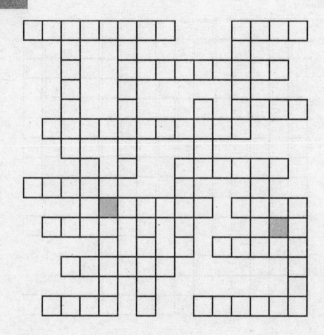

4 letters
EGGS
FISH
HATS
LAMB
LILY
PALM
TOMB

5 letters
APRIL
BUNNY
CHICK

CROSS
JESUS
TRIAL

6 letters
BASKET
BONNET
CHURCH
HEAVEN
PARADE
SUNDAY

7 letters
FLOWERS

8 letters
DAFFODIL
DUCKLING

9 letters
CHOCOLATE

11 letters
CRUCIFIXION

Get Active

4 letters
SPRY

5 letters
AGILE
ALERT
BRISK
MANIC
VITAL
ZIPPY

6 letters
NIMBLE
PROMPT

7 letters
FERVENT
FORWARD
ON THE GO
RUNNING

8 letters
BUSTLING

DILIGENT
FORCEFUL
FRENETIC
VIGOROUS

9 letters
ENERGETIC
OPERATIVE

12 letters
ENTHUSIASTIC

Under Repair

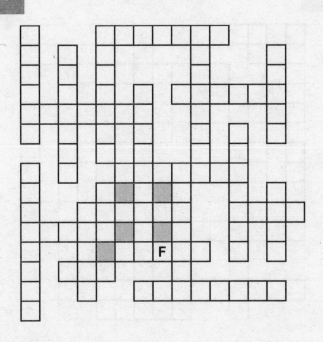

3 letters
FIX
SEW

4 letters
DARN
HEAL

5 letters
AMEND
REFIT
REJIG
RENEW

6 letters
ADJUST
COBBLE
REVAMP

7 letters
CORRECT
PATCH UP
RECTIFY
REDRESS
REPOINT
RESTORE
SERVICE

8 letters
OVERHAUL
PUT RIGHT
RENOVATE

9 letters
MELIORATE

Shifty Ways

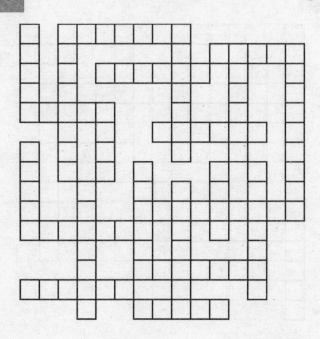

4 letters
DUPE
HOAX

5 letters
BOGUS
CHEAT
DODGY
FRAUD
SPOOF

6 letters
ARTFUL
DECEIT
FAKERY
HUMBUG
PHONEY

7 letters
CUNNING
MISLEAD
PERJURY
PRETEND

SWINDLE
TREASON
TRUMP UP

8 letters
TWO-FACED

9 letters
CHICANERY
TREACHERY

What a Commotion

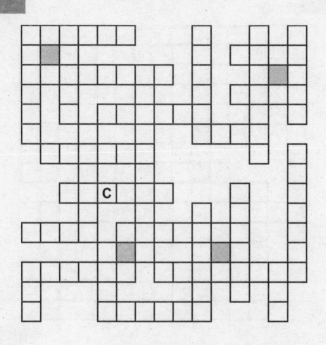

3 letters
ADO
ROW

4 letters
FUSS
RIOT
RUSH
STIR
TO-DO

5 letters
STORM
WHIRL

6 letters
FLURRY
FURORE
HOO-HAH
HUBBUB
HUSTLE
RACKET
RUCKUS
RUMPUS
SPLASH
TUMULT
UPROAR

7 letters
CLAMOUR
GARBOIL
RUCTION

8 letters
BROUHAHA
UPHEAVAL

10 letters
HURLY-BURLY

TV Time

4 letters
LIVE
NEWS
QUIZ

5 letters
DRAMA
FILMS
ON AIR
OPERA
SOUND

6 letters
ADVERT
SCREEN
SERIAL
TRAVEL
VOLUME
VOTING

7 letters
CARTOON
CREDITS
EPISODE
STATION

8 letters
BULLETIN
NATIONAL
WILDLIFE

9 letters
INTERVIEW

12 letters
BROADCASTING

Words Containing AND

5 letters
CANDY
PANDA
SANDY

6 letters
BRANDY
CANDLE
ERRAND
HANDLE
RANDOM
RIBAND

TANDEM
UGANDA
WANDER

7 letters
BANDAGE
ORLANDO
VERANDA

8 letters
BLANDEST
GRANDSON

MANDARIN
MANDIBLE
TANDOORI

9 letters
BROADBAND
DEMANDING

US State Capitals

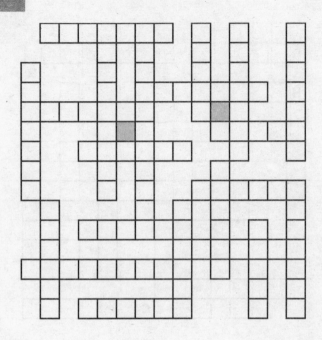

5 letters
BOISE
DOVER
SALEM

6 letters
ALBANY
AUSTIN
BOSTON
DENVER
HELENA
JUNEAU
PIERRE

7 letters
ATLANTA
CONCORD
LANSING
OLYMPIA
PHOENIX
RALEIGH
SANTA FE
TRENTON

9 letters
ANNAPOLIS
FRANKFORT

11 letters
TALLAHASSEE

'U' Words

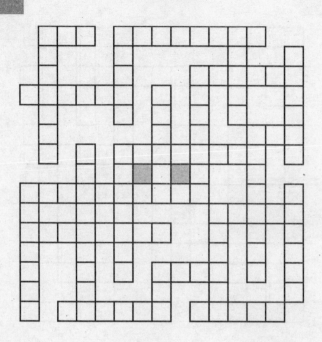

3 letters
URN
USA
USE

4 letters
UGLI

5 letters
UDDER
ULCER
UPSET
URBAN

6 letters
ULLAGE
UMPIRE
UNLOAD
UPWIND
URCHIN
UTMOST
UTOPIA

7 letters
UKULELE
UPSTART
URANIUM
URGENCY

8 letters
ULTERIOR
UNIONIST
UTENSILS
UXORIOUS

9 letters
UNIVERSAL

10 letters
ULTIMATELY

Weeding

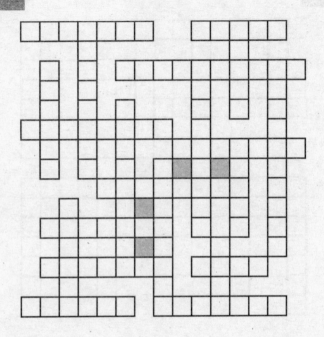

4 letters
DOCK
MOSS

5 letters
TANSY
TARES
VETCH

6 letters
FAT HEN
HENBIT

OXALIS

7 letters
DAISIES
NETTLES
RAGWORT
THISTLE
TREFOIL

8 letters
CLEAVERS
FLEABANE

KNOTWEED
PLANTAIN

9 letters
HORSETAIL
PEARLWORT

10 letters
COUCH GRASS
SILVERWEED

Very Abrupt

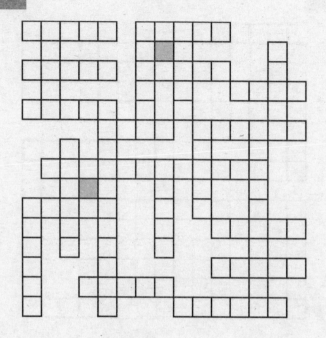

4 letters
CURT
RUDE

5 letters
BRISK
GRUFF
HARSH
HASTY
JERKY
QUICK
RAPID

ROUGH
SHARP
SHEER
SHORT
STEEP
STIFF
TERSE

6 letters
BROKEN
DIRECT
JAGGED

SNAPPY
SUDDEN

10 letters
DISMISSIVE

11 letters
PRECIPITATE

12 letters
DISCOURTEOUS

Fruits and Nuts

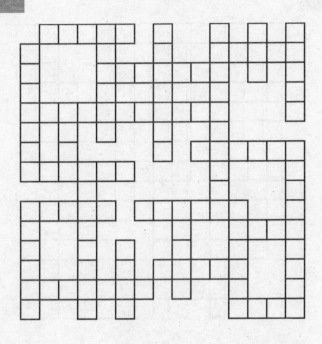

3 letters
FIG

4 letters
DATE
LIME
MAST
SLOE

5 letters
LEMON
MANGO
OLIVE
PEACH

PECAN
PRUNE

6 letters
ALMOND
NUTMEG
ORANGE
PAPAYA
PAWPAW
PEANUT

7 letters
APRICOT
AVOCADO

COCONUT
PUMPKIN

8 letters
MANDARIN

9 letters
TANGERINE

10 letters
GOOSEBERRY

11 letters
POMEGRANATE

Rather Risky

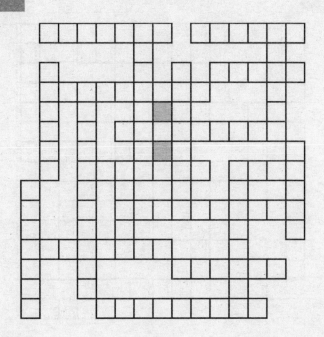

4 letters
BOMB

5 letters
ABYSS
FLOOD
ROCKS

6 letters
AMBUSH
SQUALL
SWORDS

VORTEX

7 letters
TORNADO
TSUNAMI
VOLCANO

8 letters
BLIZZARD
CHAINSAW
JOYRIDER
MELTDOWN

9 letters
BOY RACERS
LANDSLIDE
OPERATION

10 letters
CORROSIVES

11 letters
ELECTRICITY

Windy

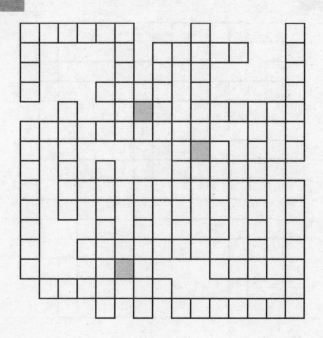

4 letters
BLOW
GALE

5 letters
BLAST
FOEHN
FORCE
ZONDA

6 letters
BOREAS

BREATH
BREEZE
CALIMA
SQUALL
ZEPHYR

7 letters
CHINOOK
CYCLONE
MISTRAL
MONSOON
SIROCCO
THERMAL

TORNADO
TWISTER

8 letters
HEADWIND
TAILWIND

9 letters
HARMATTAN

10 letters
TURBULENCE

Time for Tea

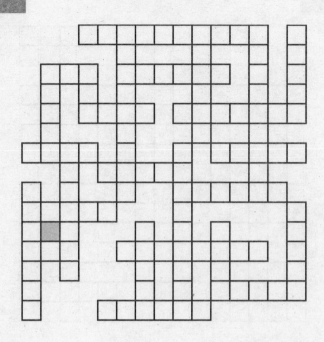

3 letters
CUP
POT
URN

4 letters
BAGS
BOIL
TRAY

5 letters
ASSAM
CADDY
CHINA

GREEN
INDIA
JAPAN
LEMON
WATER

6 letters
DOOARS
HERBAL
LEAVES
TAIWAN

7 letters
BADULLA

GINSENG
TEA COSY

8 letters
CAMEROON

9 letters
GUNPOWDER
INDONESIA
RATNAPURA

10 letters
DARJEELING

Carnival

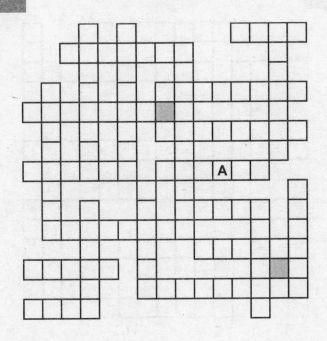

4 letters
FETE
GALA

5 letters
BANDS
MUSIC

6 letters
AWARDS
CLOWNS
FLOATS

GUILDS
HORSES
POLICE
STREET

7 letters
HOLIDAY
LORRIES
REVELRY

8 letters
CHILDREN

COSTUMES
FESTIVAL
JUGGLERS
PENNANTS
SPONSORS

9 letters
STREAMERS

10 letters
YOUTH CLUBS

440 Sailing

4 letters
BEAM
MAST
PROW
REEF
SURF
WASH

5 letters
ABAFT
BELOW
BERTH
BOATS

CABIN
FLOAT
KNOTS
PITCH
SAILS
STERN
TIDES
WHARF

6 letters
MARINA
VESSEL

7 letters
CHANNEL
CLIPPER
COMPASS
CURRENT
PASSAGE
YARDARM

8 letters
FOREDECK

10 letters
LIFE JACKET

445

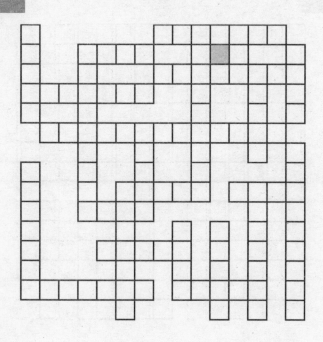

3 letters
AGA

4 letters
IMAM
KING
POPE
SHAH
TSAR

5 letters
GUIDE
KALIF

MAHDI
MAYOR
MOGUL
QUEEN
RULER

7 letters
CAPTAIN
EMPEROR
EMPRESS
MAHATMA
MANAGER
SUPREMO

8 letters
OLIGARCH

9 letters
COMMANDER
PRESIDENT
PRINCIPAL

13 letters
PRIME
  MINISTER

'V' Words

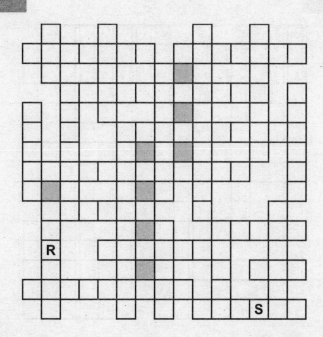

3 letters
VAN
VIM

5 letters
VAGUE
VERVE
VISOR
VISTA
VIXEN

6 letters
VELVET

VENICE
VERGER
VERSES
VOYAGE

7 letters
VACCINE
VANILLA
VINEGAR
VITRIOL
VULPINE
VULTURE

9 letters
VERMILION

10 letters
VETERINARY
VICTORIOUS
VULNERABLE

11 letters
VITICULTURE

12 letters
VAINGLORIOUS

European Capitals

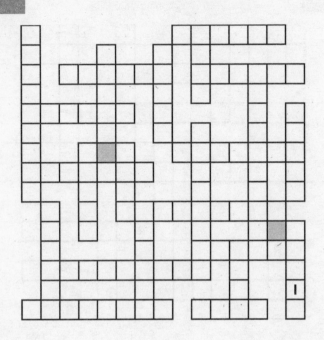

4 letters
KIEV
OSLO
RIGA
ROME

5 letters
BERNE
MINSK
PARIS
SOFIA
VADUZ

6 letters
ATHENS
LISBON
LONDON
MADRID
SKOPJE
TIRANA
VIENNA

7 letters
NICOSIA
TALLINN

8 letters
BELGRADE
VALLETTA

9 letters
AMSTERDAM
PODGORICA
SAN MARINO

10 letters
BRATISLAVA

Small-scale

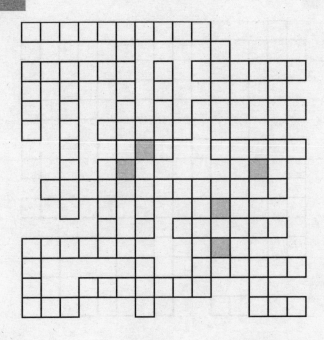

3 letters
BIT
DOT
NIT
TAD

4 letters
MEAN
POKY
TINY

5 letters
ELFIN
MINOR

WEENY
YOUNG

6 letters
ATOMIC
LITTLE
MEAGRE
MINUTE
PALTRY
PETITE
SCANTY
TIDDLY

7 letters
LIMITED
SHRIMPY
SLENDER
TRIVIAL

8 letters
TRIFLING

10 letters
UNDERSIZED

13 letters
INFINITESIMAL

Things You Can Peel

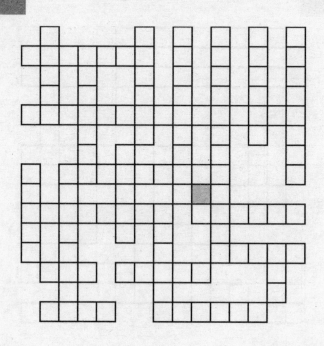

3 letters
WAX
YAM

4 letters
SKIN

5 letters
GRAPE
LABEL
ONION
PAINT
PRAWN

6 letters
BANANA
CARROT
ORANGE
POTATO
TOMATO

7 letters
SATSUMA
STICKER

8 letters
BEETROOT
MUSHROOM

TREE BARK

9 letters
TRANSFERS
WALLPAPER

12 letters
POSTAGE
STAMP

15 letters
STICKING
PLASTER

Winning Words

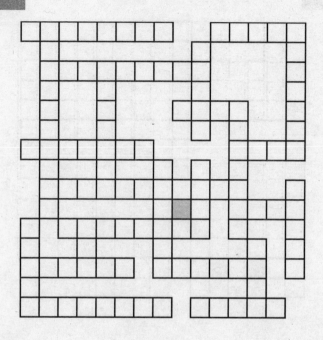

3 letters
CUP

4 letters
CASH
EDGE
GAME
PASS
STAR

5 letters
GRANT
MATCH
MONEY

PRIZE
RELAY

6 letters
FINALS
SHIELD
TROPHY

7 letters
CONTEST
LAURELS
SUCCESS
TRIUMPH

8 letters
ACCOLADE
HAT-TRICK
MARATHON

9 letters
CHECKMATE

10 letters
ASCENDANCY

11 letters
CERTIFICATE

Wales

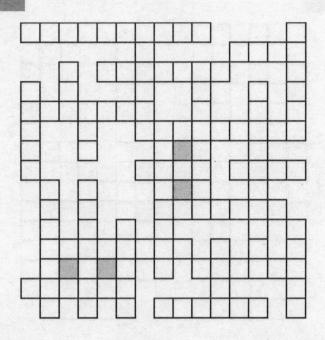

3 letters
DEE
USK

4 letters
BALA
NEBO
RHYL
TAFF

5 letters
BARRY
NEFYN
POWYS

6 letters
BANGOR
CARMEL
CORRIS
MAERDY
TREFOR

7 letters
CARDIFF
CWMBRAN
OAKDALE
TINTERN
WREXHAM

8 letters
BETHESDA
FERNDALE
LLANWNDA

9 letters
LLANBERIS

10 letters
ABERSYCHAN
PORTHMADOG

Too Much Noise!

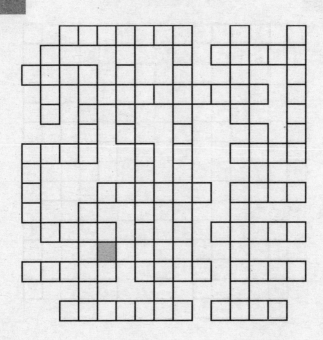

4 letters
BANG
BARK
ECHO
FIZZ
HISS
HONK
HOWL
SLAM
THUD
WAIL
WHAM
YELP

YOWL

5 letters
CHIME
CLANG
CRACK
STOMP
WHINE

6 letters
CRUNCH
SQUEAL
TUMULT

7 letters
CLATTER
PEALING
SCRATCH
SQUELCH
WHISTLE

10 letters
TRUMPETING

13 letters
REVER-
   BERATION

Silver...

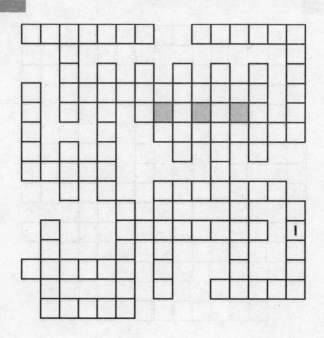

3 letters
FIR
FOX

5 letters
BEECH
BELLS
BIRCH
MEDAL
MINES
PERCH
SPOON

STARS
SWORD

6 letters
BULLET
IODIDE
SCREEN
TONGUE
WATTLE
WILLOW

7 letters
BROMIDE
JUBILEE
TANKARD
WEDDING

8 letters
CHLORIDE
NECKLACE

11 letters
CERTIFICATE

Finance

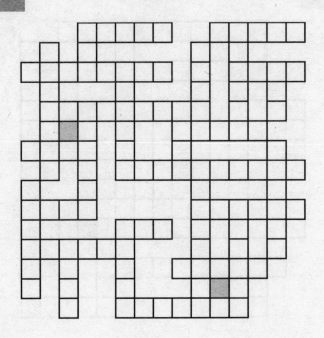

3 letters
DUN
FEE
SUM

4 letters
BANK
CASH
COST
NETT
SAFE

5 letters
ASSET
AUDIT

DEBIT
FUNDS
NOTES
TILLS

6 letters
BORROW
INCOME
MARKET
OFFICE
REBATE
SETTLE
STOCKS
USURER

7 letters
MANAGED
TRUSTEE

8 letters
DISCOUNT
RATEABLE

9 letters
ASSURANCE

10 letters
WITHDRAWAL

Human Types

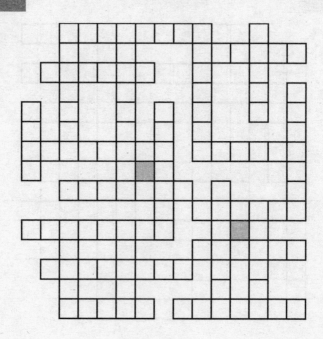

4 letters
FOOL

5 letters
IDIOT
KNAVE
MISER
TOPER

6 letters
CARPER
DODGER

GENIUS
MADMAN
PEDANT
VANDAL

7 letters
CHARMER
EGGHEAD
FANATIC
HOTHEAD
LOUNGER

PARAGON
PEASANT

8 letters
OPTIMIST
PARASITE
WHIZZ KID
WISEACRE

9 letters
AMAZONIAN

Go

4 letters
EXIT
HEAD
MOVE

5 letters
BEGIN
DRIVE
LEAVE
QUICK
SCRAM
START

6 letters
DEPART
EMBARK
GET OUT
PASS ON
TRAVEL

7 letters
ABSCOND
ADVANCE
MAKE FOR
PROCEED

RELEASE
RETREAT
SCARPER

8 letters
PROGRESS

9 letters
DISAPPEAR

Summer

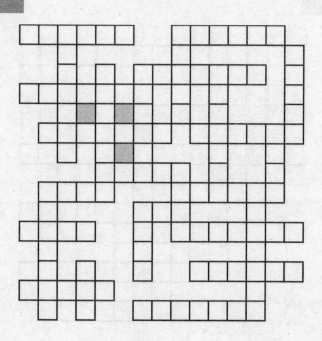

3 letters
HAY
SUN

4 letters
HEAT
PLAY
SAND
SWIM
TENT

5 letters
BEACH
ROSES
SALAD
WASPS

6 letters
AUGUST
AWNING
BIKINI
PICNIC
SHORTS
TENNIS

7 letters
AIRPORT
CAMPING
CARAVAN
DAY TRIP
FISHING
HOLIDAY
SEASIDE
SURFING
TANNING
TRAFFIC

UP Ended

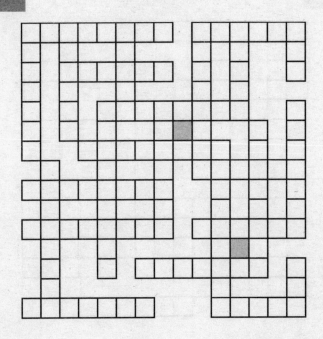

3 letters
PUP
SUP

5 letters
ACT UP
DIG UP
PAL UP

6 letters
DRAG UP
PERK UP
PUMP UP

RING UP
WIND UP

7 letters
CREEP UP
ICING UP
SPEAK UP
SWEPT UP
THINK UP

8 letters
DIVIDE UP
FATTEN UP

POPPED UP
SPICED UP
STITCH UP
STRIKE UP
STRING UP
TOPPED UP

9 letters
PULLING UP
SLACKEN UP

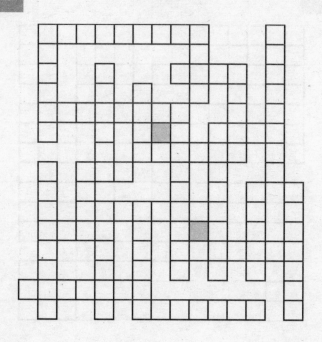

3 letters
PEN

4 letters
BIRO
DESK
NOTE
POST
RSVP
TEXT

5 letters
COMMA
PAPER

6 letters
LETTER
MINUTE
OPENER
PENCIL
STAMPS

7 letters
ADDRESS
GRAMMAR
INVOICE
READING

8 letters
FRANKING
FULL STOP
PRINTING
SPELLING
TELEGRAM

9 letters
GREETINGS
SHORTHAND

TOP First

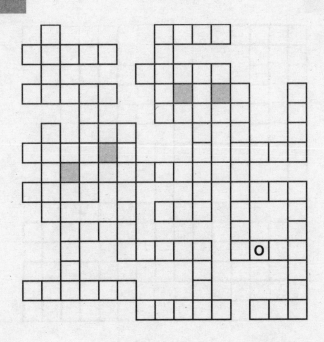

3 letters
CAT
DOG
HAT

4 letters
GEAR
HOLE
KNOT
LESS
MOST
PING
SAIL
SIDE

SOIL
SPIN
STAR

5 letters
BRASS
CLASS
GRADE
HEAVY
LEVEL
MARKS
SHELF
STONE

6 letters
BANANA
SECRET

7 letters
GALLANT
THE BILL

8 letters
DRESSING

9 letters
EXECUTIVE
OF THE POPS

Sports and Games

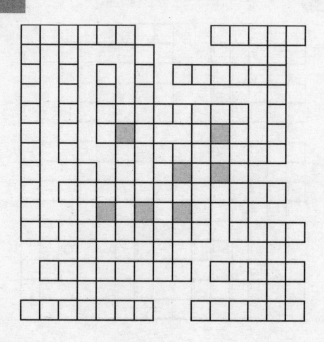

4 letters
GOLF
LUDO

5 letters
CHESS
DARTS
LOTTO
RELAY
RUGBY

6 letters
PELOTA
SLALOM
SOCCER

7 letters
BOATING
BOBSLED
CHASING
CRICKET
CURLING
HURDLES
SAILING

8 letters
DRAUGHTS
DRESSAGE
ROUNDERS

10 letters
GYMNASTICS

11 letters
SHOT-PUTTING

12 letters
POLE-VAULTING

Valentine

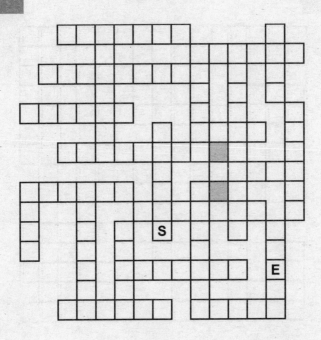

4 letters
BEAU
EROS
HUGS

5 letters
CARDS
CUPID
GIFTS
GUESS

6 letters
HEARTS
KISSES
LOVERS
POETRY
SECRET
SENDER
TENDER

7 letters
ADMIRER
DARLING
DEAREST

DREAMER
PASSION
ROMANCE

8 letters
PARAMOUR

9 letters
CHAMPAGNE

10 letters
CHOCOLATES

'W' Words

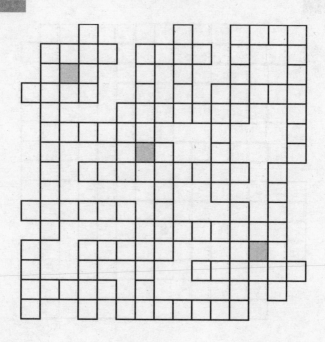

4 letters
WAIT
WASH
WEST
WHEW
WITH
WOAD
WOOD
WOWS

5 letters
WAGER
WELSH
WHIRL

WHOSE
WIVES
WOMAN
WRECK

6 letters
WAGGLE
WANTON
WEAVER
WEIGHT
WHENCE
WIGWAM

7 letters
WASSAIL
WHITEST
WORKING
WRESTLE

8 letters
WEAKNESS

9 letters
WEDNESDAY

10 letters
WAINWRIGHT

Things with Wings

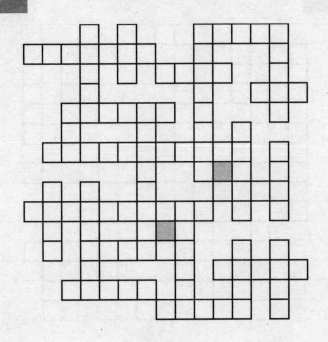

3 letters
BAT
FLY
ROC

4 letters
BIRD
CROW
GNAT
HAWK
MOTH
WASP

5 letters
ANGEL
CRANE
EAGLE
FAIRY
MIDGE
PLANE
STORK

6 letters
BEETLE
DRAGON
GLIDER
HORNET

7 letters
SPARROW

8 letters
LADYBIRD
MOSQUITO

10 letters
MICROLIGHT

11 letters
PTERODACTYL

British Monarchy Forenames

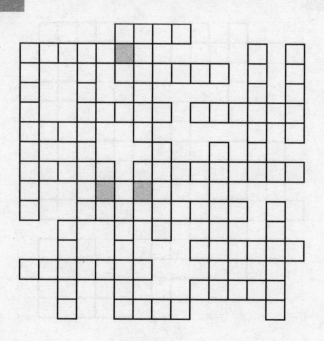

4 letters
ANNE
MARY
ZARA

5 letters
ALICE
ANGUS
DAVID
HELEN
JAMES
PETER
SARAH

6 letters
ANDREW
ARTHUR
EDWARD
LOUISE
SOPHIE

7 letters
EUGENIE
MICHAEL
WILLIAM

8 letters
VICTORIA

9 letters
ALEXANDRA
CATHERINE
ELIZABETH
GABRIELLA

Help

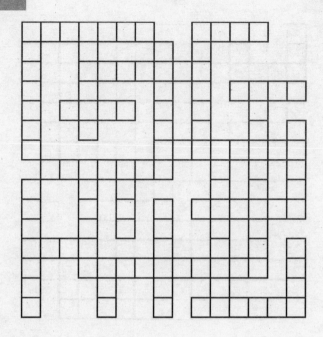

3 letters
AID

4 letters
ALMS
BACK
EASE
FUND
HELP
SAVE

5 letters
SERVE

6 letters
DONATE
FOLLOW
RELIEF
SECOND
SUPPLY

7 letters
BENEFIT
BOLSTER
FURTHER
PROMOTE
SPEED UP

SUBSIDY
SUPPORT

8 letters
EXPEDITE

9 letters
ENCOURAGE

10 letters
ASSISTANCE
FACILITATE

Link Together

3 letters
TIE

4 letters
ALLY
BIND
BOND
FUSE
GLUE
JOIN
KNOT
MELD
TEAM
YOKE

5 letters
CHAIN
CLAMP
MERGE
TOUCH
UNITE

6 letters
ADHERE
ATTACH
HOOK UP
LIAISE

7 letters
CIRCUIT
COMBINE
CONNECT
NETWORK
SHACKLE

8 letters
JUNCTION

9 letters
ASSOCIATE

Whodunnit

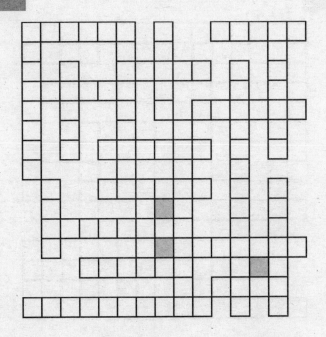

4 letters
BODY
LOVE

5 letters
ALIBI
CLUES
CRIME
MONEY
TRIAL

6 letters
KILLER
MOTIVE
POLICE
SOLVED
VICTIM
WEAPON

7 letters
ENEMIES
MYSTERY
STORIES

8 letters
DISGUISE
SUSPECTS

9 letters
DETECTIVE

10 letters
DENOUEMENT
FOOTPRINTS

13 letters
INCRIMINATION

Vegetable Plot

4 letters
BEAN
BEET
KALE
LEEK
PEAS
SAGE
SOYA

5 letters
CRESS
MAIZE
SWEDE

6 letters
ADZUKI
ENDIVE
GARLIC
GREENS
RADISH

7 letters
CABBAGE
HARICOT
LETTUCE
PARSLEY
SHALLOT

8 letters
CELERIAC
CHICKPEA
ZUCCHINI

9 letters
ASPARAGUS

11 letters
HORSERADISH

The Castle

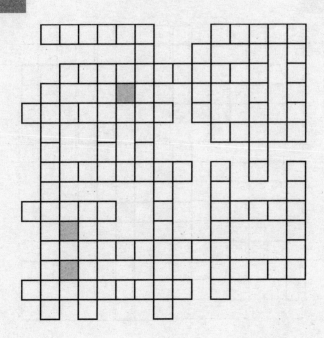

4 letters
KEEP

5 letters
DITCH
MOATS
REDAN
TOWER
VICES

6 letters
CHAPEL
ESCARP

NORMAN
SIEGES
TURRET

7 letters
BATTERY

8 letters
BUTTRESS
CASEMATE
FORTRESS
PALISADE
SOLDIERS

9 letters
INNER WARD

10 letters
DRAWBRIDGE

11 letters
BATTLEMENTS

12 letters
FOREBUILDING

Plumbing

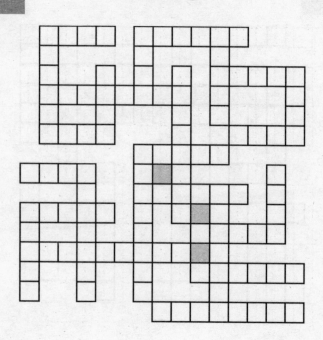

4 letters
BATH
BEND
FLUX
PLUG
PUMP
SINK
TANK
TRAP

5 letters
BASIN

BIDET
ELBOW
FLOAT
FORCE
O-RING

6 letters
BOILER
FAUCET
HOT TAP
THREAD

7 letters
AIRLOCK
HEATING

8 letters
BATHROOM
CYLINDER
PRESSURE
SOAKAWAY

9 letters
RADIATORS

468   Hotel Stay

4 letters
AWAY
CHEF
POOL
STAY
TAXI

5 letters
CHAIN
FOYER
GRILL
GUIDE
LODGE

ROOMS
SAUNA
TABLE

6 letters
GARAGE
GUESTS
LOUNGE
RESORT
RESTED
STAIRS

7 letters
EN SUITE
PARKING
SERVICE

8 letters
FIVE-STAR
SOLARIUM

9 letters
CORRIDORS
RECEPTION
THREE-STAR

Herbs and Spices

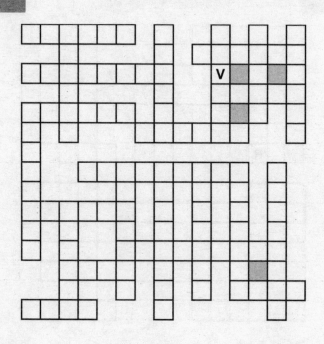

4 letters
DILL
MACE
SAGE

5 letters
ANISE
BASIL

6 letters
BORAGE
CELERY
CLOVES

GARLIC
GINGER
HYSSOP
LOVAGE
NUTMEG
SAVORY
SORREL

7 letters
CAYENNE
MUSTARD
PARSLEY

8 letters
CAMOMILE
GALANGAL
LAVENDER
ROSEMARY

9 letters
HYPERICUM
LEMON BALM

Over…

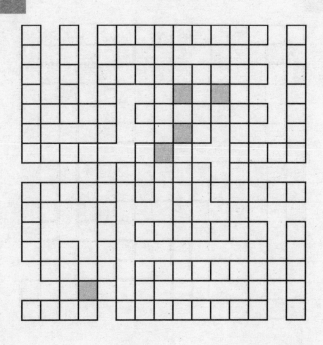

3 letters
ATE
TAX

4 letters
ALLS
AWED
CAME
CAST
DONE
PASS
SEAS

5 letters
DRESS

DRIVE
GROWN
HASTY
NIGHT
POWER
SHIRT

6 letters
EXPOSE
HAULED
SHADOW

7 letters
CROWDED
INSURED

STOCKED
WORKING
ZEALOUS

8 letters
REACTION

9 letters
AMBITIOUS
EMPHASISE
POPULATED

11 letters
SPECULATION

Salad Bowl

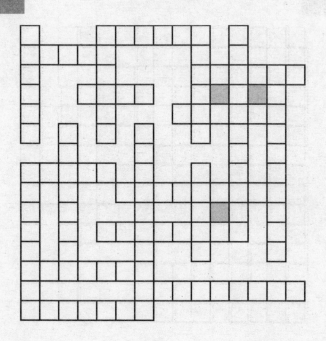

4 letters
PEAS

5 letters
CRESS
HERBS
OLIVE

6 letters
CAESAR
CELERY
CHEESE

FENNEL
POTATO
ROCKET

7 letters
LETTUCE
WALNUTS

8 letters
BEETROOT
COLESLAW
CUCUMBER

9 letters
RED PEPPER
SWEETCORN

10 letters
SALAD CREAM
WATERCRESS

11 letters
GREEN PEPPER

Swimming Pool

4 letters
COLD
DEEP
TUBE

5 letters
BOARD
FENCE
FLUME
RAFTS
WATER

6 letters
BIKINI
LOTION
MUSCLE
POSERS
SHOWER
SLIDES
SPLASH
TRUNKS
WADING

7 letters
WHISTLE

8 letters
FLOATING
SUNSHINE
SWIMSUIT
TAKE A DIP
UMBRELLA

9 letters
BUTTERFLY

Types of Buildings

3 letters
HUT
PUB

4 letters
BANK
HALL
MILL
SHED

5 letters
DAIRY
DEPOT
HOUSE

KIOSK
SHACK

6 letters
CHURCH
CLINIC
HOSTEL
MOSQUE
PALACE
SCHOOL

7 letters
FACTORY
LIBRARY

MANSION
THEATRE

8 letters
OUTHOUSE

9 letters
APARTMENT
CATHEDRAL

11 letters
SUPERMARKET

Toys

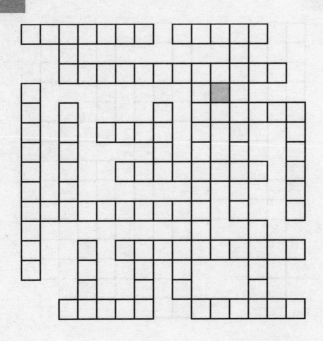

3 letters
CAR
TOP

4 letters
BALL
DOLL
KITE
YO-YO

5 letters
FURBY
SLIDE

YACHT

6 letters
BRICKS
PINATA
SKATES
SLEDGE

7 letters
MECCANO

8 letters
HULA HOOP

10 letters
BARBIE DOLL
HELICOPTER
HOBBY-HORSE
PEASHOOTER
SKATEBOARD

12 letters
ROCKING
  HORSE

Paris Metro Stations

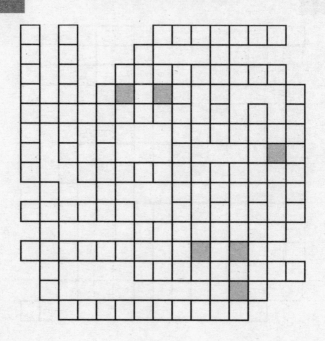

4 letters
ROME

6 letters
ANVERS
PICPUS
TEMPLE
TERNES

7 letters
BERAULT
LIBERTE

PASTEUR
RASPAIL
SIMPLON

8 letters
GAMBETTA
MIRABEAU
RANELAGH

9 letters
BIR-HAKEIM
BOUCICAUT

TROCADERO

10 letters
LE PELETIER
TELEGRAPHE

11 letters
CAMPO FORMIO

12 letters
SAINT-FARGEAU

Soft Words

4 letters
KIND

5 letters
BALMY
BLAND
CUSHY
DOWNY
MISTY
MUSHY
PULPY
QUIET

6 letters
DULCET
FACILE
SMOOTH

7 letters
LENIENT
PLIABLE
SQUASHY
VELVETY

8 letters
DIFFUSED
TEMPERED
YIELDING

9 letters
MALLEABLE

10 letters
IRRESOLUTE

11 letters
UNPROTECTED

Look in a Book

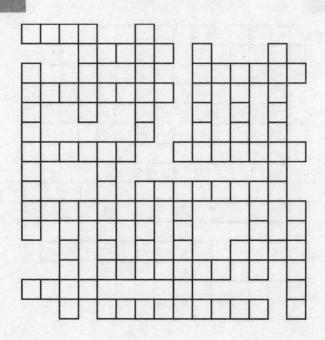

4 letters
PLOT
TALE
TEXT

5 letters
COVER
INDEX
NOVEL
SCI-FI
TITLE

6 letters
ANNALS
ANNUAL
AUTHOR
MANUAL
REVIEW
SEQUEL

7 letters
CLASSIC
EDITION
EPISTLE

FICTION
FLYLEAF

8 letters
EPILOGUE
HARDBACK
SOFTBACK

9 letters
CHRONICLE
REFERENCE

Not on a Diet

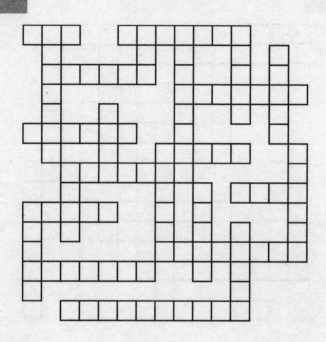

3 letters
ALE
JAM

4 letters
BEER
BUNS
WINE

5 letters
CAKES
CANDY
CHIPS

CREAM
ROLLS
SUGAR
SYRUP

6 letters
CHEESE
CRISPS
SWEETS
TOFFEE

7 letters
ALCOHOL

BURGERS
PEANUTS
TREACLE
WAFFLES

8 letters
FRITTERS
SAUSAGES

10 letters
CHOCOLATES

Silent 'H'

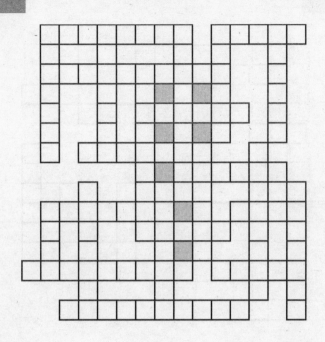

4 letters
ECHO
LOCH
SIKH

5 letters
ROUGH
SARAH
TOUGH

6 letters
ANCHOR
CHORUS

ENOUGH
GHETTO
RHESUS

7 letters
CHEETAH
CHOLERA
MONARCH
RHIZOME
STOMACH
VEHICLE
WHITHER

8 letters
CHARISMA
HONORARY

9 letters
ARCHITECT
AYATOLLAH
CHARACTER

10 letters
EXHILARATE
RHEUMATISM

Very Clever

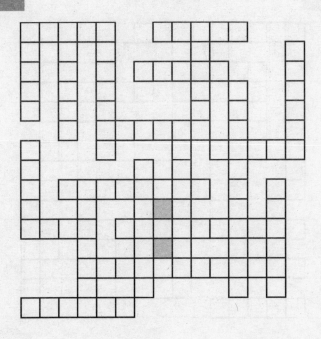

4 letters
KEEN

5 letters
ALERT
CANNY
QUICK
READY
SHARP
SMART

6 letters
ADROIT
ARTFUL
ASTUTE
BRAINY
BRIGHT
EXPERT

7 letters
CUNNING
LEARNED
TRAINED

8 letters
ACADEMIC
RATIONAL

9 letters
TRENCHANT

11 letters
CLEAR-HEADED
INTELLIGENT

'X' Words

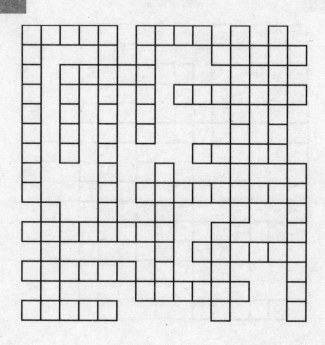

4 letters
XMAS

5 letters
XEBEC
XENON
XEROX
XHOSA
X-RAYS
XYLEM
XYRIS

6 letters
XAVIER
XENIAL
XERXES
XYLENE
XYSTUS

7 letters
XENICUS
XYLARIA
XYLOPIA

8 letters
XENOLITH
XYLOCOPA

9 letters
XEROPHYTE
XYLOPHONE

10 letters
XYLOGRAPHY

11 letters
XEROGRAPHIC

Calendar

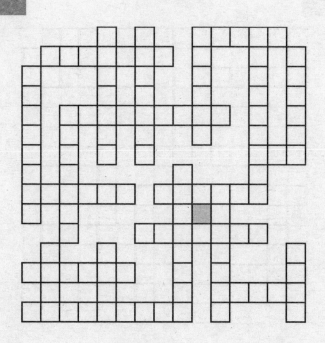

3 letters
MAY

4 letters
DATE
JULY
JUNE

5 letters
APRIL
MARCH

6 letters
EASTER
FRIDAY
MONDAY
MONTHS
SUNDAY

7 letters
HOLIDAY
NEW YEAR
OCTOBER
TUESDAY

WEEKEND
WHITSUN

8 letters
DECEMBER
NOVEMBER

9 letters
CHRISTMAS
SEPTEMBER
WEDNESDAY

In the Park

4 letters
CAFE
LAKE

5 letters
FENCE
GRASS
LAWNS
PATHS
PONDS
ROSES
SEATS

SWANS
TREES

6 letters
AVIARY
BUSHES
PEOPLE
SEESAW
STATUE
TENNIS

7 letters
BENCHES
FLOWERS

8 letters
FOUNTAIN
PAVILION

9 letters
BANDSTAND

10 letters
PLAYGROUND

Juicy Fruits

4 letters
KIWI
LIME
PEAR

5 letters
APPLE
GRAPE
GUAVA
LEMON
MANGO

MELON
PEACH

6 letters
CHERRY
ORANGE
PAPAYA
TOMATO

7 letters
APRICOT

8 letters
BILBERRY

9 letters
CRANBERRY
NECTARINE
RASPBERRY

10 letters
GOOSEBERRY
STRAWBERRY

Dry

E

3 letters
SEC

4 letters
ARID
BRUT
SEAR
SERE

5 letters
BAKED
PLAIN

SOBER
SOLID

6 letters
WILTED

7 letters
DRIED UP
DRY-EYED
PARCHED
SHRIVEL
THIRSTY

8 letters
MILKLESS
RAINLESS
SCORCHED
SUN-BAKED
WITHERED

9 letters
KILN-DRIED
MEDIUM-DRY

Colours

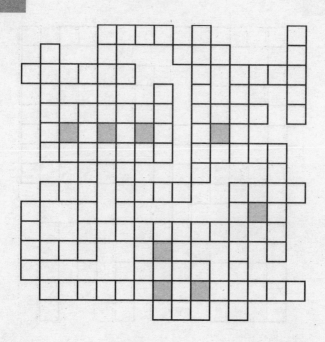

3 letters
BAY
JET
RED

4 letters
BLUE
CORK
CYAN
FAWN
GREY
LIME
RUBY
RUST

SAGE
SAND

5 letters
CORAL
CREAM
FLESH
LILAC
MAUVE
STEEL

6 letters
CHERRY
CLARET

COFFEE
COPPER

7 letters
CRIMSON
EMERALD
FUCHSIA
SCARLET

8 letters
CHESTNUT
MARIGOLD

11 letters
ULTRAMARINE

487   Looking Good

4 letters
CUTE
FAIR
FINE

5 letters
BONNY
SMART

6 letters
DAPPER
LOVELY
PRETTY

7 letters
ELEGANT
SHAPELY
STYLISH
WINSOME

8 letters
CHARMING
GORGEOUS
STUNNING

9 letters
BEAUTIFUL
EXQUISITE
GLAMOROUS
SALACIOUS

10 letters
PERSONABLE

Don't Be Miserable

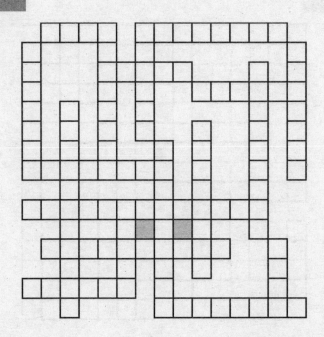

4 letters
BLUE
GLUM

5 letters
SORRY
UPSET

6 letters
DISMAL
DREARY
GLOOMY

7 letters
CRUSHED
JOYLESS

8 letters
DEJECTED
DESOLATE
DOWNCAST
MOURNFUL
WRETCHED

9 letters
DEPRESSED
WOEBEGONE

10 letters
DISTRESSED

11 letters
LOW-SPIRITED

13 letters
GRIEF-
STRICKEN

Double 'N'

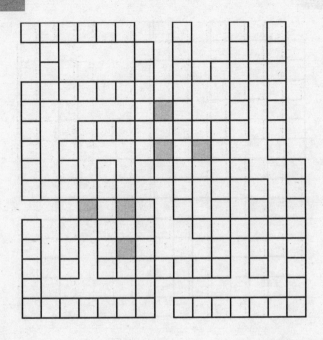

4 letters
ANNE

5 letters
ENNUI
HENNA
SUNNY

6 letters
BANNED
DINNER
LINNET
MINNOW

PUNNET
SKINNY
TENNIS
TUNNEL
ZINNIA

7 letters
ANNULAR
ANTENNA
FINNISH
MANNERS
NUNNERY
WINNING

8 letters
ANNOYING
SAVANNAH

9 letters
PERENNIAL
PERSONNEL

10 letters
MILLENNIUM

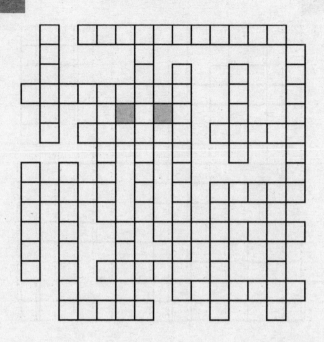

490 Ironing Session

4 letters
FLEX

5 letters
CHORE
CUFFS
LINEN
NYLON
SEAMS
STAND

6 letters
COLLAR
PLEATS
SCORCH

7 letters
CLOTHES
CREASES
FLATTEN
SLEEVES

8 letters
MATERIAL

TROUSERS
WOOLLENS

9 letters
DAMP CLOTH

10 letters
PILOT LIGHT
THERMOSTAT

11 letters
TEMPERATURE

Architectural Details

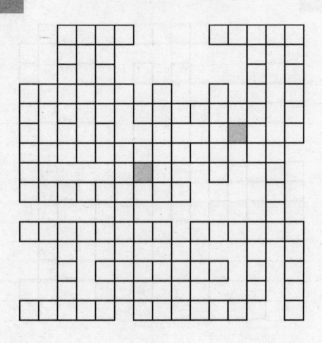

4 letters
DOME
PIER
TILE

5 letters
DORIC
LEDGE
MITRE
PANEL
SPIRE
WALLS

6 letters
COLUMN
COPING
LINTEL
SCROLL
SOFFIT
TURRET

7 letters
CORNICE
DOORWAY
FLUTING
MULLION

RAFTERS

8 letters
CAPSTONE
GARGOYLE

9 letters
TIMBERING

14 letters
FLYING
  BUTTRESS

Fabrics

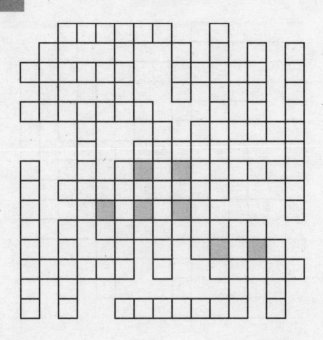

3 letters
PVC

4 letters
LACE
SILK

5 letters
DENIM
KHAKI
LISLE
SERGE
TOILE

TWEED
VOILE

6 letters
ANGORA
CANVAS
DRALON
FLEECE
MUSLIN
SATEEN
TARTAN

7 letters
FLANNEL
LEATHER
WORSTED

8 letters
CORDUROY
ORGANDIE

9 letters
CRIMPLENE
GABARDINE
GEORGETTE
HORSEHAIR

Curtains

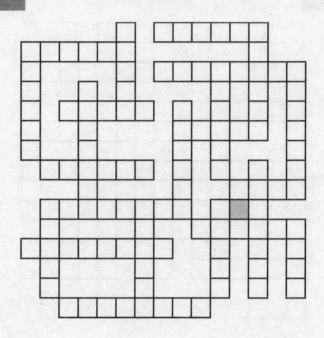

4 letters
LACE
NETS

5 letters
FRILL
HOOKS
LINED
RAILS
TRACK

6 letters
BLINDS
CHINTZ
CLOSED
COLOUR
COTTON
FABRIC
SAFETY
SHOWER
SINGLE

7 letters
PATTERN
THEATRE
VALANCE

8 letters
BLACKOUT
MATERIAL
TIEBACKS
WASHABLE

Archaeological Dig

4 letters
HUTS
KILN
OVEN

5 letters
BONES
COINS
DITCH
FLINT
HENGE
HOARD

RELIC
SITES
TOOLS

6 letters
BARROW
DATING
MENHIR
SPHINX

7 letters
IRON AGE

8 letters
ARTEFACT
CERAMICS
FIGURINE
STONE AGE

9 letters
BRONZE AGE
EXCAVATED

10 letters
PALAEOLITH

Food for Animals

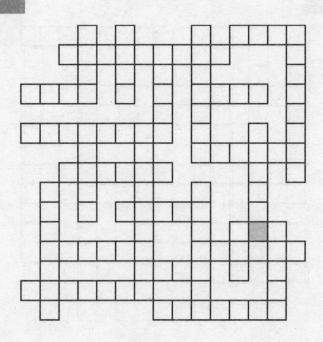

3 letters
HAY

4 letters
ANTS
MEAT
MICE
NUTS
OATS
RATS

5 letters
BONES

MAIZE
SEEDS
SWEDE
WHEAT

6 letters
FODDER
LEAVES
NECTAR
SILAGE

7 letters
BERRIES

DOG FOOD
INSECTS
LOCUSTS
PELLETS

8 letters
TERMITES
WAXWORMS

9 letters
MEALWORMS
SUGAR BEET

Can't Keep a Secret

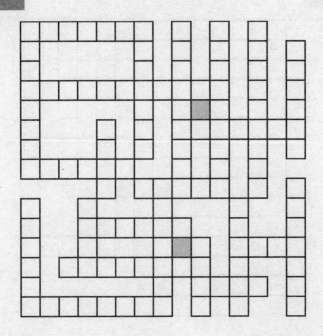

4 letters
BLAB
LEAK
RUIN
TELL
UNDO

5 letters
LET ON

6 letters
EXPOSE

REVEAL
SQUEAL
UNFOLD
UNMASK

7 letters
CONFESS
DIVULGE
ENSNARE
EXHIBIT
UNCOVER

8 letters
DISCLOSE
DISCOVER
INDICATE

9 letters
BROADCAST
DELIVER UP
MAKE KNOWN

11 letters
COMMUNICATE

Found

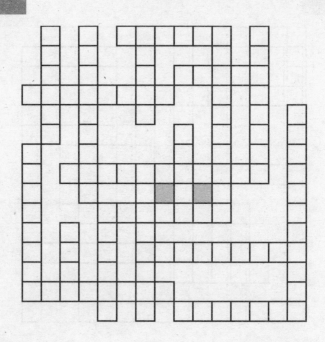

4 letters
FELT

5 letters
PLANT
RULED
SET UP

6 letters
CAME UP
GROUND
LAUNCH

7 letters
GOT HOLD
LOCATED

8 letters
DETECTED
HAPPENED
OBTAINED
RECEIVED
REGAINED

9 letters
ESTABLISH
INSTITUTE

10 letters
DETERMINED

11 letters
ASCERTAINED
ENCOUNTERED

Gardening

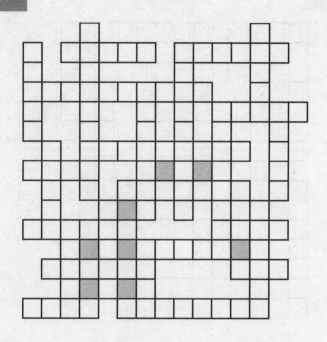

3 letters
IVY

4 letters
DILL
ILEX
TAGS
WREN

5 letters
AGAVE
GORSE
LILAC
MOWER

SALIX
SUMAC
THUJA
TRAYS
VIOLA

6 letters
ACACIA
BARROW
DAHLIA
WEEVIL

7 letters
RAGWORT

TRELLIS

8 letters
ASPHODEL
GLOXINIA

9 letters
BUTTERFLY
DRAGONFLY
FLOWERPOT

10 letters
MARGUERITE

On Your Head Be It

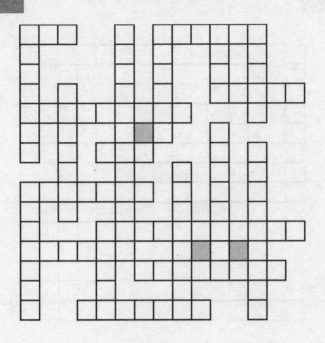

3 letters
FEZ
WIG

4 letters
HOOD

5 letters
BERET
DERBY
TIARA

6 letters
BONNET
TOP HAT
TURBAN

7 letters
FLAT CAP
HAIRNET
HOMBURG
PORK PIE
STETSON

8 letters
MANTILLA
OPERA HAT
SOMBRERO

9 letters
BALACLAVA
CLOCHE HAT

11 letters
BASEBALL CAP

12 letters
STOVEPIPE HAT

Let's Agree

4 letters
MEET
SUIT

5 letters
ALLOW
GRANT
MATCH
TALLY
UNITE
YIELD

6 letters
ACCEDE
ASSENT
COHERE
DECIDE
ENGAGE
SETTLE
SQUARE
UNISON

7 letters
BARGAIN
CONSENT

8 letters
COINCIDE

9 letters
ACQUIESCE

10 letters
UNDERSTAND

11 letters
FIT TOGETHER

US Presidents

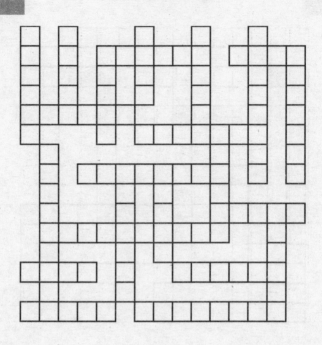

4 letters
BUSH
POLK
TAFT

5 letters
ADAMS
HAYES
NIXON
OBAMA
TYLER

6 letters
ARTHUR
CARTER
HOOVER
MONROE
PIERCE
TAYLOR
TRUMAN

7 letters
CLINTON
HARDING
KENNEDY

8 letters
BUCHANAN
COOLIDGE
MCKINLEY

9 letters
CLEVELAND

10 letters
EISENHOWER

Things That Get Lost

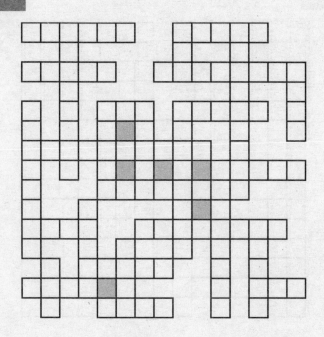

3 letters
CAR
CAT
DOG
PEN

4 letters
FACE
GAME
HOPE
KEYS
TIME

5 letters
CAUSE
MONEY
PLACE
PRIDE
SENSE
SHAPE
SHEEP
TRACK
TRIBE

6 letters
WEIGHT

8 letters
ELECTION
FEELINGS
IDENTITY
INTEREST
MOMENTUM
POSITION
PROPERTY

9 letters
DIRECTION

10 letters
ENTHUSIASM

Shopping List

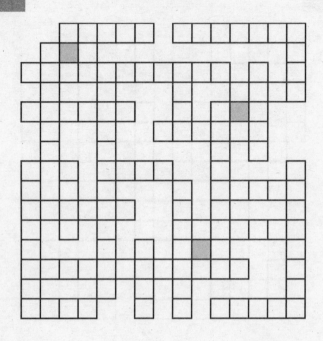

3 letters
TEA

4 letters
EGGS
MEAT
MILK
NUTS
PEAS
RICE
SALT

5 letters
CAKES
JELLY

PASTA
STEAK

6 letters
CEREAL
PICKLE
POLISH
SALMON

7 letters
CAT FOOD
CHICKEN
TISSUES

8 letters
DESSERTS
SAUSAGES

9 letters
MEAT PASTE

11 letters
TOMATO PUREE

12 letters
RUBBER
   GLOVES
TALCUM
   POWDER

'Y' Words

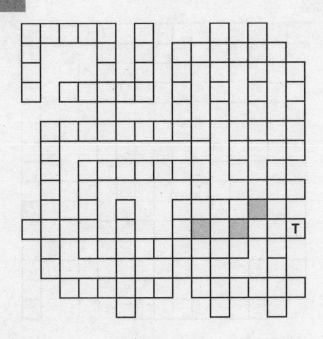

3 letters
YET
YEW
YOU

4 letters
YAKS
YEAH
YETI
YOLK
YOWL
YO-YO

5 letters
YAHOO
YOGIC
YOUTH
YPRES
YUCCA
YUCKY
YUMMY

6 letters
YANKEE
YEASTY
YELLED
YEMENI

YIPPEE
YOGURT
YUPPIE

7 letters
YOBBISH

8 letters
YEARBOOK
YOSEMITE

9 letters
YELLOWING
YESTERDAY

Goodbye

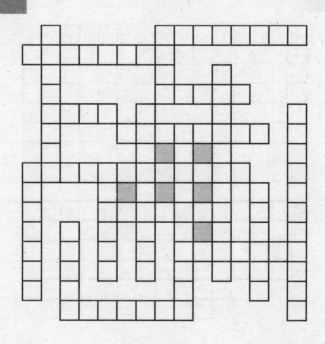

4 letters
TA-TA
WAVE

5 letters
ADIEU
ADIOS

6 letters
BYE-BYE
SO LONG

7 letters
GOODBYE
LEAVING
PARTING
SEND-OFF

8 letters
FAREWELL
GODSPEED
SAYONARA
TOODLE-OO

9 letters
GOING AWAY

10 letters
SETTING OFF

11 letters
ARRIVEDERCI
BE SEEING YOU

12 letters
PLEASANT TRIP

Intelligence Test

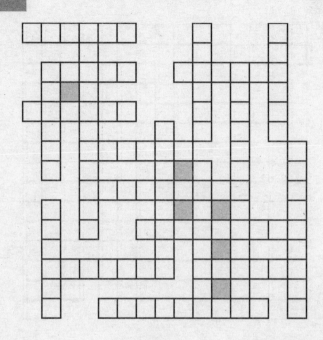

5 letters
SHARP

6 letters
ACUMEN
ASTUTE
BRAINY
BRIGHT
CLEVER
GENIUS
MENTAL
SHREWD
WISDOM

7 letters
TUTORED

8 letters
SENSIBLE
WELL-READ

9 letters
ENLIGHTEN
INTELLECT
KNOWLEDGE
REASONING

11 letters
IMAGINATION

13 letters
UNDER-
   STANDING

Magic

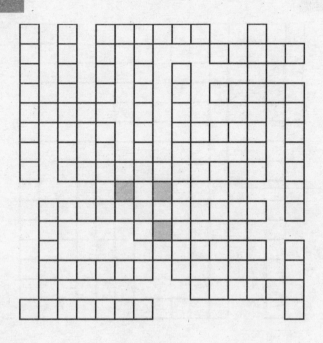

4 letters
CAPE
SHOW
WAND

5 letters
AMAZE
CURSE
LOCKS
STAGE

6 letters
MERLIN
OCCULT
SPELLS
STOOGE
VOODOO

7 letters
GLAMOUR
SECRETS
SORCERY

8 letters
ESCAPIST
MAGICIAN
TRICKERY

11 letters
ENCHANTMENT
INCANTATION
THAUMATURGY

12 letters
SUPERNATURAL

Things We Dream About

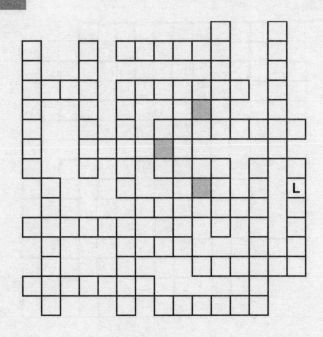

4 letters
FAME
FOOD
HOME
KIDS
WORK

5 letters
SHEEP

6 letters
CHASES
CLOUDS
CROWDS
EATING
FLYING
SCHOOL
WEALTH

7 letters
CASTLES
COFFINS

FLOWERS
HOLIDAY
STARDOM
SUCCESS
THE WIFE

8 letters
MEMORIES
MONSTERS

9 letters
CHOCOLATE

There's a RAT Inside

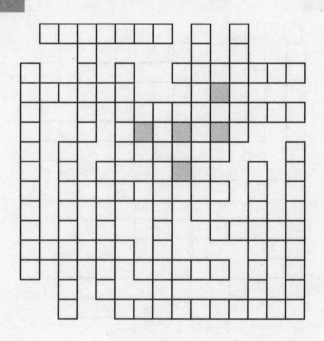

5 letters
BRATS
IRATE
SPRAT

6 letters
CRATER
ERRATA
GRATES
GYRATE
STRATA

7 letters
INGRATE
OPERATE
SCRATCH

8 letters
MARATHON

9 letters
CALIBRATE
FRATERNAL
LUCRATIVE

10 letters
ASPIRATION
IMPERATIVE
IRRATIONAL

11 letters
ACCELERATED
PARATROOPER

The Simpsons

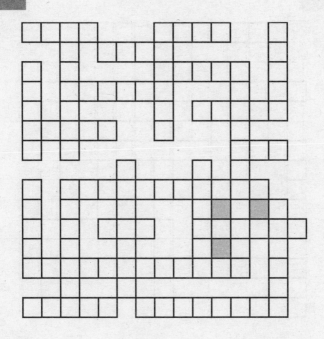

3 letters
ABE
MOE

4 letters
BART
EDNA
LISA

5 letters
FRINK
LENNY
MARGE
MAUDE

PATTY
RALPH
SELMA

6 letters
BARNEY
CLETUS
GUMBLE
MARTIN
WIGGUM

7 letters
HIBBERT
SEYMOUR

SKINNER

8 letters
FLANDERS

11 letters
HANS
MOLEMAN
SPRINGFIELD

12 letters
KENT
BROCKMAN

Rather Awkward

4 letters
RUDE
SLOW

5 letters
GAWKY
INEPT
ROUGH
STIFF
UNFIT

6 letters
CLUMSY
COARSE
GAUCHE
STICKY
TRICKY
UNEASY

7 letters
UNCOUTH

8 letters
UNWIELDY

9 letters
HAM-FISTED
MALADROIT
SLOUCHING
UNSKILFUL

10 letters
CUMBERSOME
UNENVIABLE

Mythical Creatures

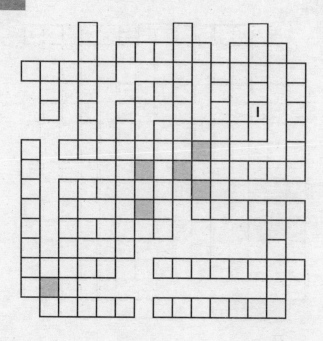

3 letters
ELF
IMP
ROC

5 letters
GENIE
GIANT
TITAN
TROLL

6 letters
DRAGON
GOBLIN
GORGON
KELPIE
KRAKEN
MEDUSA
NESSIE
SPHINX

7 letters
BANSHEE

CENTAUR
CHIMERA
CYCLOPS
PHOENIX
VAMPIRE

8 letters
BABA YAGA
BASILISK
SLEIPNIR
VALKYRIE

Ball Games

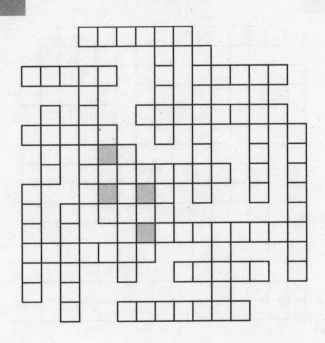

4 letters
GOLF
POLO
POOL

5 letters
BANDY
BOWLS
RINGO
RUGBY
ULAMA

6 letters
PELOTA
SHINTY
SOCCER
TENNIS

7 letters
BIRIBOL
BOWLING
CRICKET
MINITEN
SNOOKER

8 letters
JUGGLING
LACROSSE
NINEPINS
PING-PONG
RACQUETS

Boats

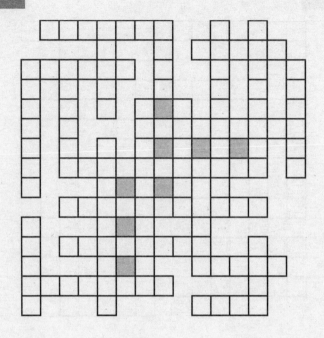

3 letters
ARK
TUG

4 letters
DHOW
RAFT
SCOW

5 letters
CANOE
KETCH
SLOOP
SMACK

6 letters
CUTTER
GALIOT
LAUNCH
LUGGER

7 letters
CLIPPER
COASTER
GALLEON

8 letters
CORVETTE
LONGBOAT

SCHOONER

9 letters
FREIGHTER
HOUSEBOAT

10 letters
PADDLE BOAT
SHRIMP BOAT

11 letters
HERRING BOAT

Occupational Surnames

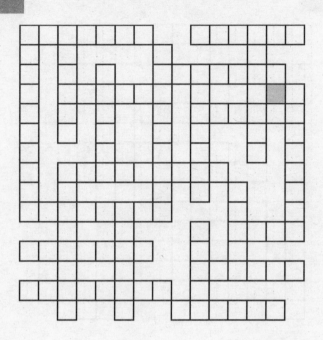

4 letters
DYER

5 letters
RIDER
ROPER

6 letters
BARBER
BOOKER
BREWER
COOPER

DRAPER
HARPER
PARKER
TAYLOR

7 letters
COLLIER
GODDARD
LATIMER
WEBSTER
WHEELER

8 letters
CHANDLER
CROWTHER
SHEPHERD
THATCHER

9 letters
CARPENTER
SCRIVENER

10 letters
WAINWRIGHT

Landlocked Countries

4 letters
CHAD
LAOS
MALI

5 letters
NEPAL
NIGER

6 letters
KOSOVO
MALAWI

SERBIA
UGANDA

7 letters
ARMENIA
BELARUS
BOLIVIA
BURUNDI
LESOTHO

8 letters
BOTSWANA

MONGOLIA
PARAGUAY
ZIMBABWE

9 letters
SAN MARINO

10 letters
TAJIKISTAN

11 letters
AFGHANISTAN

In the Spring

3 letters
MAY

4 letters
BUDS
EGGS
LENT
LILY

5 letters
BUNNY
FRESH
GREEN
GUSTY

LAMBS
MARCH
NESTS

6 letters
CALVES
GROWTH
SHOOTS
SPRING
TULIPS

7 letters
ANEMONE
PUDDLES

RAINBOW
SHOWERS

8 letters
SNOWDROP

9 letters
NARCISSUS

13 letters
MORRIS
  DANCERS

Creatures

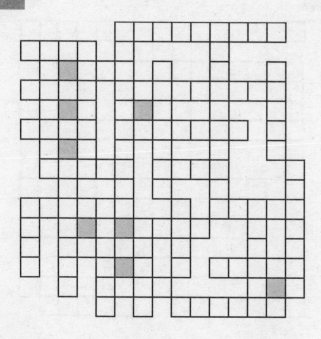

3 letters
OWL

4 letters
BEAR
BOAR
FAWN
GNAT
IBEX
LAMB
SEAL
SLUG

5 letters
GENET
HORSE
HYENA
KOALA
SNAIL
SNAKE

6 letters
ALPACA
EARWIG
FERRET
JAGUAR

7 letters
BULLOCK
GORILLA
LIONESS
NARWHAL
POLECAT
WALLABY

9 letters
DRAGONFLY
WOLVERINE

10 letters
RHINOCEROS
WILDEBEEST

European Countries

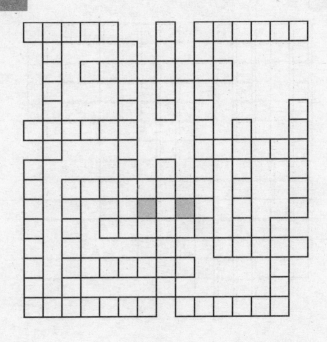

5 letters
ITALY
MALTA
SPAIN
WALES

6 letters
FRANCE
GREECE
NORWAY
POLAND

RUSSIA
SERBIA

7 letters
ANDORRA
AUSTRIA
BELARUS
CROATIA
ESTONIA
ROMANIA

8 letters
BULGARIA
SLOVAKIA
SLOVENIA

10 letters
MONTENEGRO

11 letters
SWITZERLAND

In Black and White

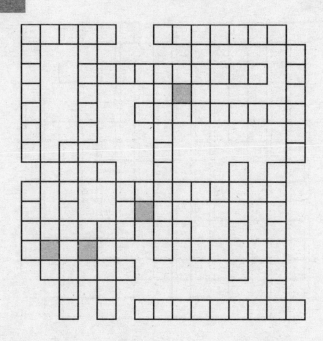

3 letters
COW

4 letters
DICE
FILM

5 letters
ICONS
LEMUR
PANDA
PRINT
SKUNK

6 letters
DOMINO
MAGPIE
PEARLS

7 letters
PELICAN
UNIFORM

8 letters
NEGATIVE

9 letters
CLOCK FACE
CROSSWORD
GOLF SHOES
NEWSPAPER
PIANO KEYS

10 letters
CHESSBOARD
MUSIC NOTES

Playing Cards

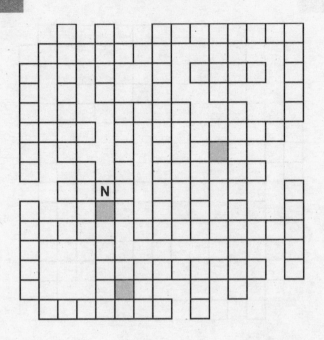

3 letters
ACE
SIX

4 letters
DEAL
FIVE
FOUR
KING
NINE
PACK
PAIR

5 letters
CHIPS

DEUCE
EIGHT
ROYAL
STOCK
THREE

6 letters
BANKER
CHANGE
HEARTS
PIQUET

7 letters
CALLING
KALOOKI

PARTNER

8 letters
WILD CARD

9 letters
ADVERSARY
GRAND SLAM

10 letters
LITTLE SLAM

11 letters
WINNING HAND

Drinks

3 letters
ALE
GIN
TEA

4 letters
MEAD
MILK
OUZO
WINE

5 letters
COCOA

JULEP
PERRY
VODKA

6 letters
BRANDY
GRAPPA
PERNOD
SCOTCH
SHANDY
SHERRY
WHISKY

7 letters
BACARDI
BOURBON
CAMPARI
LIQUEUR
MARTINI
TEQUILA

8 letters
COCKTAIL

9 letters
HERBAL TEA

Birthday Party

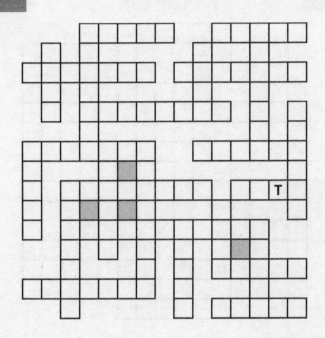

4 letters	SONGS	GLASSES
CAKE	THEME	INDOORS
DATE		MARQUEE
FOOD	**6 letters**	NAPKINS
HATS	GUESTS	
	SPEECH	**8 letters**
5 letters	WISHES	ICE CREAM
CARDS		LAUGHTER
DANCE	**7 letters**	SURPRISE
GAMES	BANNERS	
GIFTS	CANDLES	**11 letters**
MUSIC	FRIENDS	DECORATIONS

Capital Cities

4 letters
BAKU
DILI
DOHA
MALE
ROME
SUVA

5 letters
AMMAN
PARIS
SEOUL

6 letters
ATHENS
BERLIN
BOGOTA
KIGALI
MUSCAT
TEHRAN
TIRANA
VIENNA

7 letters
CAYENNE

8 letters
BRASILIA
BRUSSELS
DAMASCUS
MELEKEOK
MONROVIA
SANTIAGO

9 letters
NUKU'ALOFA

14 letters
ANDORRA LA
VELLA

Containers

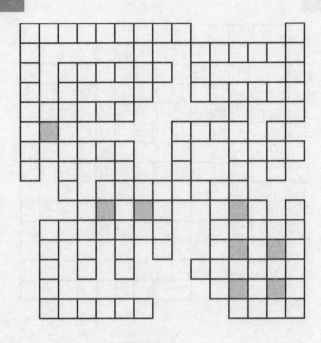

3 letters
JUG
TUB

4 letters
BOOT
BOWL
BUTT
DISH
EWER
TRAY
TRUG

5 letters
CHURN
CRATE
TRUNK

6 letters
BEAKER
BOTTLE
BUNKER
CARTON
CASKET
GOBLET
IN-TRAY
JAM JAR
KETTLE

PACKET
SHEATH

7 letters
CISTERN
HANDBAG
THIMBLE

8 letters
ENVELOPE
SUITCASE

9 letters
STRONGBOX

Healthy Eating

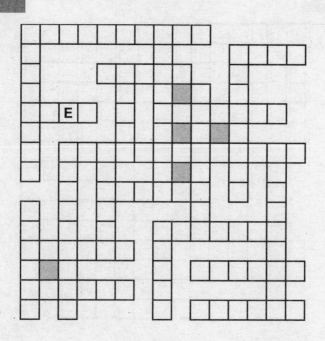

4 letters
SOUP
STEW

5 letters
CREPE
ROAST
SALAD

6 letters
CARROT
LENTIL
MUESLI

POTATO
PULSES
RECIPE
TOMATO

7 letters
RHUBARB
SPINACH

8 letters
COLESLAW
SOYA BEAN
ZUCCHINI

9 letters
ASPARAGUS
CASSEROLE
SPAGHETTI

10 letters
CHEESE BAKE

13 letters
COTTAGE
  CHEESE

Dictionary

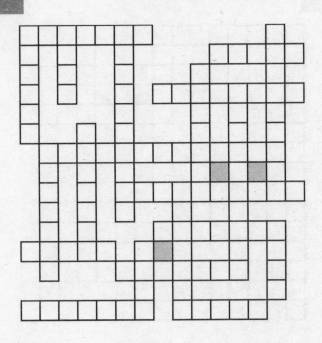

4 letters
BOOK
GIST
TEXT

5 letters
NOUNS
PAGES
SLANG

6 letters
SPEECH

7 letters
ARCHAIC
DIALECT
EDITION
FOREIGN
LEXICON
LISTING
PLURALS
SUBJECT

8 letters
ABRIDGED

9 letters
REFERENCE

10 letters
ADJECTIVES
COLLOQUIAL
DEFINITION

13 letters
PRONUN-
CIATION

BACK at the Front

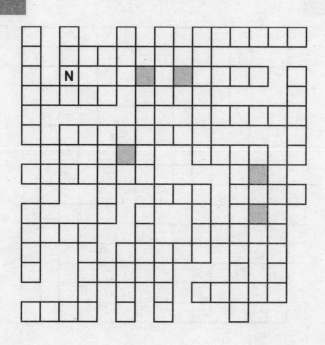

3 letters
END
OFF
SAW

4 letters
ACHE
AWAY
BEAT
BONE
CHAT
DOWN
DROP
HAND
LASH

ROOM
SPIN
WARD
YARD

5 letters
BACON
DATED
ORDER
PORCH
SPACE
SWEPT
TOOTH
TRACK
WATER

6 letters
CIRCLE
NUMBER
STROKE

7 letters
CHANNEL
PASSAGE
TO FRONT

8 letters
AND FORTH
ENTRANCE

9 letters
SCRATCHER

Flowery Girls' Names

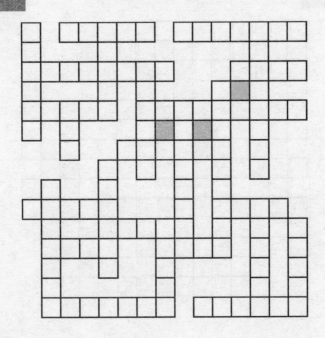

3 letters
IVY

4 letters
FERN
IRIS
LILY
SAGE

5 letters
DAISY
FLORA
OLIVE

PANSY
POPPY
TANSY
VIOLA

6 letters
BRYONY
CICELY
CLOVER
DAHLIA
DAVIDA
LAUREL

7 letters
HEATHER
NIGELLA
SAFFRON

8 letters
HYACINTH
LAVENDER
VERONICA

9 letters
AMARYLLIS
COLUMBINE

It's All Wrong

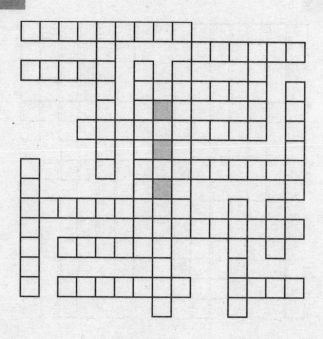

3 letters
BAD

4 letters
EVIL

5 letters
FALSE
UNFIT

6 letters
FAULTY

SINFUL
UNJUST
UNTRUE
WICKED

7 letters
IMMORAL
IMPIOUS
INEXACT

8 letters
UNTIMELY

9 letters
ERRONEOUS
IMPRECISE
INCORRECT
MISGUIDED
UNETHICAL

10 letters
DEPLORABLE
VILLAINOUS

Rainy Day

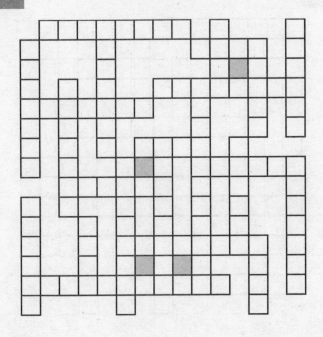

4 letters
DAMP
GAMP
HATS
HOOD
RAIN

5 letters
STORM

6 letters
ANORAK

CLOUDS
PUDDLE
SODDEN
SQUALL

7 letters
PELTING
POURING
SOAKING
TEEMING
WETNESS

8 letters
DOWNPOUR
DROPLETS
GALOSHES
OILSKINS
SPITTING

11 letters
LOW PRESSURE
WINDCHEATER

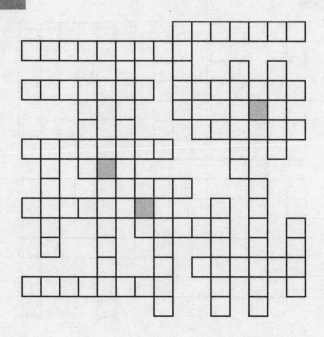

532 Nuts and Seeds

4 letters
DILL

5 letters
ANISE
BETEL
CUMIN
PECAN
POPPY

6 letters
ALMOND
BRAZIL
CELERY
CONKER
FENNEL
PEANUT
SESAME

7 letters
ANNATTO
COCONUT

FILBERT
PINE NUT
PUMPKIN

8 letters
CHESTNUT
HAZELNUT

9 letters
CORIANDER
PISTACHIO

In the Larder

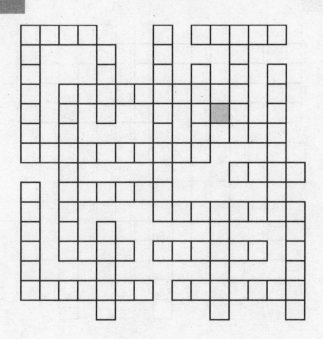

4 letters
MACE
SAGE
SALT
SOUP

5 letters
CUMIN
HONEY
SUGAR
YEAST

6 letters
FENNEL
GINGER
NUTMEG
PEPPER
PICKLE
PRUNES

7 letters
MUSTARD
RAISINS
TREACLE

8 letters
STUFFING
TARRAGON

9 letters
SPLIT PEAS

10 letters
DRIED FRUIT
SALAD CREAM
STOCK CUBES

Words of Love

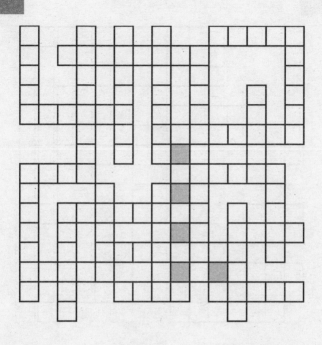

4 letters
EROS
KISS
ROSE

5 letters
AMOUR
BRIDE
CUPID
CUTIE
GROOM
VENUS
YEARN

6 letters
DESIRE
GENTLE
JOYOUS
LOVING
REVERE
TENDER

7 letters
FAIREST
ROMANCE
WORSHIP

8 letters
DEVOTION
GORGEOUS
INTIMATE
MARRIAGE
PARAMOUR

12 letters
RELATIONSHIP

Puzzles

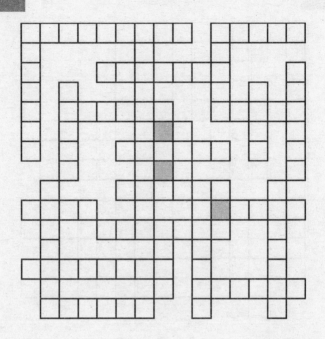

4 letters
FILL
GAME
GRID
QUIZ
SUMS

5 letters
CLUES
LINKS
LOGIC
THINK

6 letters
ANSWER
DOMINO
HANJIE
JIGSAW
KAKURO
VISUAL

7 letters
ANAGRAM
FITTING
JIGWORD

PLAYING
RIDDLES
TANGRAM

8 letters
NONOGRAM

9 letters
FUTOSHIKI

11 letters
IMAGINATION

Types of Literature

4 letters
EPIC
PULP
SAGA

5 letters
CRIME
DRAMA
PROSE
TRIAD
VERSE

6 letters
COMEDY
PARODY
POSTIL
SATIRE

7 letters
CLASSIC
FANTASY
FICTION
POLEMIC
TRAGEDY

8 letters
APOLOGUE
LIBRETTO
TREATISE

9 letters
BIOGRAPHY
CHILDREN'S

10 letters
HISTORICAL

Verbs

3 letters
FIX

4 letters
CHOP
FAZE
GROW
JOIN
LOOK
WASH
YAWN

5 letters
BREAK

CHANT
FRISK
HURRY
JOUST
REACT
SCOWL
STUDY
TWIST
YEARN

6 letters
ATTACK
GATHER
HUDDLE

RECANT
RECITE
VERIFY

7 letters
COLLECT
TESTIFY
UNRAVEL
WHISPER

8 letters
LANGUISH
PERSPIRE

Words Ending in 'X'

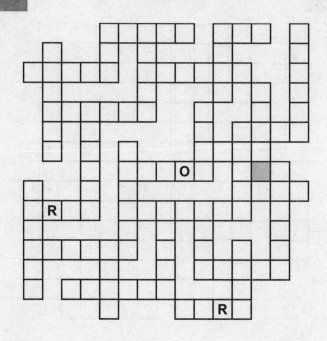

3 letters
COX
FOX

4 letters
APEX
COAX
CRUX
FLAX
IBEX
KNOX
MANX
MARX
ONYX

ORYX
ROUX

5 letters
CODEX
DETOX
LATEX
REMIX
UNBOX
UNFIX
XEROX

6 letters
CAUDEX

COCCYX
COWPOX
DUPLEX
OUTFOX
PREMIX
SKY BOX
THORAX
VERTEX
VORTEX

7 letters
FLUMMOX

Young Animals

3 letters
CUB
EFT
FRY
KID

4 letters
CALF
COLT
CRIA
FAWN
FOAL
JOEY
LAMB

PARR

5 letters
ELVER
FILLY
NYMPH
OWLET
POULT
PUPPY
WHELP

6 letters
EAGLET
KITTEN

PIGLET

7 letters
LEVERET
TADPOLE

8 letters
YEARLING

9 letters
FLEDGLING

10 letters
SPIDERLING

'Z' Words

3 letters
ZIP
ZOO

4 letters
ZANY
ZERO
ZEST
ZINC
ZOOM

5 letters
ZAIRE
ZEBRA

ZILCH
ZONAL

6 letters
ZAMBIA
ZANTAC
ZEALOT
ZENITH
ZEPHYR
ZIGZAG
ZIMMER
ZODIAC
ZOMBIE
ZYGOTE

7 letters
ZAMBEZI
ZEALAND
ZEALOUS

8 letters
ZANZIBAR
ZIGGURAT

9 letters
ZECHARIAH

Redecorating

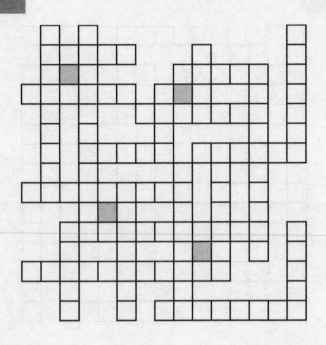

4 letters
GLUE
RAGS

5 letters
NAILS
PAINT
PASTE
PLANS
VINYL

6 letters
DESIGN
SCREWS

7 letters
CEILING
COLOURS
PLASTER
TOPCOAT

8 letters
CLEANING
EGGSHELL

9 letters
STEP STOOL
UNDERCOAT

10 letters
TURPENTINE

11 letters
LINING PAPER
PREPARATION
SCAFFOLDING

Sounds

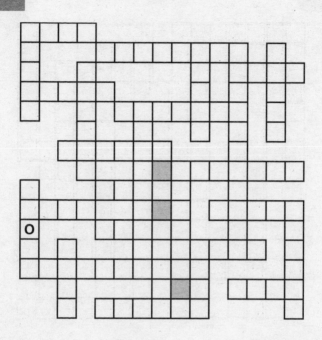

4 letters
BANG
BUZZ
ECHO
HISS
HOOT
TONE

5 letters
BLAST
CLICK
LAUGH
MUSIC
SHOUT

THUMP
TWANG
VOICE
WHOOP

6 letters
BELLOW
HOARSE
MUTTER
SCREAM
TINKLE

7 letters
CADENCE

CLATTER
SCREECH

8 letters
SPLUTTER

9 letters
ACOUSTICS

10 letters
PIANISSIMO

11 letters
REVERBERATE

Languages

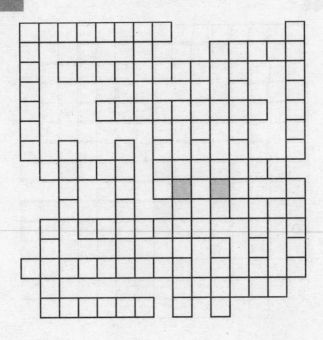

4 letters
THAI
URDU

5 letters
AZERI
GREEK
LATIN
ORIYA
SUNDA
TAMIL
XIANG

6 letters
ARABIC
GAELIC
KOREAN

7 letters
CATALAN
ENGLISH
KANNADA
MARATHI
TAGALOG
WALLOON

8 letters
CROATIAN
MAITHILI

9 letters
CANTONESE
HUNGARIAN
NORWEGIAN
UKRAINIAN

Things That Can Be Broken

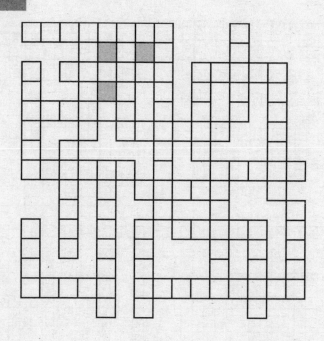

4 letters
CAMP

RANKS
SLEEP

7 letters
PROMISE
SILENCE

5 letters
BONES
BREAD
COVER
HEART
LIMBS
PEACE
PLATE
RADIO

6 letters
ARCHES
BOTTLE
BRANCH
HABITS
PENCIL
SPIRIT
STRIDE
TREATY

8 letters
CONTRACT
DEFENCES

9 letters
AGREEMENT

10 letters
TELEVISION

Solutions

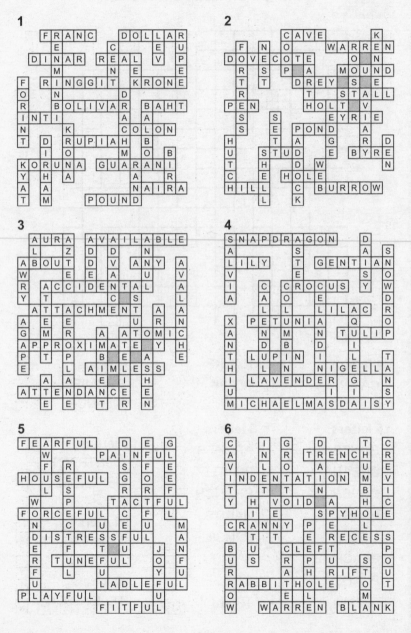

Solutions

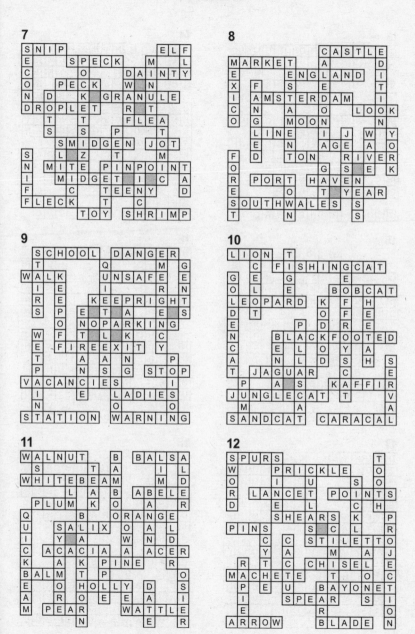

Solutions

13

O C T A H E D R O N   P
Y   E   O   V A   O R B   S
L   A   D   A   I   P
I   R   E L L I P S E   H
N   T   C   M   E
D   C   A   R   R
H E M I S P H E R E   C O N E
  R   R   E   E   U
    C   D E C A G O N   H
    L   R   T L D   E
C U B E   N O N A G O N   X
R   S   N   G B   A
O   K I T E   G E   G
S   A   L   O
S Q U A R E   P E N T A G O N

14

  B A L L   N I B L I C K
  A   L   F
S T U M P S   E T R I E R
  O   C   S   M   A
  N   P U C K   B   M
S   W   B I   Q U I V E R
K N E E P A D S   N   I
A   D   A   T O B O G G A N
T   G   D   I A R   G
E   E   D I S C U S   O A R S
  J   L   K   K P
M A L L E T   E P E E
  C   U   B A T   C
  K   G   O   U
  N E T S   W H I S T L E

15

  W A   F L O W E R
N U P T I A L   E   E
  L   F   T O A S T S   G
W E   C A M E R A   S   T I
E   N   R   T   C A R S
D R E S S   T   G T E
I   H   T P A R
N   S P E E C H   R A R
G   H   N O   O R Y
  M O R N I N G S U I T
U   W   I   F   S Y   S
S   E   G U E S T S   M
C H U R C H   T   E   I
E   T T   A   L
B R I D E   L I M O U S I N E

16

H A M P T O N C O U R T   G
O   O   H E I R
W   E D W A R D   R   E
A   E   D I V O R C E
R   M A R Y   N   N
D   R E   P O P E   W
  T O   A   I
  T H O M A S M O R E   C
N   U A   A L   W H
O   C R A N M E R   I   I
N   L   R A N N E
S   V   K   I M D
U   E   I J A N E   S O N
C L E M E N T   G N   O
H   S   G   J E S T E R

17

D E C A Y E D   G   M
E   O   R U I N O U S
B   R   O   U   I
A T R O C I O U S   L   N
S   U   S   B A D   F
E   P   A Y   U
D E T R I M E N T A L   L
  M   J   E   S
  S H A M E F U L   F O U L Y
R   O   R   U
A   C R I M I N A L
N   A   O W   M E A N
C R U E L   U F   V
I   D I S G U S T I N G
D   L   L

18

R H U B A R B   P O T   P
  U   U   P   O
  V   T A M A L E   T
  F   E T   P   C   A
M E R I N G U E   K   T A R T   T
U   E   E   R A I S I N   O
D   S   T   S   N N
  H   A   C   D
C   B   O   P O R K   C
C H O C O L A T E   U   R
E   H   E   C   G C   U
F R I E D   S H E P H E R D S
R   E   A   E   T
Y   S   O V E N   A
  M E A T   L E M O N

Solutions

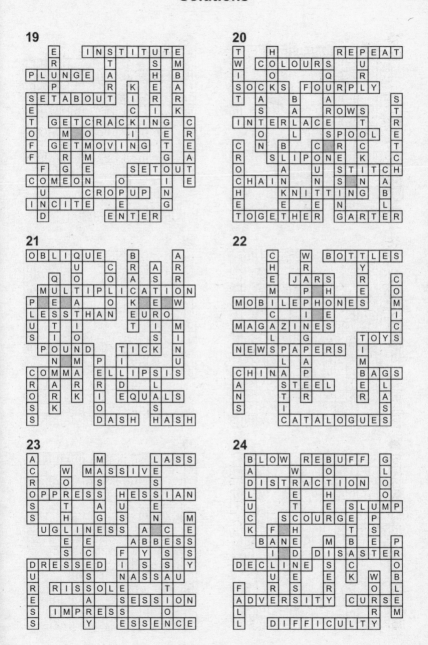

Solutions

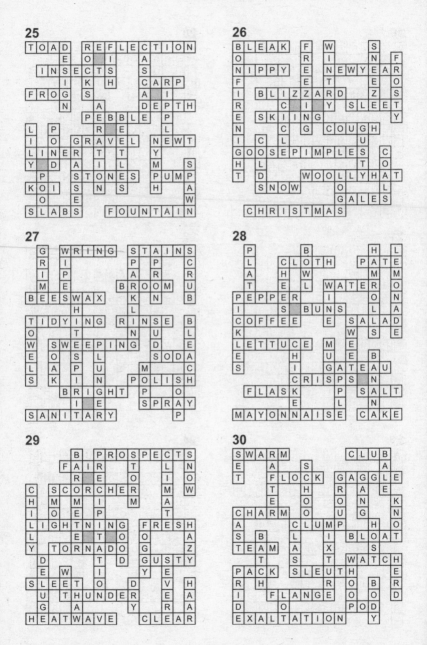

Solutions

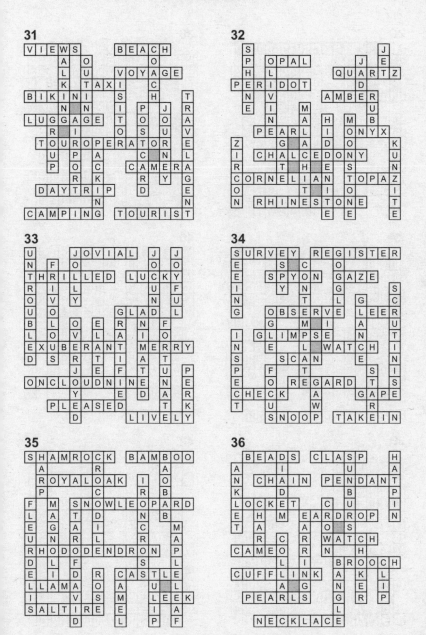

31

VIEWS BEACH VOYAGE TAXI BIKINI LUGGAGE TOUROPERATOR CAMERA DAYTRIP CAMPING TOURIST

32

OPAL JET QUARTZ PERIDOT AMBER PEARL ONYX CHALCEDONY ZIRCON CORNELIAN TOPAZ RHINESTONE KUNZITE

33

JOVIAL THRILLED LUCKY GLAD EXUBERANT MERRY ONCLOUDNINE PLEASED LIVELY

34

SURVEY REGISTER SPYON GAZE OBSERVE GLIMPSE WATCH SCAN REGARD CHECK GAPE SNOOP TAKEIN

35

SHAMROCK BAMBOO ROYALOAK SNOWLEOPARD RHODODENDRON CASTLE LLAMA LEEK SALTIRE

36

BEADS CLASP CHAIN PENDANT LOCKET EARDROP WATCH CAMEO BROOCH CUFFLINK PEARLS NECKLACE

Solutions

37

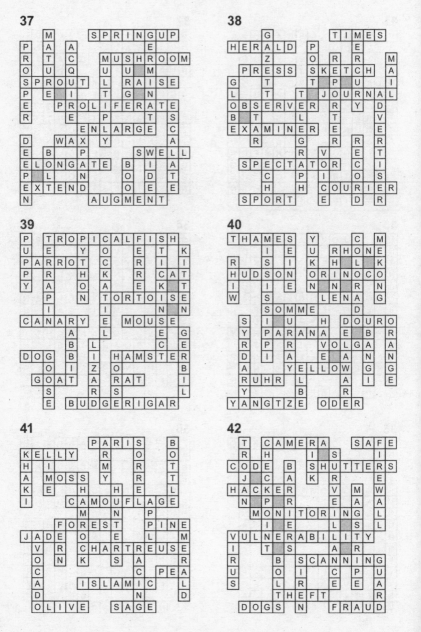

38

39

40

41

42

556

Solutions

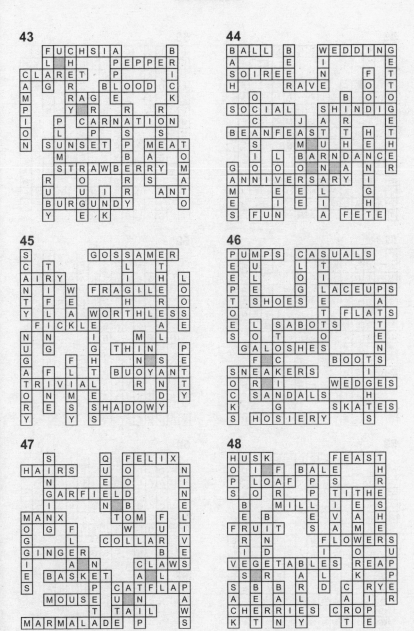

Solutions

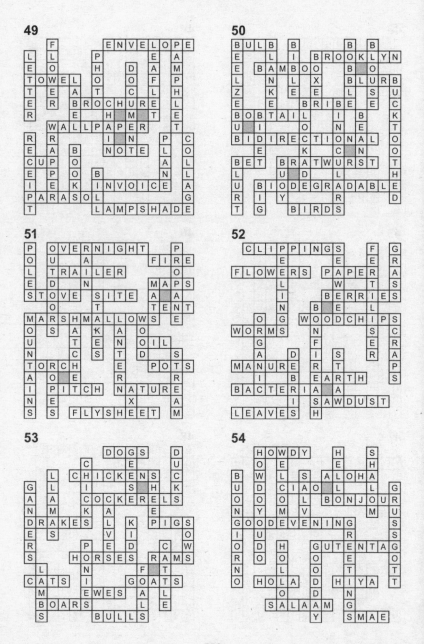

Solutions

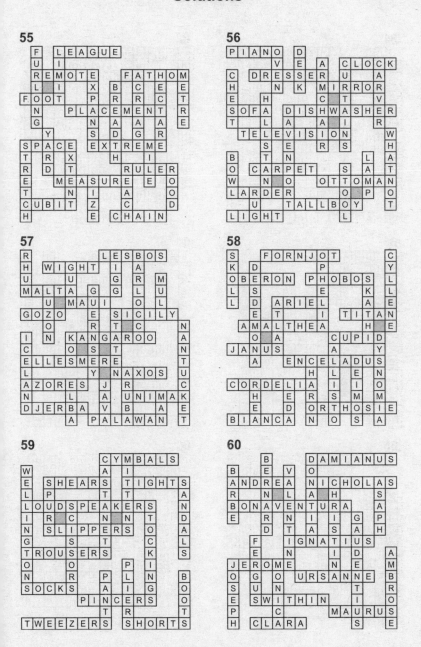

Solutions

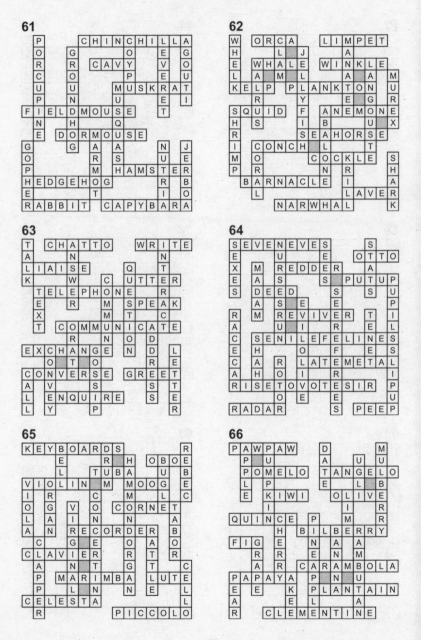

61 **62**

63 **64**

65 **66**

Solutions

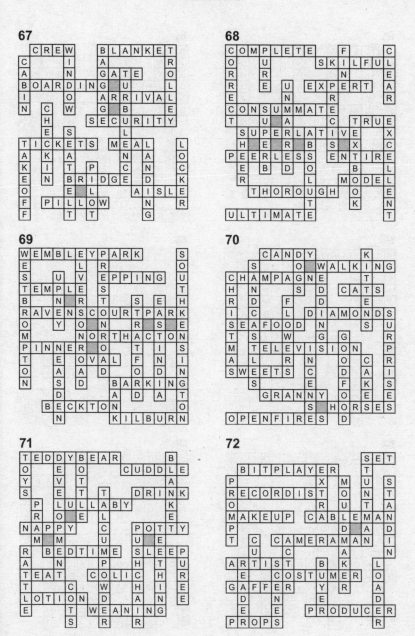

Solutions

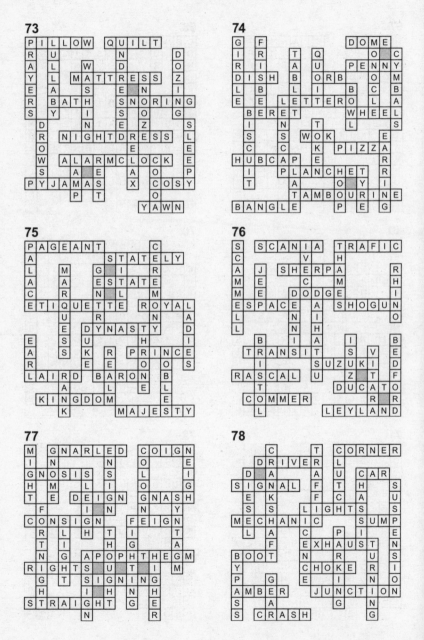

73

PILLOW QUILT
RAY QU L D
ALL U W DOZ
YE L MATTRESS E Z
ERS BATH SNORING
S Y H SO G
D I NE Z S
DR NIGHTDRESS L
OW E E
WS ALARMCLOCK E
S A E AX O P
PYJAMAS T COSY
P T O
YAWN

74

G F DOME
GIR F T Q O C
RI RI TAB QU PENNY Y
DISH B L ORB O O M
LE BE LI B C BA
BERET LETTERO L L
BE I T WHEEL S
IS N T E A
SC SC WOK E R
K PIZZA A
HUBCAP E R R
IT P PLANCHET T I
P A O Y N
TAMBOURINE E
BANGLE P E G

75

PAGEANT C
S STATELY R
ALA M GI R
LAC MAR ESTATE E
C R N L M
ETIQUETTE ROYAL L
U R N A
QUE DYNASTY Y L
ESS U H I
E SS UK RE PRINCE S
AR K E O O S
LAIRD BARONE B
A L E L
KINGDOM E
K MAJESTY

76

S SCANIA TRAFIC
SC V H
CA J SHERPA M R
MM EE C M RH
ME EE DODGE A I
ESPACE N SHOGUN O
LL N H O
L B I I B
TRANSIT S V E
I SUZUKI Z D
RASCAL U Z T F
T DUCATO R O
COMMER R R
L LEYLAND

77

M GNARLED COIGN
I N N E
GNOSIS S S I
HM M L I G
T E DEIGN GNASH
F I N N Y
CONSIGN FEIGN
R L H T T
T I I I A
N G APOPHTHEGM
RIGHTS U T M
G T SIGNING
H I H N H
STRAIGHT G E
N R

78

C T CORNER
DRIVER L
D A A U CAR
SIGNAL F T H S
E K F C A U
S S LIGHTS S
MECHANIC SUMP
L A C P E
A F EXHAUST N
BOOT N R U S
Y CHOKE I I
PA G E N O
AMBER JUNCTION
SS A N
S CRASH G

562

Solutions

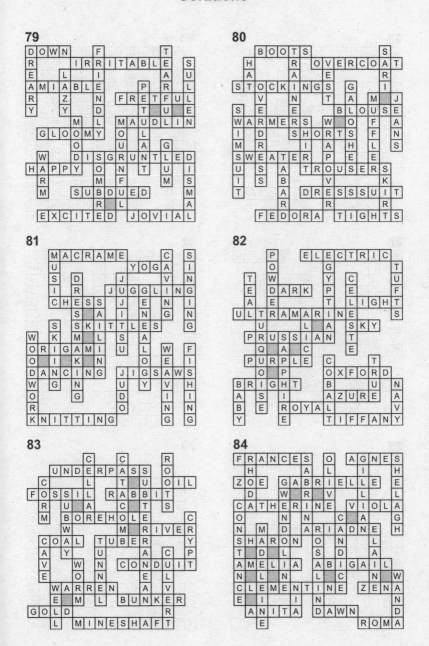

79

DOWN · F · T
IRRITABLE · S
R · L · I · A · U
AMIABLE · P · R · L
RY · Z · N · FRETFUL · L
Y · Y · D · T · U · E
M · L · MAUDLIN
GLOOMY · O · L
O · U · A · G
W · DISGRUNTLED
HAPPY · O · N · T · U · I
R · M · F · M · S
M · SUBDUED · M · A
R · L · A
EXCITED · JOVIAL

80

BOOTS · S
H · R · OVERCOAT
HA · A · E · R · T
STOCKINGS · G · I
V · N · T · A · M · J
SE · E · BLOUSE · E
WARMERS · W · O · F · A
ID · SHORTS · F · N
M · I · A · H · L · S
SWEATER · P · E · E
US · A · TROUSERS · S
II · S · AB · V · K
T · A · DRESSSUIT
R · R · R
FEDORA · TIGHTS

81

MACRAME · C · S
YOGA · A · I
US · D · J · V · N
SI · R · JUGGLING · G
CHESS · E · N · I
S · A · I · N · N
S · SKITTLES · A · G
W · K · M · L · S · A
ORIGAMI · U · L · W · F
O · I · K · N · O · E · I
DANCING · JIGSAWS · S
W · G · U · Y · V · H
O · N · D · I · I
R · G · O · N · N
KNITTING · G · G

82

P · ELECTRIC · C
O · G · T
TW · Y · C · U
EA · DARK · P · E · F
A · E · T · LIGHT · S
ULTRAMARINE · E
U · L · A · SKY
PRUSSIAN · T
Q · A · C · E
PURPLE · C · T
O · P · OXFORD
BRIGHT · B · U · N
A · S · I · A · AZURE · A
B · E · ROYAL · L · V
Y · E · TIFFANY

83

C · C · R
UNDERPASS · O
CL · T · U · OIL
FOSSIL · RABBIT · S
R · U · A · C · T
M · BOREHOLE · C
W · M · RIVER · Y
COAL · TUBER · P
A · Y · U · A · C
V · W · N · CONDUIT
E · O · N · E · L
WARREN · A · V
E · M · L · BUNKER
GOLD · R
L · MINESHAFT

84

FRANCES · O · AGNES
H · A · L · I · H
ZOE · GABRIELLE · E
D · W · R · V · L · L
CATHERINE · VIOLA
O · N · N · C · A · G
N · M · D · ARIADNE · H
SHARON · O · N · L
T · D · L · S · D · A
AMELIA · ABIGAIL
N · L · N · L · C · N · W
CLEMENTINE · ZENA
E · I · I · N · A
ANITA · DAWN · D
E · ROMA

563

Solutions

85

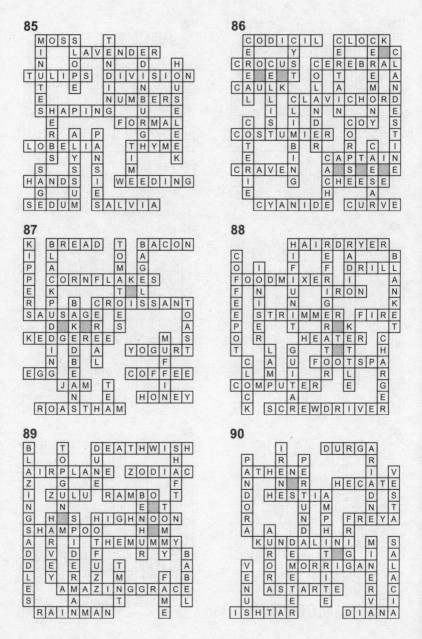

MOSS · T
IN · LAVENDER
IN · O · N · D
TULIPS DIVISION
T · E · I · N · U
E · NUMBERS
SHAPING · U · E
E · R · A · P · FORMAL · E
LOBELIA · THYME
S · Y · N · I · K
S · S · I · M
HANDS · WEEDING
G · U · E
SEDUM SALVIA

86

CODICIL CLOCK
E · Y · E · E · C
CROCUS CEREBRAL
E · E · T · O · T · A
CAULK · L · A · M · N
L · L · CLAVICHORD
I · I · L · N · N · E
C · S · L · D · COY · S
COSTUMIER · O · R · T
T · B · R · C · I
E · I · CAPTAIN
CRAVEN · A · S · E · E
I · G · CHEESE
E · H
CYANIDE CURVE

87

K · BREAD · T · BACON
I · L · O · A
P · A · M · G
P · CORNFLAKES
E · K · T · L
R · P · B · CROISSANT
SAUSAGE · E · S · O
D · K · R · S · A
KEDGEREE · M · S
I · D · A · YOGURT
N · B · L · F
EGG · E · COFFEE
JAM · T · I
N · E · HONEY
ROASTHAM

88

HAIRDRYER
C · I · E · A · B
O · I · F · F · DRILL
FOODMIXER · I · A
F · N · U · IRON · N
E · I · N · K
E · STRIMMER · FIRE
P · E · T · R · K · T
O · R · HEATER · C
T · L · G · T · T · H
C · A · U · FOOTSPA
L · M · I · L · R
COMPUTER · E · G
C · A · E
K · SCREWDRIVER

89

B · T · DEATHWISH
L · O · H
AIRPLANE ZODIAC
Z · G · E · F
I · ZULU RAMBO · T
N · N · E · T
G · H · S · HIGHNOON
SHAMPOO · H · M
A · R · I · THEMUMMY
D · V · D · F · R · Y · B
D · E · E · U · T · A
L · Y · R · Z · M · F · B
E · AMAZINGGRACE
S · A · T · M · L
RAINMAN · E

90

I · DURGA
P · R · P · R · I
ATHENE · R · I · V
N · N · R · HECATE
DORA HESTIA · D · S
O · U · M · N · T
R · A · N · P · FREYA
A · A · D · H · R
KUNDALINI · M · S
R · E · T · G · I · A
V · O · MORRIGAN · L
E · R · E · I · E · A
N · ASTARTE · R · C
U · E · E · V · I
ISHTAR · DIANA

564

Solutions

91

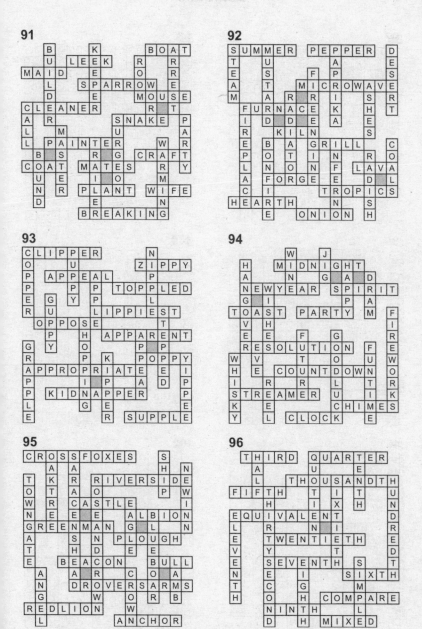

92

93

94

95

96

Solutions

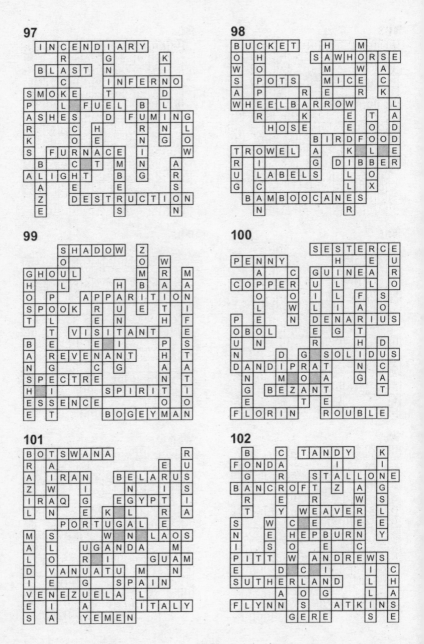

97

98

99

100

101

102

Solutions

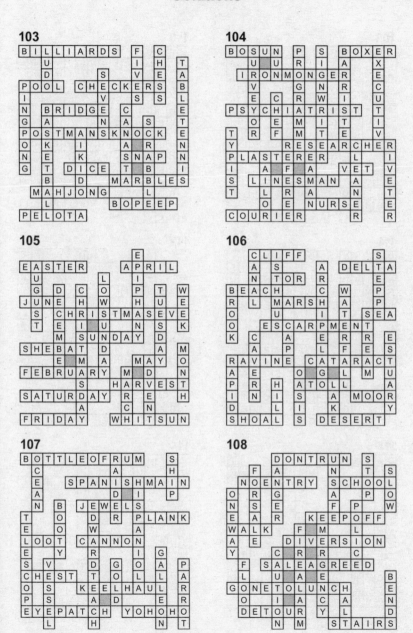

103

BILLIARDS F C
Fivechess TABLE
SS SS
POOL CHECKERS
BRIDGE
POSTMANSKNOCK
SNAP
DICE B
MARBLES
MAHJONG
BOPEEP
PELOTA

104

BOSUN P S BOXER
IRONMONGER
PSYCHIATRIST
RESEARCHER
PLASTERER VET
LINESMAN
NURSE
COURIER

105

EASTER APRIL
JUNE
CHRISTMASEVE
SUNDAY
SHEBAT MAY
FEBRUARY
HARVEST
SATURDAY
FRIDAY WHITSUN

106

CLIFF S
DELTA
BEACH
MARSH SEA
ESCARPMENT
RAVINE CATARACT
ATOLL MOOR
SHOAL DESERT

107

BOTTLEOFRUM
SPANISHMAIN
JEWELS
PLANK
LOOT CANNON
CHEST
KEELHAUL
EYEPATCH YOHOHO

108

DONTRUN
NOENTRY SCHOOL
KEEPOFF
WALK DIVERSION
SALEAGREED
GONETOLUNCH
DETOUR STAIRS

567

Solutions

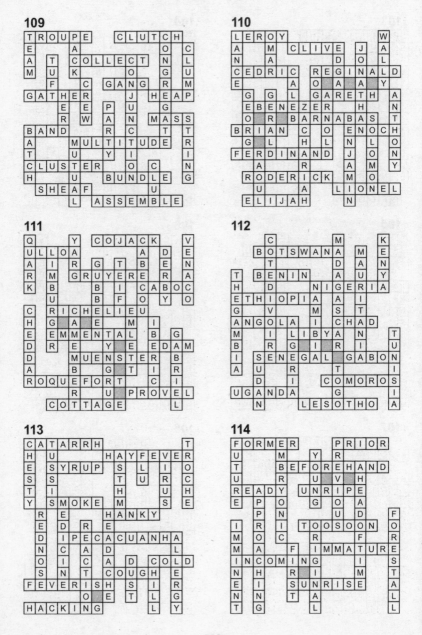

109

TROUPE · CLUTCH
TEAM · COLLECT · CLUM
MU K · CO · NG · LUM
F C GANG · R M
GATHER · J HEAP
ERW PUN G
ER PARC MASS
BAND · ARC T ST
AT MULTITUDE RI
CLUSTER O C N
H U BUNDLE E G
SHEAF U
L ASSEMBLE

110

LEROY · W
AN M CLIVE JO AL
N A D OL L
CEDRIC REGINALD
E A OAAY
GG G L GARETH AN
EBENEZER H T
OR BARNABAS H
BRIAN CO ENOCH O
GL H L N LN
FERDINAND J OY
A R A MY
RODERICK M O
U A LIONEL
ELIJAH N

111

Q Y COJACK V
ULLOA A D E N
ARI RGT BE RA
ARK M GRUYERE RC O
KBU BI CABOCO
UB F OY Y
CH RICHELIEU I
HE GA E M I
ED EMMENTAL BG
DR EY E EDAM
DA MUENSTER BB
AB GT IR
ROQUEFORT CI
R U PROVEL L
COTTAGE L

112

C M K
BOTSWANA MA EN
T DA UY
TH BENIN AUA
HD NIGERIA IT
ETHIOPIA A ST
GV MS TI
ANGOLA I CHAD
MILIBYA NT
BI RGI RIU
AI SENEGAL GABON
AUR TS
DI COMOROS IA
UGANDA G IA
N LESOTHO A

113

CATARRH T
HU HAYFEVER RO
ES SYRUP ST LUIRC
ST SS THURUSHE
TY I HM US
Y SMOKE HM
RE HANKY
RE DR E
ED IPECACUANHA
NO CA D L
OS IN CT COLD
S NT COUGH ER
FEVERISH ST IL RGY
O E TL LY
HACKING LL

114

FORMER PRIOR
FU M Y R
TU BE BEFOREHAND
UU R U VH
READY UNRIPE
EE PO GOA
PN U D F
I ROC TOOSOON O
IM OC R F R
MA F IMMATURE E
INCOMING I S
NH R I M T
E NG SUNRISE A
T G T AL L

568

Solutions

115

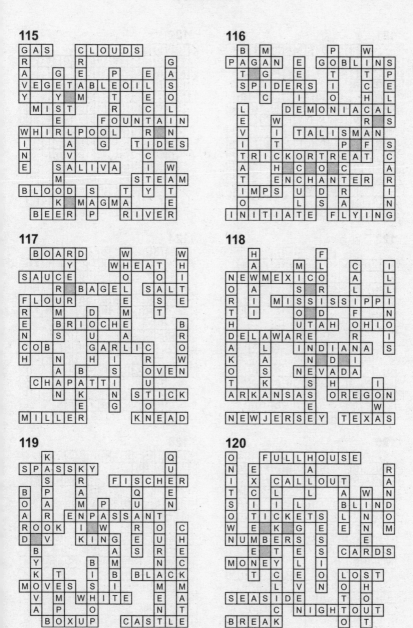

116

117

118

119

120

Solutions

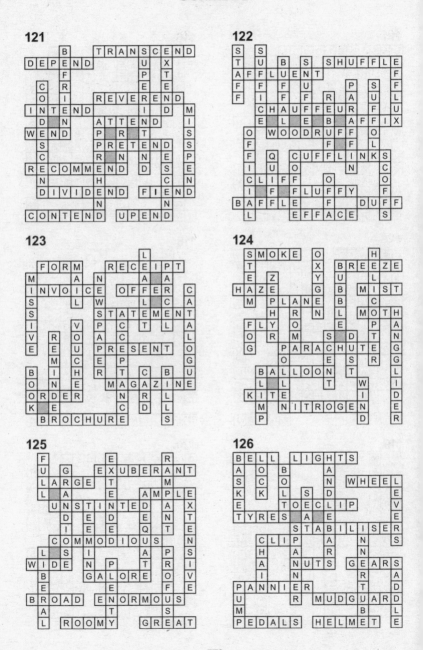

121

```
        B       T R A N S C E N D
D E P E N D     U     X
    F           P     T
  C R           E     E
  O I   R E V E R E N D
I N T E N D     I   D     M
  D   N   A T T E N D     I
W E N D   P   R   T       S
        P   R E T E N D   S
        R   N   N   E     P
R E C O M M E N D   D     S E N
E       N   H       S     C
  D I V I D E N D   F I E N D
        N           N     N
C O N T E N D   U P E N D
```

122

```
S   S
T   U   B   S   S H U F F L E
A F F L U E N T           F
F   F   F   U       P   S F
F   I   F   F   R   A   U F
  C H A U F F E U R     F L
    E   L   E   B   A F F I X
O   W O O D R U F F     O
F           F   F   F   L
F   Q   C U F F L I N K S O
I   U   O       N       C
C L I F F   O           O
I   F   F L U F F Y     F
B A F F L E     F   D U F F
L       E F F A C E     S
```

123

```
            L
  F O R M   R E C E I P T
M     A     A   A
I N V O I C E   O F F E R   C
S     L   W     L   C       A
S         S T A T E M E N T A
I     V   P   C   T   L     A
V   R O   A   C           L O
E   E U   P R E S E N T   O G
    M C   E   P           G U
B   I H   R   T   C   B   L E
O   N E       M A G A Z I N E
O R D E R     N   Z   R   L
K   E         C   R   D   L S
  B R O C H U R E
```

124

```
  S M O K E   O       H
  T       X   X   B R E E Z E
  E   Z   Y   Y   U   L
H A Z E   G   G   B   M I S T
  M   P L A N E   B   C
      H   R   N   L   M O T H
F L Y O         L   P     A
O   R M     S   D   T     N
G   P A R A C H U T E R   G
    O       E   S   R     L
  B A L L O O N T         I
  L   L       T       W   D
K I T E               I   E
  M   N I T R O G E N D   R
  P
```

125

```
  F         E         R
U L G   E X U B E R A N T
  L A R G E   T       M
  L A       E   A M P L E
  U N S T I N T E D   X
  D E E     D   N   T E
  I E E     E   Q   E N
  C O M M O D I O U S   N
L S   I       A   P R S
W I D E   N P     T R O I
  B     G A L O R E   O V
  E     E     E       F E
B R O A D E N O R M O U S
  L   R O O M Y   G R E A T
```

126

```
B E L L   L I G H T S
A   O   B       A
S   C   O       N   W H E E L
K   K   L   S   D       E
E       T O E C L I P   V
T Y R E S   A   E       E
        S T A B I L I S E R S
    C L I P   A   N
    H   A     R   N
    A   N U T S   G E A R S
    I   N         R     A
P A N N I E R     T     D
U       R   M U D G U A R D
M               B       L
P E D A L S   H E L M E T   E
```

570

Solutions

127

128

129

130

131

132

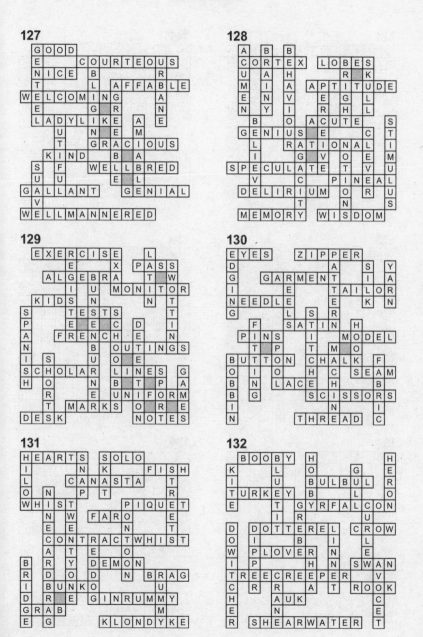

Solutions

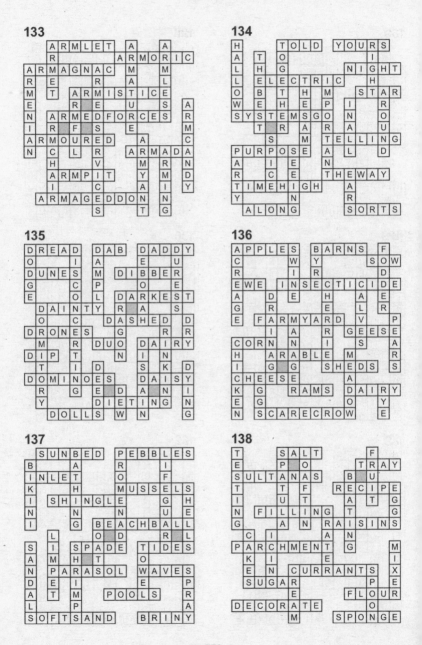

133

ARMLET A A
R ARMORIC
ARMAGNAC M M
A E R A L
ARME T ARMISTICE
MEN R E U S AR
NI ARMEDFORCES R
I RFS E M
IARMOURED A UC
N C L R ARMADA A
H V MRND
ARMPIT YMINY
IC AT
ARMAGEDDON T G
S T

134

H TOLD YOURS
A T O I
LL TH OG NIGHT
LO ELECTRIC H
OW B TH HE M STAR
S SYSTEMSGO I RO
T S AAR NU
S M TELLING
PURPOSE AL D
ARIE N
R CE THEWAY
TIMEHIGH AR
Y N R
ALONG SORTS

135

DREAD DAB DADDY
O I A E U
DUNES AMP DIBBER
GE C P O E
E OL DARKEST
DAINTY RA S
OC DASHED D
DRONES G RR
M R DUO DAIRY
DIP T N IN
TI D S K D
DOMINOES DAISY
R GE D AN I
Y DIETING N
DOLLS W N G

136

APPLES BARNS F
C W Y SOW
R I R D
EWE INSECTICIDE
A D E H A E
G R E L R
E FARMYARD V P
I A R GEESE E
CORN N I S A
I ARABLE M R
I GG SHEDS S
CHEESE A
K G RAMS DAIRY
E G O Y
N SCARECROW E

137

SUNBED PEBBLES
B A R I
INLET O F
K H MUSSELS
IN SHINGLE GH
N N N UE
I G BEACHBALL
L O D RL
S LI SPADE TIDES
AN M HT O
ND PARASOL WAVES
A E I E P
L T M POOLS R
L P A
SOFTSAND BRINY

138

T SALT F
E P O TRAY
SULTANAS B U
T T F RECIPE
I U T A T G
N FILLING T G
G A N RAISINS
C I A N
PARCHMENT G M
K I E IX
E N CURRANTS E
SUGAR P
E FLOUR
DECORATE O
M SPONGE

572

Solutions

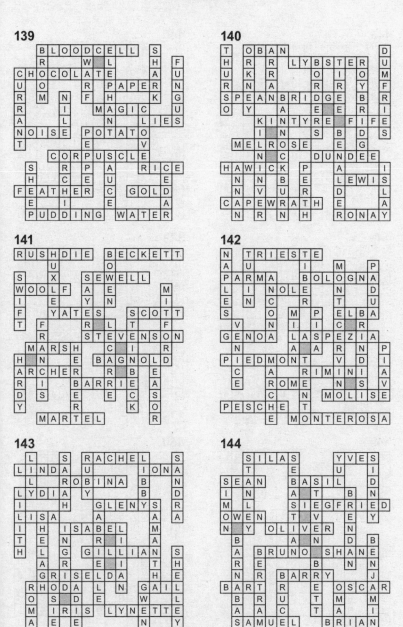

139

140

141

142

143

144

Solutions

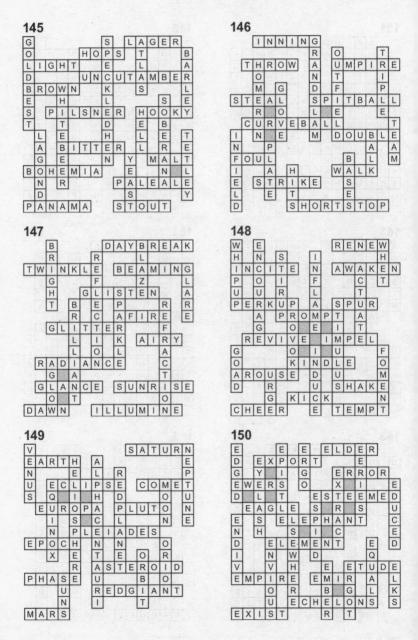

145

146

147

148

149

150

Solutions

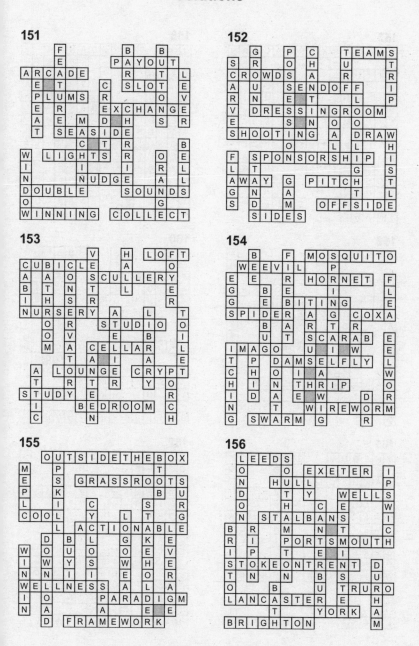

Solutions

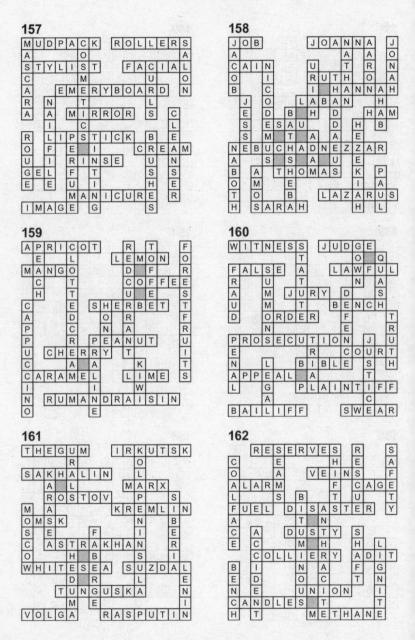

157 158 159 160 161 162

Solutions

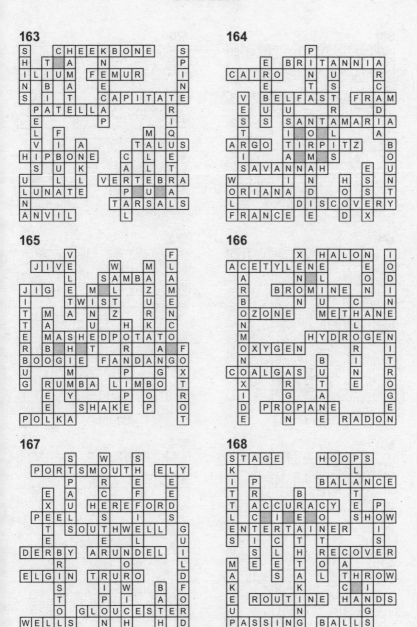

163

164

165

166

167

168

577

Solutions

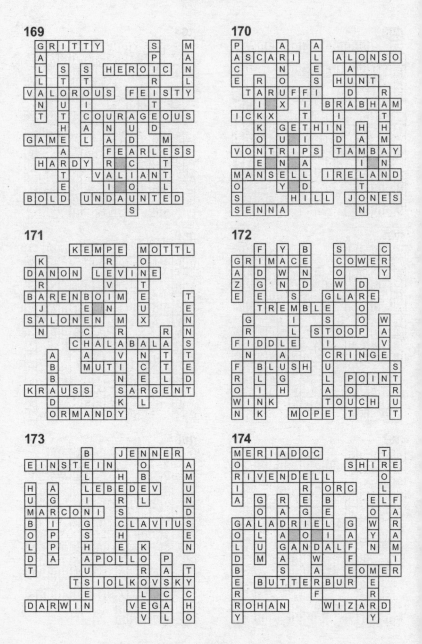

169

GRITTY · SP · MAN · ALL · HEROIC · VALOROUS · FEISTY · COURAGEOUS · GAME · FEARLESS · HARDY · VALIANT · BOLD · UNDAUNTED

170

PASCARI · ALES · ALONSO · HUNT · TARUFFI · BRABHAM · ICKX · GETHIN · VON TRIPS · TAMBAY · MANSELL · IRELAND · HILL · JONES · SENNA

171

KEMPE · MOTTL · DANON · LEVINE · BARENBOIM · SALONEN · CHALABALA · MUTI · KRAUSS · SARGENT · ORMANDY

172

GRIMACE · COWER · CRY · GLARE · TREMBLE · STOOP · FIDDLE · CRINGE · BLUSH · POINT · WINK · TOUCH · MOPE

173

JENNER · EINSTEIN · LEBEDEV · MARCONI · CLAVIUS · APOLLO · TSIOLKOVSKY · DARWIN · VEGA

174

MERIADOC · SHIRE · RIVENDELL · ORC · ELF · GALADRIEL · GANDALF · EOMER · BUTTERBUR · ROHAN · WIZARD

Solutions

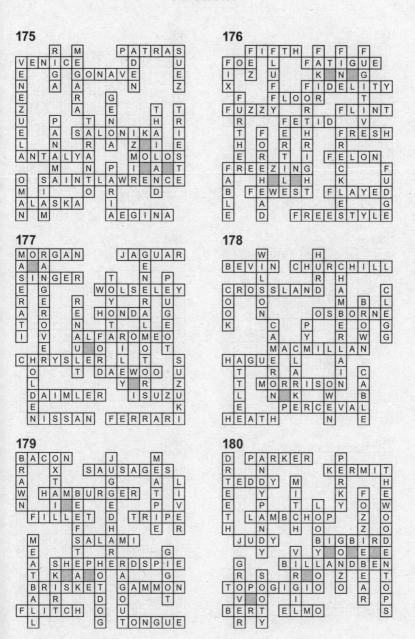

175

176

177

178

179

180

Solutions

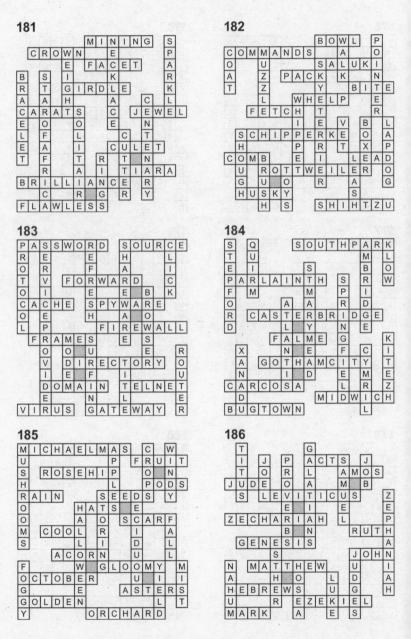

181

MINING S
CROWN E P
E FACET A
B S I K R
R T GIRDLE K
A A H A L
CARATS C JEWEL
E O O E N
L F L C T
E A I CULET
T F T R T N
R A I T TIARA
BRILLIANCE R Y
C R G R
FLAWLESS

182

BOWL P
COMMANDS A O
O U SALUKI N
A Z PACK K T
T Z Y BITE
L WHELP E R
FETCH T
I E V B L
SCHIPPERKE O A
H P R T X P
COMB E I LEAD O
U ROTTWEILER R G
G U O R A
HUSKY S
H S SHIHTZU

183

PASSWORD SOURCE
R E E H L
O R F A I
T V FORWARD C
O I E B K
CACHE SPYWARE
O E H A O
L P FIREWALL
FRAMES E S
O O U E R
V DIRECTORY O
I E F I U
DOMAIN TELNET
E N L E
VIRUS GATEWAY R

184

S Q SOUTHPARK
T U M L
E I S B O
PARLAINTH S R W
F M M P I
O A A R D
R CASTERBRIDGE
D L Y N E
FALME G K
X N E F C I
A GOTHAMCITY T
N I D E M E
CARCOSA L R Z
D MIDWICH
BUGTOWN L

185

MICHAELMAS C W
U P FRUIT T
S ROSEHIP O N
H L PODS Y
RAIN SEEDS
O HATS E
O A O SCARF
M COOL R I A
S L I D L
ACORN U L
F W GLOOMY M
OCTOBER U I I
G E ASTERS S
GOLDEN L T
Y ORCHARD

186

T G
I J P ACTS J
T O R L AMOS
JUDE O A M B
S LEVITICUS Z
E I E E
ZECHARIAH L P
B N RUTH
GENESIS
S JOHN
N MATTHEW U I
A H O L D A
HEBREWS U G H
U R EZEKIEL
MARK A S

580

Solutions

187

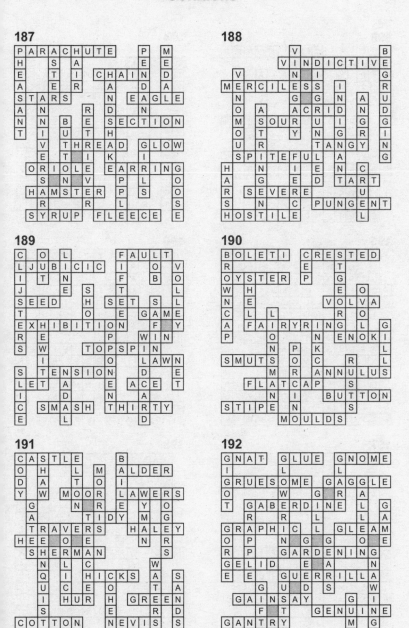

P A R A C H U T E — P — M
H — S — A — E — E
E — T — I — C H A I N — D
— — E — R — A — D — A
S T A R S — — N — E A G L E
A — N — R E — D — N
N — N — B — E — S E C T I O N
T — I — U — T — H
— V — T H R E A D — G L O W
— E — T — I — K — I
— O R I O L E — E A R R I N G
— S — N — V — P — L — O
— H A M S T E R — P — S — O
— R — R — L — — S
— S Y R U P — F L E E C E — E

188

— — — V — — — — — B
— — V I N D I C T I V E — E
— V — N — I — — — G
M E R C I L E S S — I — R
— N — G — G — N — A — U
— O — A — A C R I D — N — D
— M — S O U R — U — I — G G
— O — T — Y — N — G R — I
— U — R — — T A N G Y — N
— S P I T E F U L — A — G
H — N — I — E — N — C
A — G — E — D — T A R T
R — S E V E R E — U
S — N — C — P U N G E N T
H O S T I L E — L

189

C — O — L — F A U L T
L J U B I C I C — I — O — V
I — T — N — F — B — O
J — E — S — T — S — L
S E E D — H — S E T — S — L
T — O — E — G A M E — E
E X H I B I T I O N — F — Y
R — E — P — W I N
S — W — T O P S P I N
— I — O — L A W N
S T E N S I O N — D — E
L E T — A — E — A C E — T
I — D — E — A
C — S M A S H — T H I R T Y
E — L

190

B O L E T I — C R E S T E D
R — — E — T
O Y S T E R — P — G E — O
W — H — E — V O L V A
N — E — L — R — O
C — L L — R — O
A — F A I R Y R I N G — L — G
P — O — N — E N O K I
— N — P — K — L
S M U T S — O — C — R — L
— M — A N N U L U S
— F L A T C A P — S
— N — I — B U T T O N
S T I P E — N — S
— M O U L D S

191

C A S T L E — B
O — H — L — M — A L D E R
D — A — T — O — I
Y — W — M O O R — L A W E R S
— G — N — R — E — Y — O
— A — — T I D Y — M — G
— T R A V E R S — H A L E Y
H E E — O — E — N — R
— S H E R M A N — S
— N — L — C — W
— Q — I — H I C K S — A — S
— U — C — E — O — T — A
— I — H U R — H — G R E E N
— S — E — R — D
C O T T O N — N E V I S — S

192

G N A T — G L U E — G N O M E
I — L — L
G R U E S O M E — G A G G L E
O — W — G — R — A
T — G A B E R D I N E — L — G
— R — R — L — L — A
G R A P H I C — L — G L E A M
O — P — N — G — O — E
R — P — G A R D E N I N G
G E L I D — E — A — N
E — E — G U E R R I L L A
— G — U — D — S — W
G A I N S A Y — G — I
— F — T — G E N U I N E
G A N T R Y — M — G

Solutions

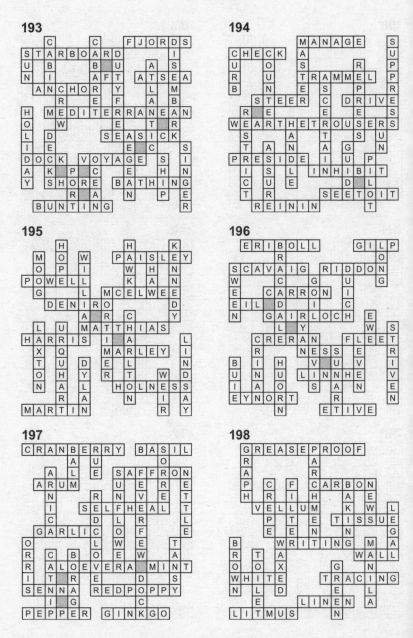

193

		C				C			F	J	O	R	D	S
S	T	A	R	B	O	A	R	D					I	
U		B			B		U			A			S	
N		I			A	F	T		A	T	S	E	A	
	A	N	C	H	O	R		Y		L		M		
		R			E		F			A		B		
H		M	E	D	I	T	E	R	R	A	N	E	A	N
O		W			E			T		T		R		
L		D			S	E	A	S	I	C	K			
I		E			E			E		C		S		
D	O	C	K		V	O	Y	A	G	E		S	I	
A		K		P		C		E		H		I	N	
Y		S	H	O	R	E		B	A	T	H	I	N	G
				R		A		N				P		E
	B	U	N	T	I	N	G							R

194

				M	A	N	A	G	E				S	
C	H	E	C	K		A							U	
U		O			S			R				P		
R		U		T	R	A	M	M	E	L		P		
B		N			E		S		P		R			
	S	T	E	E	R		C		D	R	I	V	E	
R		E			E		E		E		S			
W	E	A	R	T	H	E	T	R	O	U	S	E	R	S
S				A			T		S		U			
T		A	N			A	G			N				
P	R	E	S	I	D	E		I	U		P			
I		S		L		I	N	H	I	B	I	T		
C		U		E					D			L		
T		R				S	E	E	T	O	I	T		
	R	E	I	N	I	N						T		

195

		H				H			K	
M		O		W		P	A	I	S	L	E	Y
O		P		I		W		H		N	
P	O	W	E	L	L		K		A		N	
G			L		M	C	E	L	W	E	E	
	D	E	N	I	R	O			D		Y
		A		R		C			Y	
L		U		M	A	T	T	H	I	A	S
H	A	R	R	I	S		I		A		L
X		Q			M	A	R	L	E	Y		I
T		U		D		E	L			N
O		H		Y		R	T		W		D
N		A		L			H	O	L	N	E	S	S
		R		A			N			I		A
M	A	R	T	I	N				R		Y

196

	E	R	I	B	O	L	L			G	I	L	P	
			R										O	
S	C	A	V	A	I	G		R	I	D	D	O	N	
W			C			G			U				G	
E		C	A	R	R	O	N		I					
E	I	L		D			I		C					
N		G	A	I	R	L	O	C	H		E			
			L		Y					W		S	
	C	R	E	R	A	N		F	L	E	E	T	
	R			N	E	S	S		E		T	R	
B	I		H		V		U		V			R	
U	N		U		L	I	N	N	H	E		I	
I	A		O		S			A	N			V	
E	Y	N	O	R	T			R				E	N
	N						E	T	I	V	E		

197

C	R	A	N	B	E	R	R	Y		B	A	S	I	L	
		A		U							O				
		L		E			S	A	F	F	R	O	N		
	A	R	U	M			U		E		R		E		
	N			R		S	E	L	F	H	E	A	L		
	I			D			L		O		F		L		
	G	A	R	L	I	C		O		F		E		
O				L		W		W		E		T		
R		C		B		O		E		W		A		
R		A	L	O	E	V	E	R	A		M	I	N	T
I		T		R		E			D			S		
S	E	N	N	A		R	E	D	P	O	P	P	Y	
		I		G					C					
P	E	P	P	E	R		G	I	N	K	G	O		

198

	G	R	E	A	S	E	P	R	O	O	F		
R					A			A		R			
A							P		C	A	R	B	O	N
P		C		F			C	H		A		E		
H		R		I			H			K		W		L
	V	E	L	L	U	M			K		W		L
		P		T		E		T	I	S	S	U	E
		E		E		N		N				G	
B			W	R	I	T	I	N	G		M		A
R		T		A					W	A	L	L	
O		O		X				G			A		N
W	H	I	T	E			T	R	A	C	I	N	G
N		L		D				E			L		A
		E			L	I	N	E	N		A		
L	I	T	M	U	S					N			

Solutions

199

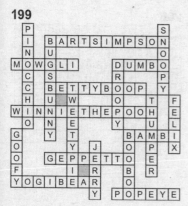

200

201

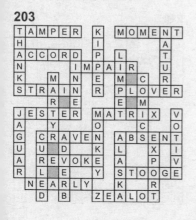

202

203

204

Solutions

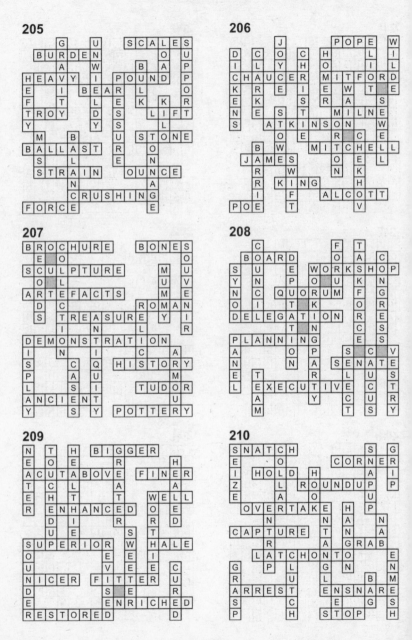

Solutions

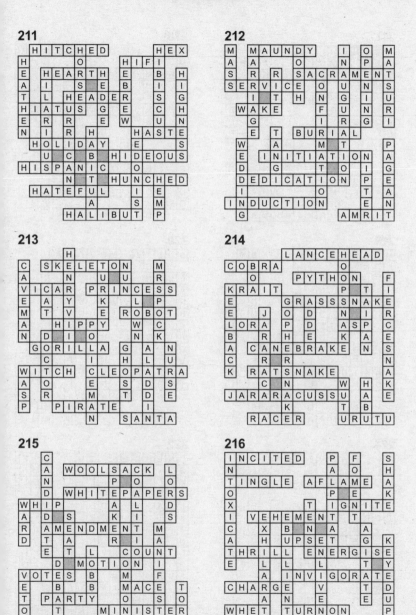

211

212

213

214

215

216

Solutions

217

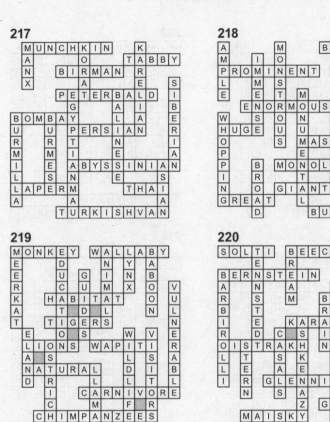

```
M U N C H K I N      K
A           O        T A B B Y
N      B I R M A N    R
X           A         E        S
      P E T E R B A L D         I
            G         A    I    B
B O M B A Y          L    A    E
U     U    P E R S I A N        R
R     R    T         N          I
M     M    I         E          A
I     E    A B Y S S I N I A N  N
L     S    N         E         S
L A P E R M          T H A I
A          A                   A
      T U R K I S H V A N
```

218

```
A           M           B U M P E R
M      I    O                     X
P R O M I N E N T      H E F T Y
L      M    S              P    E
E      E    T    M         I    N
      E N O R M O U S      C    S
W      S    O    N    C    B I G
H U G E    U    U    O         V
O      S    S    M A S S I V E
P           E    M
P      B    M O N O L I T H I C
I      R    T         C    E
N      O    G I A N T      V A S T
G R E A T    L               V
D           B U L K Y
```

219

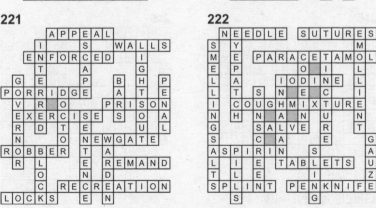

```
M O N K E Y      W A L L A B Y
E      D        N    Y    A
E      U    G    I    N    B
R      C    U    M    X    B    V
K    H A B I T A T          O    U
A      T    D    L         O    L
T    T I G E R S            N    L
   E      O S         W    V    N
L I O N S        W A P I T I    E
A    S           L    S         R
N A T U R A L    D    I         A
D    R           L    L         B
   I      C A R N I V O R E    L
   C      M         F    R
C H I M P A N Z E E S
```

220

```
S O L T I      B E E C H A M
      E        R              E
B E R N S T E I N            N
A      N       A      G O U L D
R      S    M    B         H    U
B      T         R         I    P
I      E    K A R A J A N       R
R      D  C   S         I       E
O I S T R A K H         N
L    T       S    K    P    M
L    E       A    E    R    U
I    R    G L E N N I E      T
      N    S    A    V    T
            Z    G I L E L S
M A I S K Y      N    R
```

221

```
      A P P E A L
      I        S    W A L L S
   E N F O R C E D    I
      T        A      G
   G  E        P    B H    P
P O R R I D G E    A T    E
   V  R    O       P R I S O N
   E X E R C I S E    S    O    A
   R  D    T    E          U    L
   N       O    N E W G A T E
R O B B E R    T    A
   R  L       E    R E M A N D
      O       N    D
      C    R E C R E A T I O N
L O C K S     E    N
```

222

```
   N E E D L E    S U T U R E S
S  Y              M
M  E    P A R A C E T A M O L
E  P         O    I        L
L  A    I O D I N E        L
L  T  S  N    E    C       I
I  C O U G H M I X T U R E
N  H  N  A    N    U       N
G  S A L V E       R       T
S  C  A            E       G
A S P I R I N    S         A
L  I  E  T A B L E T S     U
T  L  E            I       Z
S P L I N T  P E N K N I F E
   S              G
```

Solutions

223

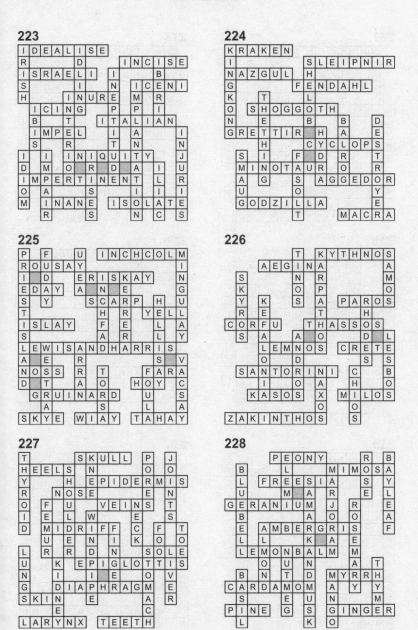

224

225

226

227

228

Solutions

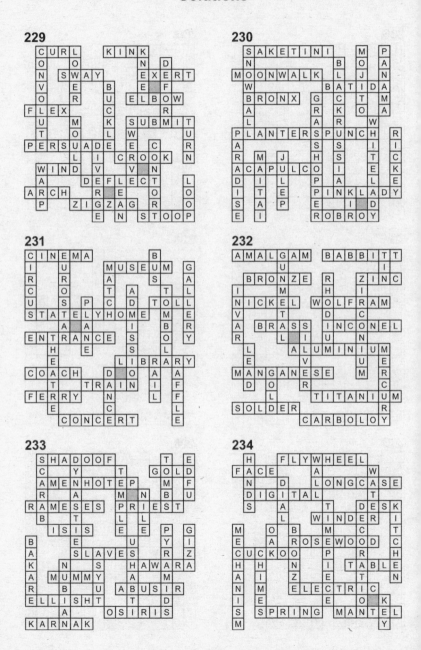

229

230

231

232

233

234

Solutions

235

236

237

238

239

240

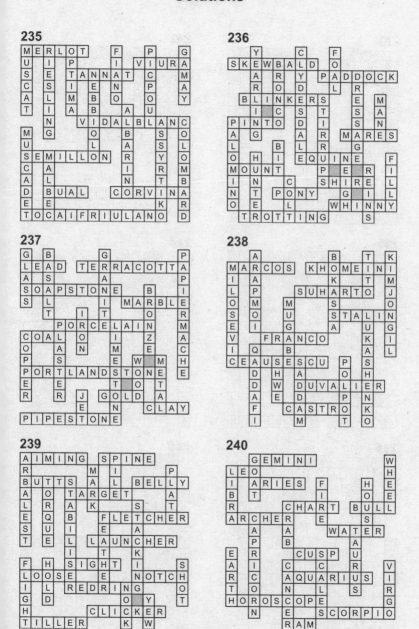

Solutions

241
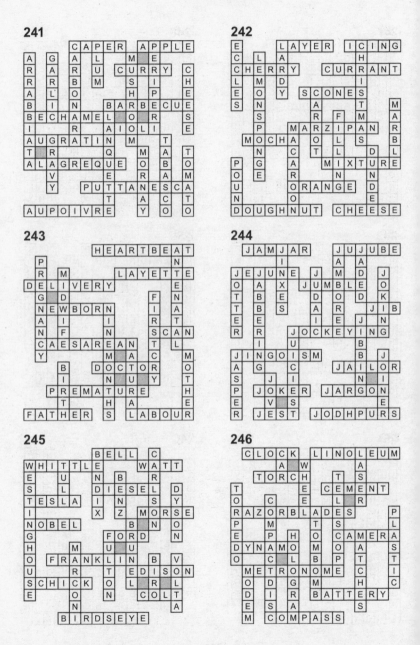

242

243

244

245

246

Solutions

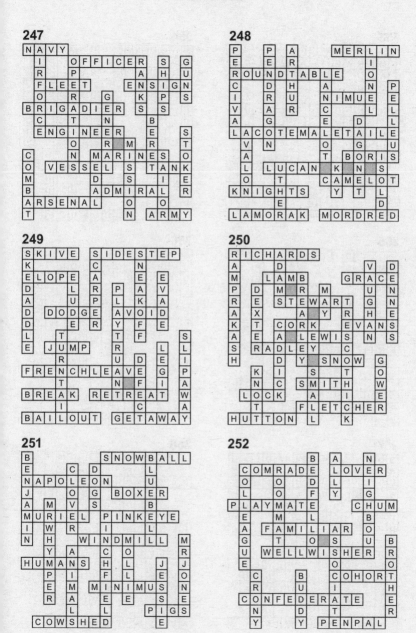

Solutions

253

254

255

256

257

258

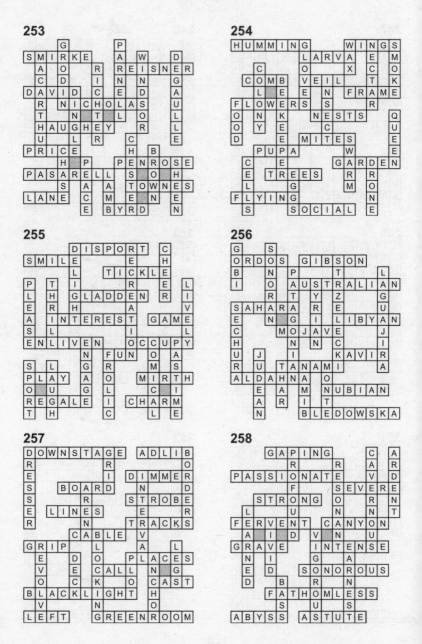

Solutions

259

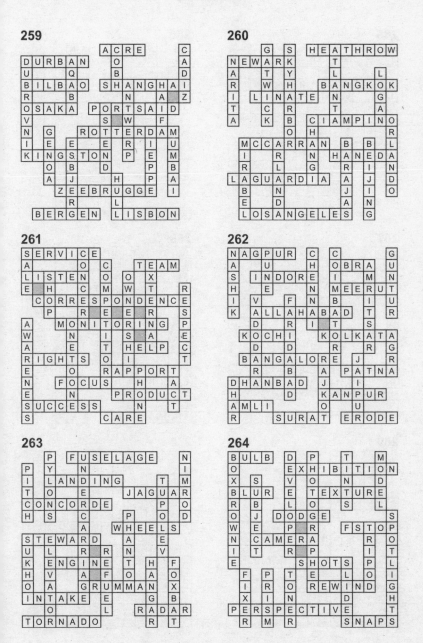

Crossword grid with answers:
ACRE, C, CAD, DURBAN, OB, BILBAO, SHANGHAI, OSAKA, PORTSAID, ROTTERDAM, KINGSTON, ZEEBRUGGE, BERGEN, LISBON

260

Crossword grid with answers:
HEATHROW, NEWARK, BANGKOK, LINATE, CIAMPINO, MCCARRAN, HANEDA, LAGUARDIA, LOSANGELES

261

Crossword grid with answers:
SERVICE, LISTEN, TEAM, CORRESPONDENCE, MONITORING, HELP, RIGHTS, RAPPORT, FOCUS, PRODUCT, SUCCESS, CARE

262

Crossword grid with answers:
NAGPUR, OBRA, INDORE, MEERUT, ALLAHABAD, KOCHI, KOLKATA, BANGALORE, PATNA, DHANBAD, KANPUR, AMLI, SURAT, ERODE

263

Crossword grid with answers:
FUSELAGE, LANDING, JAGUAR, CONCORDE, WHEELS, STEWARD, ENGINE, GRUMMAN, INTAKE, RADAR, TORNADO

264

Crossword grid with answers:
BULB, EXHIBITION, BLUR, TEXTURE, DODGE, FSTOP, CAMERA, SHOTS, REWIND, PERSPECTIVE, SNAPS

593

Solutions

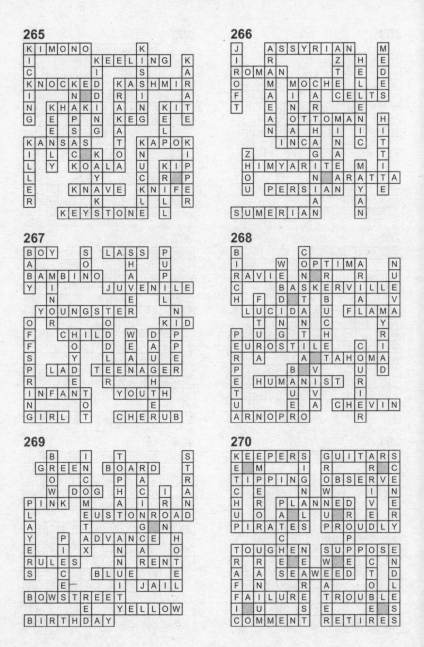

Solutions

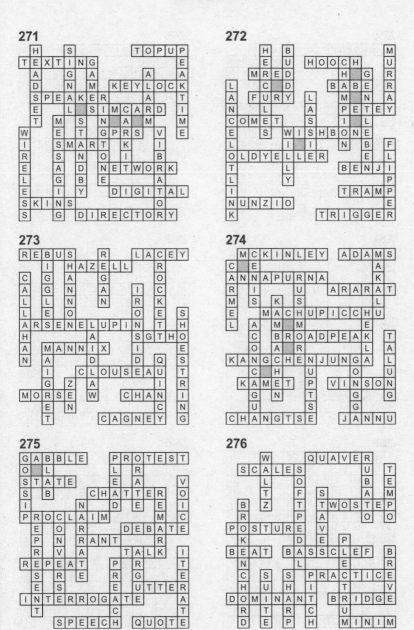

271 272 273 274 275 276

Solutions

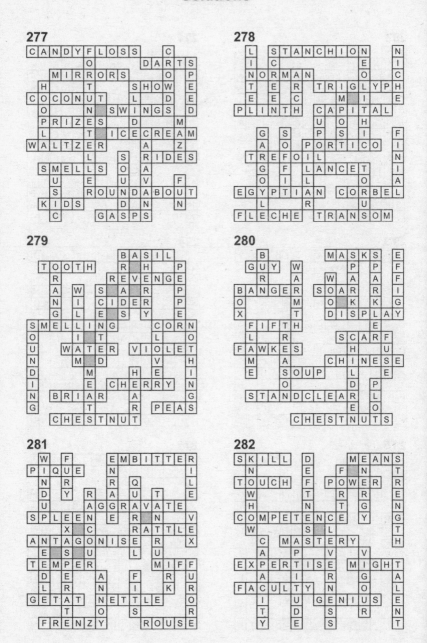

277

CANDYFLOSS · DARTS · MIRRORS · SHOW · COCONUT · SWINGS · PRIZES · ICECREAM · WALTZER · RIDES · SMELLS · ROUNDABOUT · KIDS · GASPS

278

STANCHION · NORMAN · TRIGLYPH · PLINTH · CAPITAL · PORTICO · TREFOIL · LANCET · EGYPTIAN · CORBEL · FLECHE · TRANSOM

279

BASIL · TOOTH · REVENGE · CIDER · SMELLING · CORN · WATER · VIOLET · CHERRY · BRIAR · PEAS · CHESTNUT

280

MASKS · GUY · BANGER · SOAR · OX · DISPLAY · FIFTH · SCARF · FAWKES · CHINESE · SOUP · STANDCLEAR · CHESTNUTS

281

EMBITTER · PIQUE · AGGRAVATE · SPLEEN · RATTLE · ANTAGONISE · TEMPER · MIFF · GETAT · NETTLE · FRENZY · ROUSE

282

SKILL · MEANS · TOUCH · POWER · COMPETENCE · MASTERY · EXPERTISE · MIGHT · FACULTY · GENIUS

596

Solutions

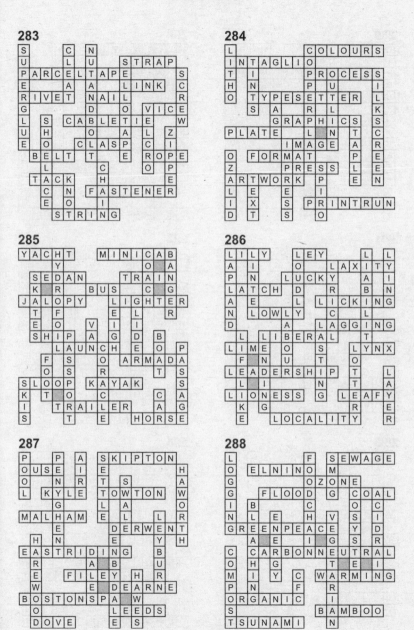

283

S · · C N
U · · L U · · · S T R A P
P A R C E L T A P E · · · · S
E · · · A A · · L I N K · · C
R I V E T · N A I L · · · · R
G · · · · D · O · · V I C E · W
L · · S C A B L E T I E · · W
U · H · · O · · A · L · Z · ·
E · O · C L A S P · C · I · ·
· B E L T · T · · E · R O P E
· L · · · C · · · · O · P ·
· T A C K · H · · · · · E ·
· C · N · F A S T E N E R
· E · O · · I
· · S T R I N G

284

L · · · C O L O U R S
I N T A G L I O · O · ·
T · I · · · P R O C E S S
H · N · · · P · U · · · I
O · T Y P E S E T T E R · L
· · S · A · · R · L · · · K
· · · G R A P H I C S · · S
P L A T E · L · N · T · · C
· · · · I M A G E · A · · R
O · F O R M A T · · P · · E
Z · · · P R E S S · L · · E
A R T W O R K · P · E · · N
L · E · · E · · I · · · ·
I · X · · S · · P R I N T R U N
D · T · · S · · O

285

Y A C H T · M I N I C A B
· · Y · · · · O · · · A
S E D A N · · T R A I N
K · R · B U S · · C · G
J A L O P Y · L I G H T E R
T · F · · E · L · R
E · O · V · I · L · I
S H I P · A · G · D · B
· L A U N C H · E · O · P
F · S · O · A R M A D A
O · S · R · · · T · · S
S L O O P · K A Y A K · S
K · T · O · · C · · C · A
I · · T R A I L E R · A · G
S · · T · · E · H O R S E

286

L I L Y · · L E Y · · L · L
A · I · · O · · L A X I T Y
P · N · L U C K Y · R · A I N
L A T C H · D · · R · B · N
A · E · · L · L I C K I N G
N · L O W L Y · C · L
D · · A · · L A G G I N G
· L · L I B E R A L · T
L I M E · O · S · L Y N X
F · N · U · T · O
L E A D E R S H I P · T · L
L · I · N · · T · A
L I O N E S S · G · L E A F Y
K · G · · · · R · E
E · · L O C A L I T Y · R

287

P · P · A · S K I P T O N
O U S E · I · E · · · · H
O · N · R · T · S · · · A
L · K Y L E · T O W T O N · W
· G · · · L · A · · L · O
M A L H A M · E · L · L · R
· · E · · · D E R W E N T H
H · N · · · E · · · Y
E A S T R I D I N G · · B
R · · · A · B · · · U
E · · F I L E Y · H · R
W · · · E · D E A R N E
B O S T O N S P A · W
O · · · · · L E E D S
D O V E · · · E · S

288

L · · · F · S E W A G E
O · E L N I N O · M
G · · · O Z O N E
G · F L O O D · G · C O A L
I · B · · C · · O · C
N · L · E · H · V · S · I
G R E E N P E A C E · Y · D
· A · E · I · G · S · R
C · C A R B O N N E U T R A L
O · H · G · · T · E · I
M · I · Y · C · W A R M I N G
P · N · · · F · R
O R G A N I C · · I
S · · · B A M B O O
T S U N A M I · · N

Solutions

289

```
C   C O M P A S S       M A P S
I                 C   F         Y
R E G I S T R A T I O N         M
C         T       L     R   D   B
L     C H A L L E N G E     I   O
E     O   R           S     R   L
      N   T   T   F I T N E S S
      T   I   R             C
    M O U N T A I N         T   W
E     U   G   I       F I N I S H
F O R M L I N E             O   I
F     S   I   E             N   S
O     I   N     R O U T E   S   T
R     T R E E S                 L
T               N A V I G A T E
```

290

```
W I D O W     P A R I S H       S
  I       E       B       U     U
  L       A       I   R E G I S T E R
  L       T       R       B     N
      C H A R T S     A   A     A
          N       H   R   N     M
          C       R E C O R D S E
B   B I B L E     H   E   I
A       E         S   V   B     L
B A N N S         E   I   L     I
Y       T   P A R E N T   I     B
        W   S     R S     N     R
    D I V O R C E         V   G A
        F   N     H       E     R
D E E D S         H I S T O R Y
```

291

```
    H           L I V Y   H
S O C R A T E S     I     O
    R       R       R     M
    A   P I N D A R   G   E
    C     S     R   C I C E R O
    E     T     I     L   U
C     M O S E S     T     R
A     T   L     T   T     I
T     U   L     O   S A P P H O
U     A E S O P     C   E   V
L         E   H E S I O D   I
L U C I A N   A     T   E S D
U         E   N     U
S O P H O C L E S   S
          A   S
```

292

```
        R           W
J A C O B     R Y E L A N D
      M   M       N       O
M     N   E       S       R
A   K E R R Y H I L L   F P
S O A Y   I   E   E   U E
H R   A   N   R   Y   G R
A A   B O R D E R D A L E
M M       W       A E   V
    A W A S S I   L   S   E
D A   N   R   C O T E N T I N
A A   C   K   E     A   D
L I N C O L N     X     E E
A     T     L L E Y N   E N
    B E L T E X     L
```

293

```
  M A T C H E S       W
  A       O       S C A R F
  P       M     B     E
F   T     P   W H I S T L E   B
I   O     A   N   R   R       L
R   R     S   G L O V E S     A
S   R     S   C   V K         N
O C K S       R U C K S A C K
T   H       C     L   N       E
A       C   L     A   B       T
I     H A T A     N   O
D       M   R     R U G
K N I F E   R     S   P H O N E
I       R         O     T
T     V A C U U M F L A S K
                  E
```

294

```
              W A L P O L E
      B L A I R         L
T       T       B A L F O U R
H E A T H           Y
A       L       A   E D E N
T       E   B   S   G
C A M E R O N   Q   P E E L
H       A   A   U   O
P E R C E V A L I   R
  R     D   R   T   G   W
    D O U G L A S H O M E I
      N     A       A   L
    B A L D W I N   J   S
      L             O   O
G L A D S T O N E   B R O W N
```

598

Solutions

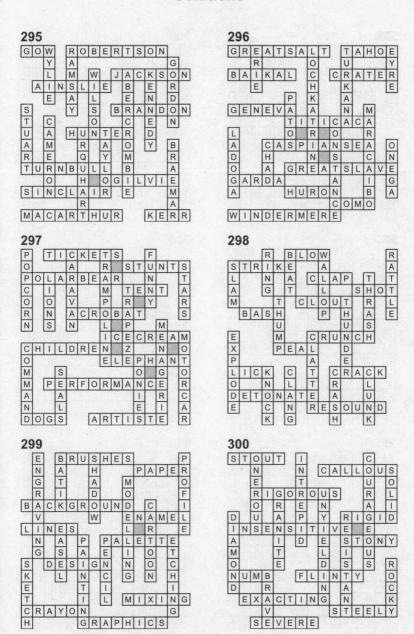

295

296

297

298

299

300

Solutions

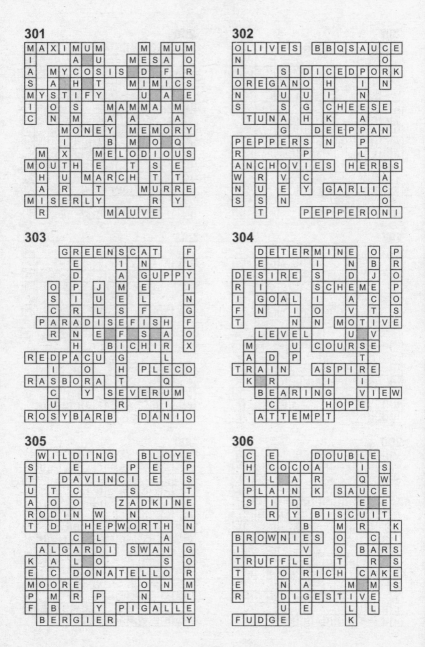

301

302

303

304

305

306

Solutions

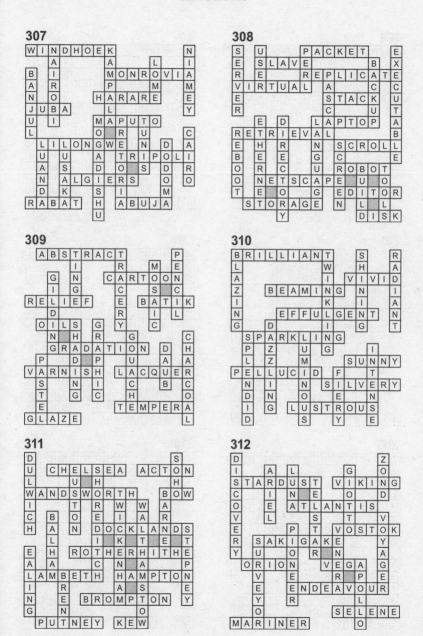

307

WINDHOEK ... NIAMEY
BANJUL / AIRO / KAMPALA
MONROVIA
JUBA / HARARE
MAPUTO
LILONGWE / TRIPOLI / DODOMA / CAIRO
ALGIERS
RABAT / ABUJA

308

SERVER / UP / PACKET / EXECUTABLE
SLAVE / REPLICATE
VIRTUAL / STACK
LAPTOP
RETRIEVAL / SCROLL
ROBOT
NETSCAPE / EDITOR
STORAGE / DISK

309

ABSTRACT / PEN
CARTOON
GIL / RELIEF / BATIK
OILS / GRADATION / CHA
VARNISH / LACQUER
GLAZE / TEMPERA

310

BRILLIANT / SH / RADIANT
VIVID
BEAMING
EFFULGENT
SPARKLING
SUNNY
PELLUCID / SILVERY
LUSTROUS

311

DULL / CHELSEA / ACTON / S
WANDSWORTH / BOW
DOCKLANDS
ROTHERHITHE
LAMBETH / HAMPTON
BROMPTON
PUTNEY / KEW

312

DISCOVERY / ZO
STARDUST / VIKING
ATLANTIS
VOSTOK
ORION / VEGA
ENDEAVOUR
SELENE
MARINER

601

Solutions

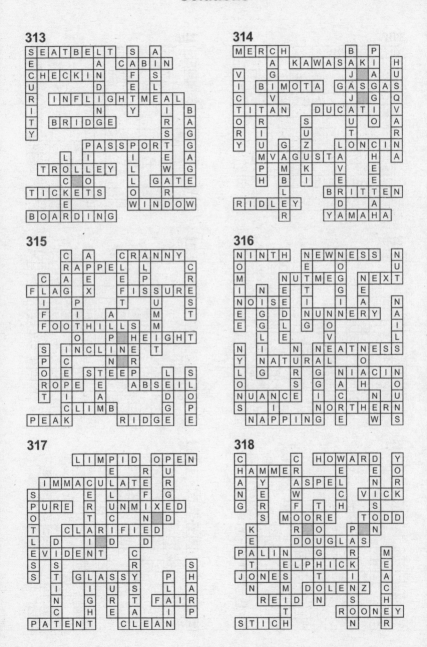

313

314

315

316

317

318

Solutions

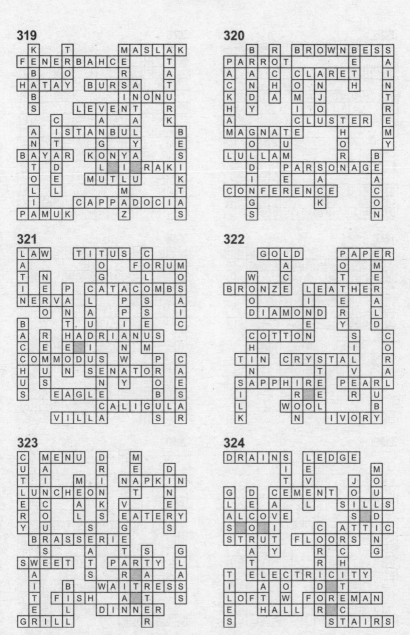

319

320

321

322

323

324

Solutions

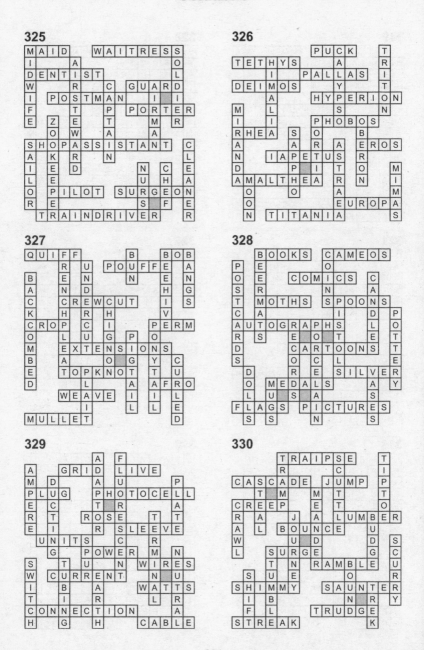

325

326

327

328

329

330

Solutions

331

332

333

334

335

336

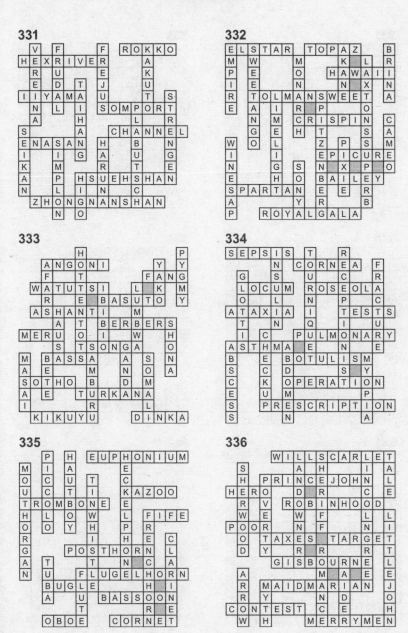

Solutions

337

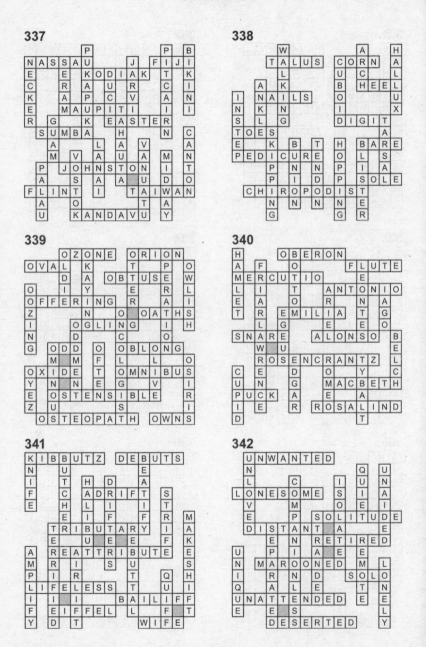

338

339

340

341

342

Solutions

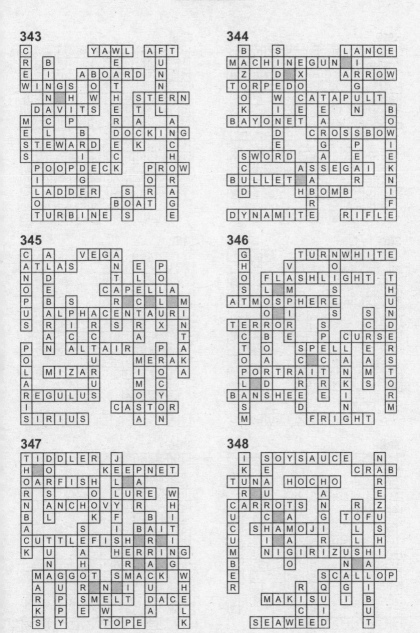

343

344

345

346

347

348

Solutions

349 **350**

351 **352**

353 **354**

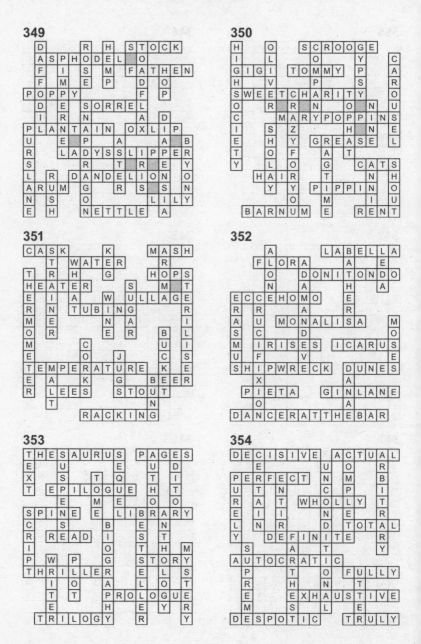

Solutions

355

356

357

358

359

360

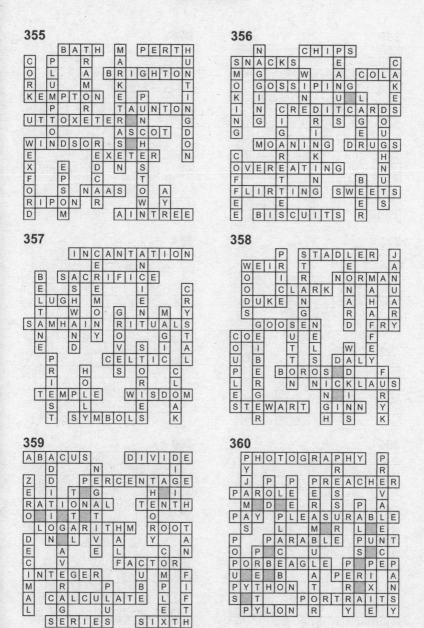

Solutions

361 **362**

363 **364**

365 **366**

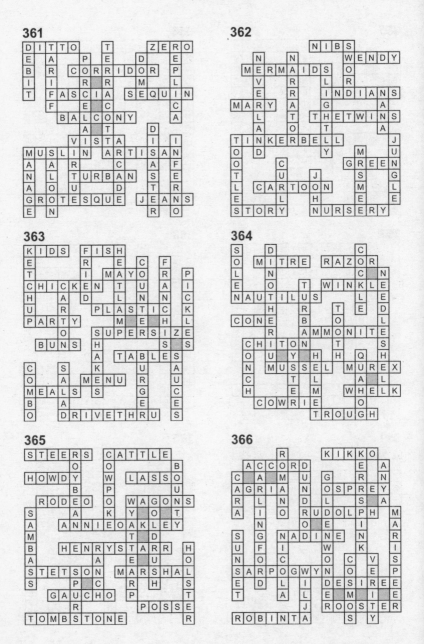

Solutions

367

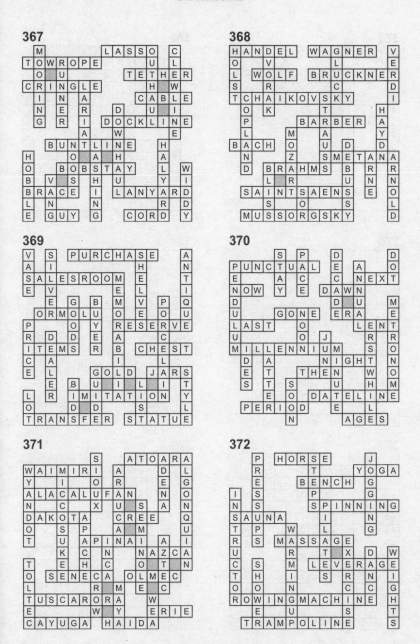

368

369

370

371

372

Solutions

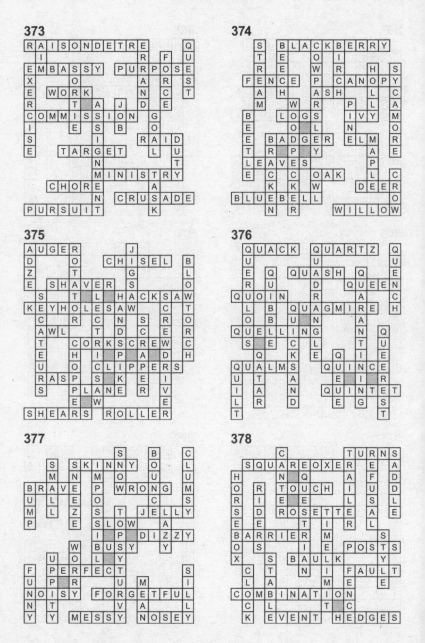

373

374

375

376

377

378

Solutions

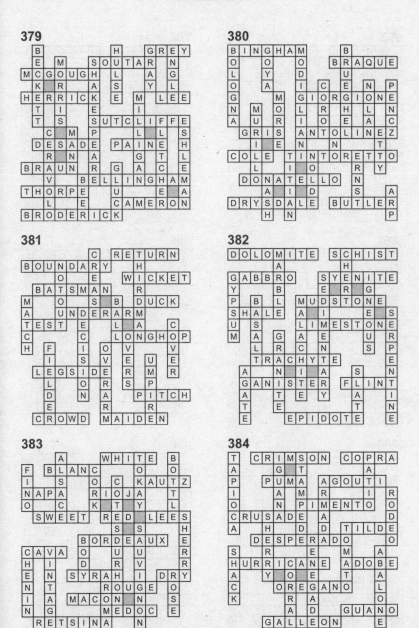

379 380

381 382

383 384

Solutions

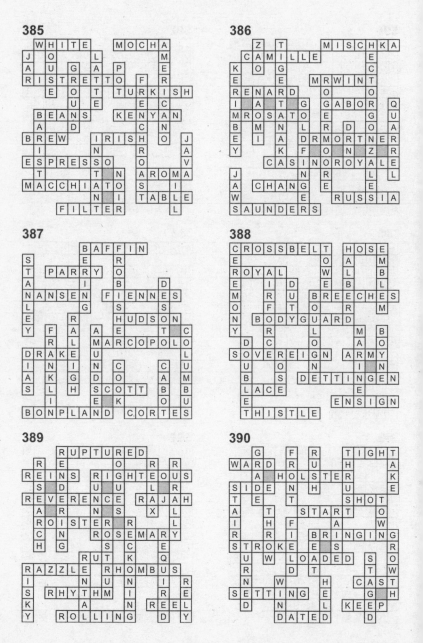

385

386

387

388

389

390

Solutions

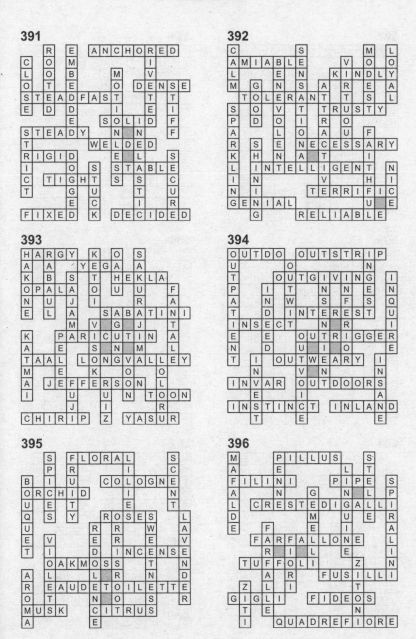

391

392

393

394

395

396

615

Solutions

397
398
399
400
401
402

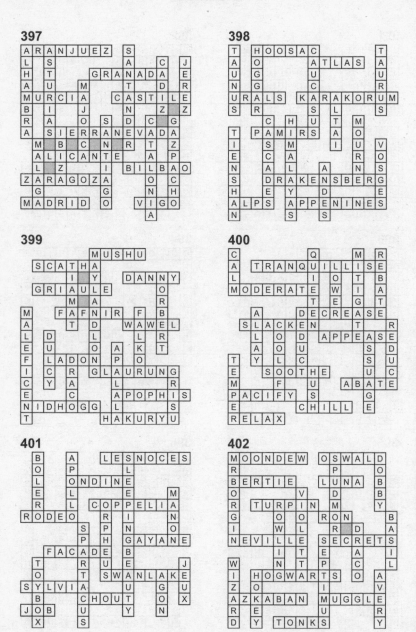

Solutions

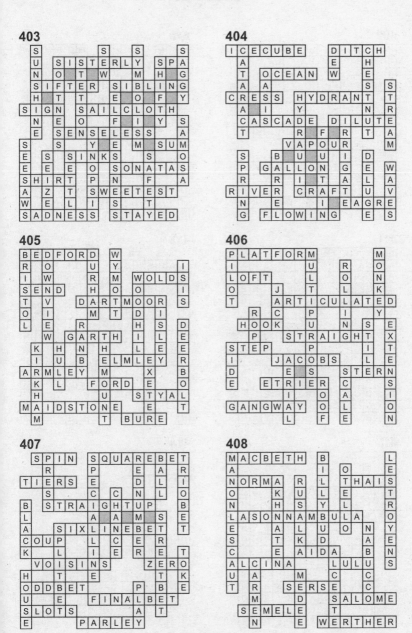

403

404

405

406

407

408

Solutions

409

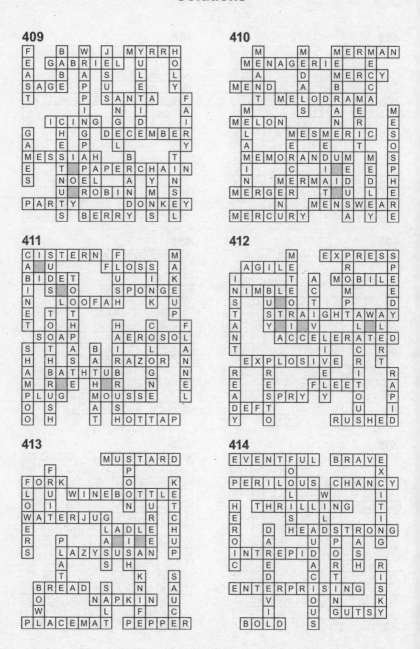

410

411

412

413

414

Solutions

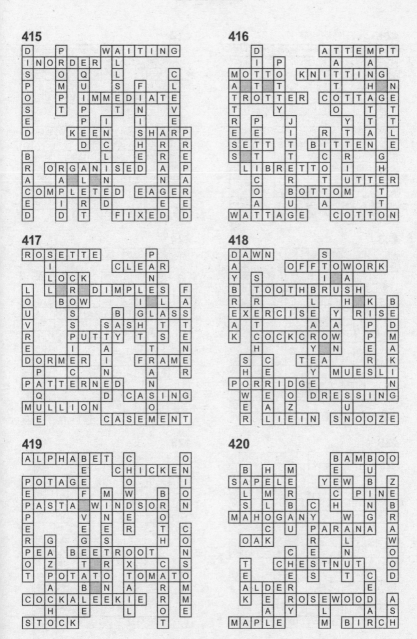

415   416

417   418

419   420

Solutions

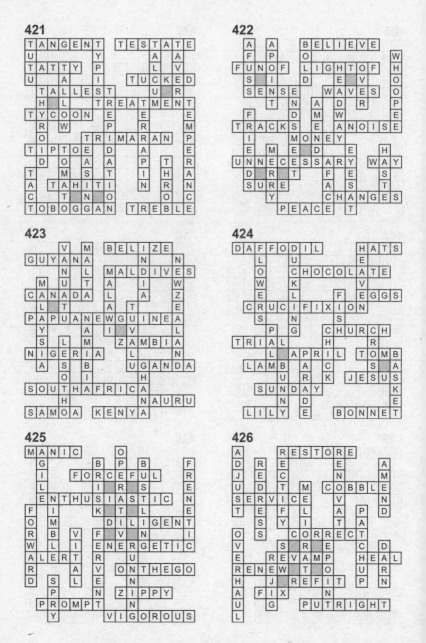

421

T	A	N	G	E	N	T		T	E	S	T	A	T	E
U					Y				A		A			
T	A	T	T	Y		P			L		V			
U		A				I		T	U	C	K	E	D	
	T	A	L	L	E	S	T		U		R			
	H	L		T	R	E	A	T	M	E	N	T		
T	Y	C	O	O	N		E			E				
R		W				E		R			M			
O			T	R	I	M	A	R	A	N		P		
T	I	P	T	O	E		D		A		P		E	
D		O		A		A		P	I	N		T	H	R
T		M		S		T			N		H	R	O	
A		T	A	H	I	T	I			O				
C		T			N		O					O		
T	O	B	O	G	G	A	N		T	R	E	B	L	E

422

A		A		B	E	L	I	E	V	E		
F		P		O								W
F	U	N	O	F		L	I	G	H	T	O	F		H
S		I		D		E			V		O	
S	E	N	S	E		W	A	V	E	S		O
		T		N		A		D		R		P
F			D		M		W			E
T	R	A	C	K	S		E		A	N	O	I	S	E
I			M	O	N	E	Y				E
E		M		E		D			E		H
U	N	N	E	C	E	S	S	A	R	Y		W	A	Y
D		R		T			F		E		S
S	U	R	E			A		S		T
Y					C	H	A	N	G	E	S
				P	E	A	C	E		T

423

			V		M		B	E	L	I	Z	E
G	U	Y	A	N	A				N		N
			N		L		M	A	L	D	I	V	E	S
	M		U		T		A		I		W
C	A	N	A	D	A		L		A		Z
L		T			T		A	T		E
P	A	P	U	A	N	E	W	G	U	I	N	E	A
Y			A		I		V		L
S		L		M		Z	A	M	B	I	A
N	I	G	E	R	I	A		L		N
A		S		B			U	G	A	N	D	A
	O		I			H
S	O	U	T	H	A	F	R	I	C	A
	H						N	A	U	R	U
S	A	M	O	A		K	E	N	Y	A

424

D	A	F	F	O	D	I	L				H	A	T	S
	L		O		U					H	E
	O		C	H	O	C	O	L	A	T	E
	W		K							V
	E		L			F		E	G	G	S
C	R	U	C	I	F	I	X	I	O	N
S					N		S
	P		G		C	H	U	R	C	H
T	R	I	A	L		H		R
	L		A	P	R	I	L		T	O	M	B
L	A	M	B		A		C		S		A
	U		R		K		J	E	S	U	S
S	U	N	D	A	Y						K
	N		D							E
L	I	L	Y		E		B	O	N	N	E	T

425

M	A	N	I	C			O
	G				B		P		B				F
	I		F	O	R	C	E	F	U	L		R
	L			I		R		S			E
	E	N	T	H	U	S	I	A	S	T	I	C
F		I		K		T		L		N
O		M			D	I	L	I	G	E	N	T
R		B	V	F		V		N		I
W		L	I	R		E	N	E	R	G	E	T	I	C
A	L	E	R	T		R		U		T
R			A		V		O	N	T	H	E	G	O
D		S	L		E		N
		P			N		Z	I	P	P	Y
P	R	O	M	P	T		N
	Y					V	I	G	O	R	O	U	S

426

A		R	E	S	T	O	R	E
D		R		E			E			A
J		E	C				N			M
U		D	T		M		C	O	B	B	L	E
S	E	R	V	I	C	E		V		E
T		E	F		L		A		P		D
	S	Y		I		T		A
O			C	O	R	R	E	C	T
V		S		R		E		C		D
E		R	E	V	A	M	P		H	E	A	L
R	E	N	E	W		T		O		U		R
H		J		R	E	F	I	T		P		N
A		F	I	X			N
U		G			P	U	T	R	I	G	H	T
L

620

Solutions

427

428

429
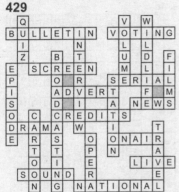

430

431
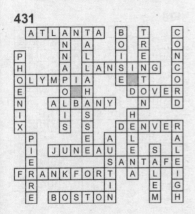

432
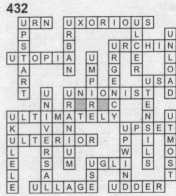

Solutions

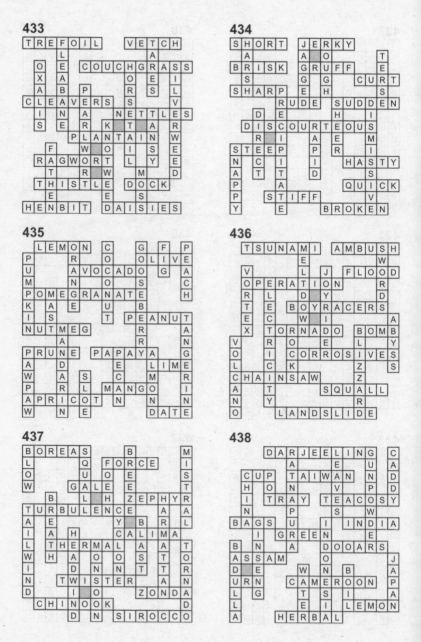

433 — TREFOIL, VETCH, COUCHGRASS, CLEAVERS, NETTLES, PLANTAIN, RAGWORT, THISTLE, DOCK, HENBIT, DAISIES, OXALIS, CRABGRASS, SPURGE, PERIWINKLE, FAT HEN, KNOTWEED, SOW THISTLE, MELONS...

434 — SHORT, JERKY, BRISK, GRUFF, CURT, SHARP, RUDE, SUDDEN, DISCOURTEOUS, STEEP, HASTY, QUICK, STIFF, BROKEN, SNAPPY, ABRUPT, RIGID, RAPID...

435 — LEMON, OLIVE, AVOCADO, POMEGRANATE, PEANUT, NUTMEG, PRUNE, PAPAYA, LIME, MANGO, APRICOT, DATE, PUMPKIN, ORANGE, COCONUT, PEACH, BANANA, PAWPAW...

436 — TSUNAMI, AMBUSH, FLOOD, OPERATION, BOYRACERS, TORNADO, BOMB, CORROSIVES, CHAINSAW, SQUALL, LANDSLIDE, VOLCANO...

437 — BOREAS, FORCE, GALE, ZEPHYR, TURBULENCE, CALIMA, THERMAL, TWISTER, ZONDA, CHINOOK, SIROCCO, MISTRAL...

438 — DARJEELING, TAIWAN, CUP, TRAY, TEACOSY, BAGS, INDIA, GREEN, DOOARS, ASSAM, CAMEROON, LEMON, HERBAL, URN, JAPAN...

Solutions

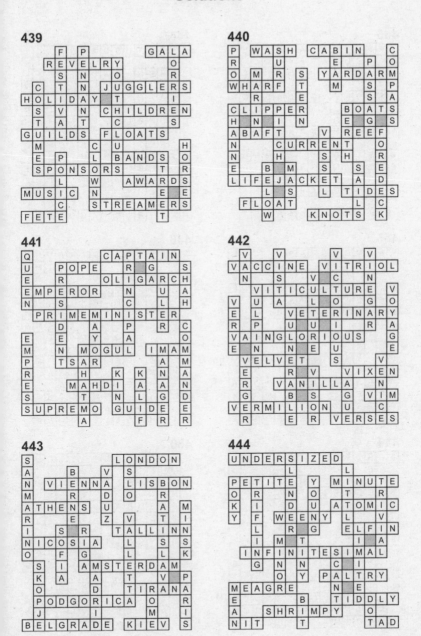

Solutions

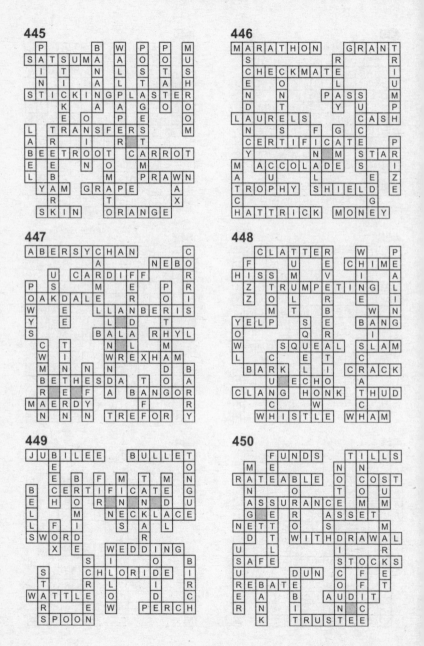

445

446

447

448

449

450

Solutions

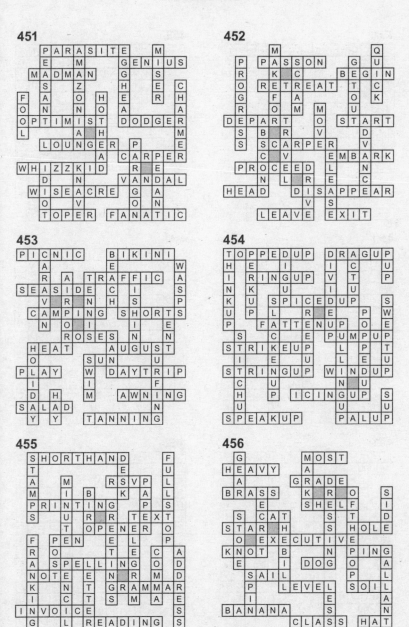

451 452

453 454

455 456

Solutions

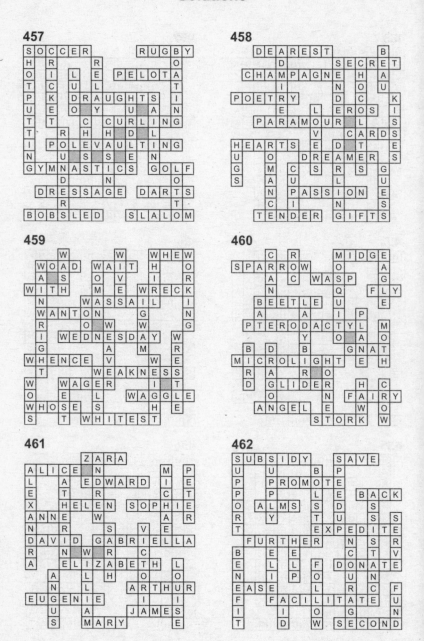

457

SOCCER · RUGBY

458

DEAREST · SECRET

459

WOAD · WAIT · WHEW

460

SPARROW · MIDGE

461

ZARA · ALICE · EDWARD

462

SUBSIDY · SAVE

Solutions

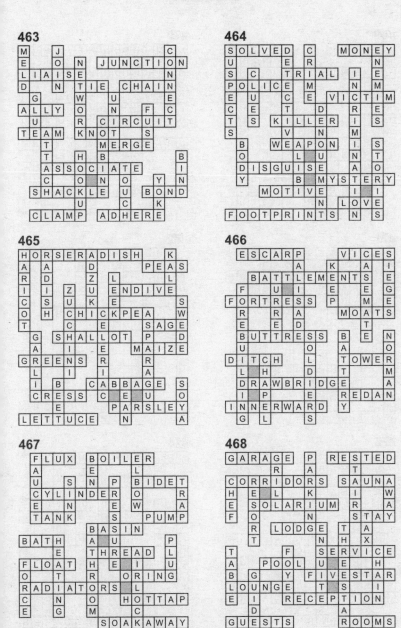

463

464

465

466

467

468

Solutions

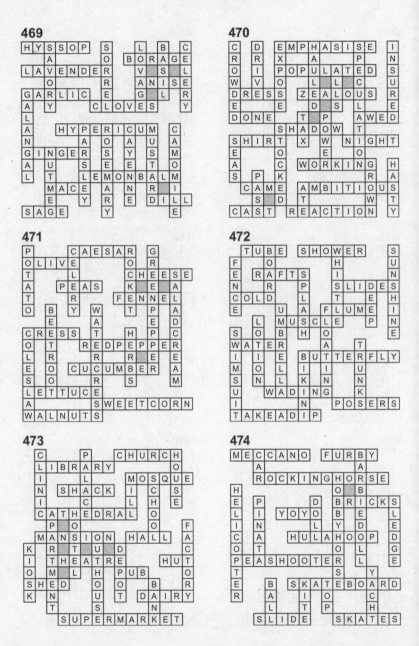

Solutions

475

476

477

478

479

480

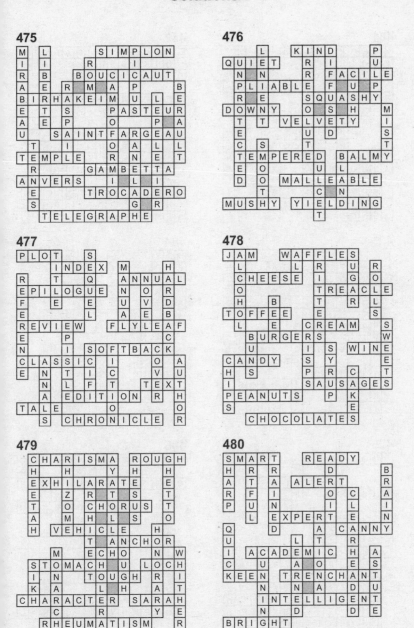

Solutions

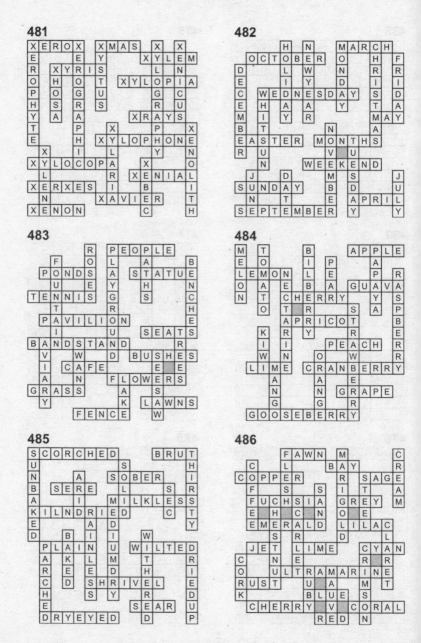

481

X E R O X | X M A S | X | X
XYLEM
XYRIS | XYLOPIA
XRAYS
XYLOPHONE
XYLOCOPA
XENIAL
XERXES
XAVIER
XENON

482

MARCH
OCTOBER
WEDNESDAY
EASTER | MONTHS
WEEKEND
SUNDAY | JULY
SEPTEMBER | APRIL

483

PEOPLE
PONDS | STATUE
TENNIS
PAVILION
SEATS
BANDSTAND
CAFE | BUSHES
FLOWERS
GRASS | LAWNS
FENCE

484

APPLE
LEMON | GUAVA
CHERRY
APRICOT
PEACH
LIME | CRANBERRY
GRAPE
GOOSEBERRY

485

SCORCHED | BRUT
SOBER
SERE | MILKLESS
KILNDRIED
PLAIN | WILTED
SHRIVEL
SEAR
DRYEYED

486

FAWN
BAY
COPPER | SAGE
FUCHSIA | GREY
EMERALD | LILAC
JET | LIME | CYAN
ULTRAMARINE
RUST
BLUE
CHERRY | CORAL
RED

Solutions

487

488

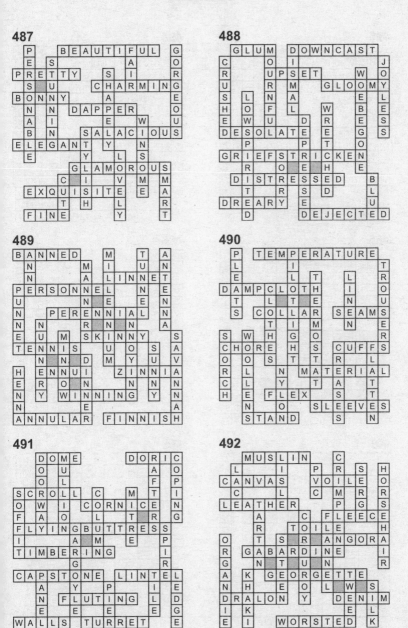

489

490

491

492

Solutions

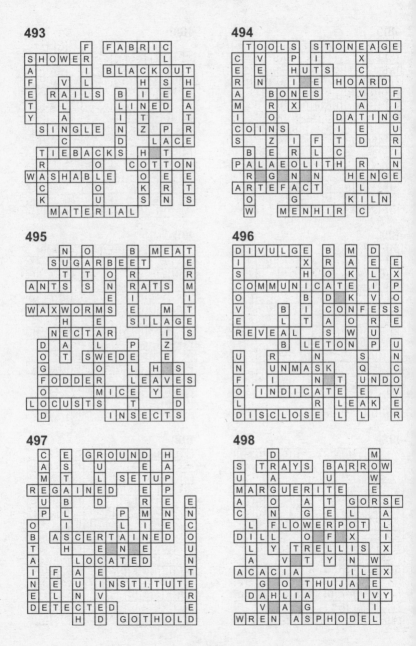

493

FABRIC
F R I C
SHOWER R L
A I BLACKOUT
FETY V L H S H
E RAILS B I E E
T L LINED A A
Y A I T P R
SINGLE N Z P R
C D LACE C
TIEBACKS H T E
R O COTTON
WASHABLE O O E T
C U K R T
K MATERIAL N S

494

TOOLS STONEAGE
C V P I X
E E HUTS C
R N I E HOARD
A BONES V F
M R X A I
I O DATING G
COINS I E U
S Z I F T R
B E R L C I
PALAEOLITH R N
R G N N HENGE
ARTEFACT L E
O G KILN
W MENHIR C

495

N O B MEAT
SUGARBEET E
T T O R R
ANTS S N RATS M
I I I
WAXWORMS E M T
H E SILAGE S
NECTAR I
D A L P Z S
O T SWEDE E
G O L H S
FODDER LEAVES
O MICE Y E
LOCUSTS T D
D INSECTS

496

DIVULGE B M D
I X R A E E
S H O K L X
COMMUNICATE E I P
O B D K V O
V B I C CONFESS
E L T A O R E
REVEAL S W U
B LETON P U
UN R N S N
UNMASK Q C
F I N T UNDO
O INDICATE E O
L R LEAK V
DISCLOSE L L R

497

C E GROUND H
CAM ST U E A
RE GAINED L SETUP P
UP B D E P
P L P M N ENC
OB A SCERTAINED OU
T H E N E N
A LOCATED T
INE F A E E
E L UN INSTITUTE R
DETECTED E
H D GOTHOLD

498

D M
S TRAYS BARROW
U A U W
MARGUERITE E
A O A T GORSE
C N G E L A
L FLOWERPOT L
DILL O F X I
L Y TRELLIS X
A V T Y N W
ACACIA ILEX
G O THUJA E
DAHLIA IVY
V A G I
WREN ASPHODEL

632

Solutions

499

500

501

502

503

504

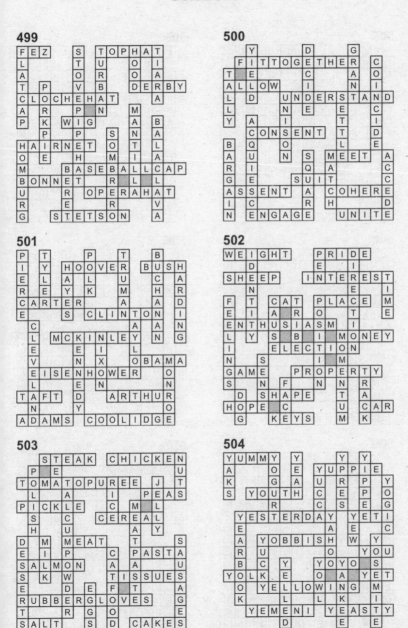

Solutions

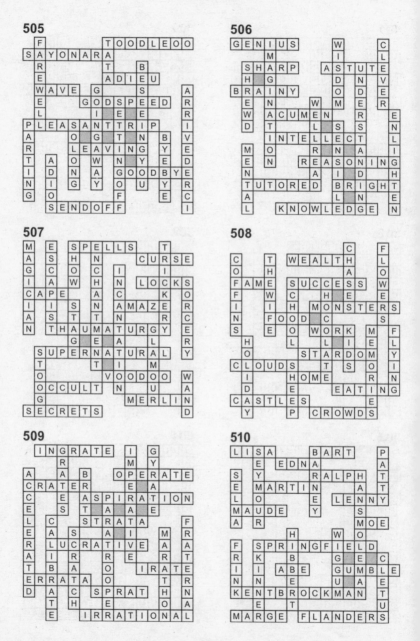

505

506

507

508

509

510

Solutions

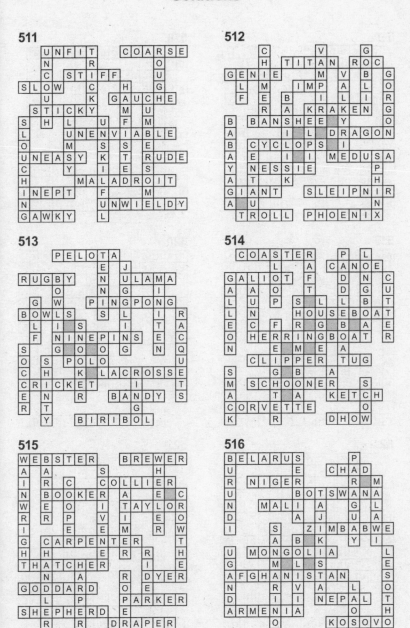

511

UNFIT COARSE
STIFF
SLOW GAUCHE
STICKY
UNENVIABLE
UNEASY RUDE
MALADROIT
INEPT
UNWIELDY
GAWKY

512

CHI TITAN ROC
GENIE
IMP
KRAKEN
BANSHEE
DRAGON
CYCLOPS
MEDUSA
NESSIE
GIANT SLEIPNIR
TROLL PHOENIX

513

PELOTA
RUGBY ULAMA
PINGPONG
BOWLS
NINEPINS
POLO
LACROSSE
CRICKET
BANDY
BIRIBOL

514

COASTER
CANOE
GALIOT
HOUSEBOAT
HERRINGBOAT
CLIPPER TUG
SCHOONER
KETCH
CORVETTE
DHOW

515

WEBSTER BREWER
COLLIER
BOOKER
TAYLOR
CARPENTER
THATCHER
DYER
GODDARD
PARKER
SHEPHERD
DRAPER

516

BELARUS
CHAD
NIGER
BOTSWANA
MALI
ZIMBABWE
MONGOLIA
AFGHANISTAN
NEPAL
ARMENIA
KOSOVO

Solutions

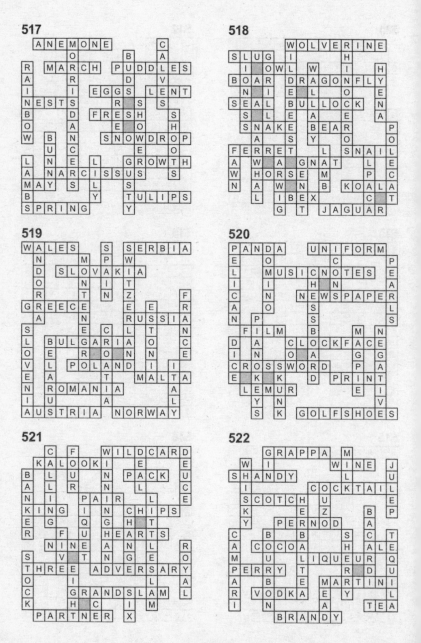

517

ANEMONE · CA
MARCH · PUDDLES · LENT
EGGS
NESTS · FRESH
SNOWDROP
GROWTH
NARCISSUS
MAY · TULIPS
SPRING

518

WOLVERINE
SLUG · OWL · DRAGONFLY
BOAR · BULLOCK
SEAL · SNAKE · BEAR
FERRET · SNAIL
HORSE · GNAT · KOALA
IBEX · JAGUAR

519

WALES · SERBIA
SLOVAKIA
GREECE · RUSSIA
BULGARIA · POLAND · MALTA
ROMANIA
AUSTRIA · NORWAY

520

PANDA · UNIFORM
MUSICNOTES
NEWSPAPER
FILM · CLOCKFACE
CROSSWORD · PRINT
LEMUR · GOLFSHOES

521

WILDCARD
KALOOKI · PACK
PAIR · CHIPS
KING · HEARTS
NINE
THREE · ADVERSARY
GRANDSLAM
PARTNER

522

GRAPPA · WINE
SHANDY · COCKTAIL
SCOTCH · PERNOD
COCOA · LIQUEUR
PERRY · MARTINI
VODKA · TEA
BRANDY

Solutions

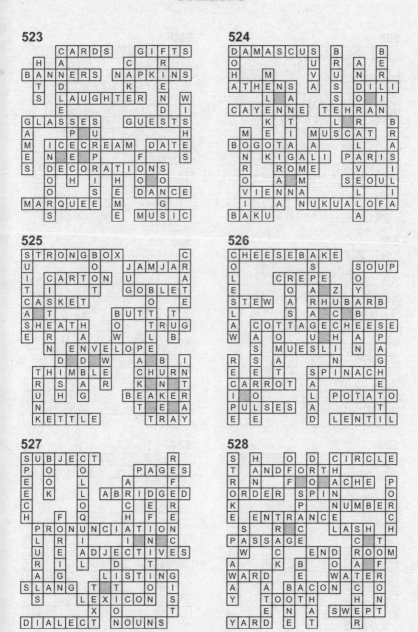

523

CARDS · GIFTS · H A · C R · BANNERS · NAPKINS · T D · K E · S LAUGHTER · N W · E · D I · GLASSES · GUESTS · A P U · H · M ICECREAM · DATE · E N E P · F · S · S DECORATIONS · O H I H O · O O S E · DANCE · MARQUEE · M · G · S · E · MUSIC

524

DAMASCUS · B · B · O U R A E · H M V A N R · ATHENS A S DILI · L A S O I · CAYENNE · TEHRAN · K T L R B · ME I MUSCAT R · BOGOTA A A L A · N KIGALI PARIS · R ROME V I · O A M SEOUL L · VIENNA L I · I A NUKUALOFA · BAKU A

525

STRONGBOX · C · U O JAMJAR A · I CARTON U R · T I T G GOBLET · CASKET O E · A T BUTT T · SHEATH O TRUG · E R A W L B · N ENVELOPE · D D W A B I · THIMBLE CHURN · R S A R K N T · U H G BEAKER · N T E A · KETTLE TRAY

526

CHEESEBAKE · O S SOUP · L CREPE O Y · E O A Z Y · STEW A RHUBARB · L A A C B · W COTTAGECHEESE · A O U H A P · S MUESLI N A · R S A N G · E E T SPINACH · CARROT A E · I O L POTATO · PULSES A T · E E D LENTIL

527

SUBJECT · R · P O O PAGES · E O L A F · E K L ABRIDGED · C L C E R · H F Q H F E · PRONUNCIATION · L R I I N C · U E I ADJECTIVES · R I L D T · A G L LISTING · SLANG T T O I · S LEXICON S · X O T · DIALECT NOUNS

528

S H O D CIRCLE · T ANDFORTH H · R N F O ACHE P · ORDER SPIN O · K P NUMBER R · E ENTRANCE C · S R C LASH H · PASSAGE C T · W C END ROOM · A K B O A F · WARD E WATER · A A BACON C O · Y TOOTH H N · E N A SWEPT · YARD E T R

637

Solutions

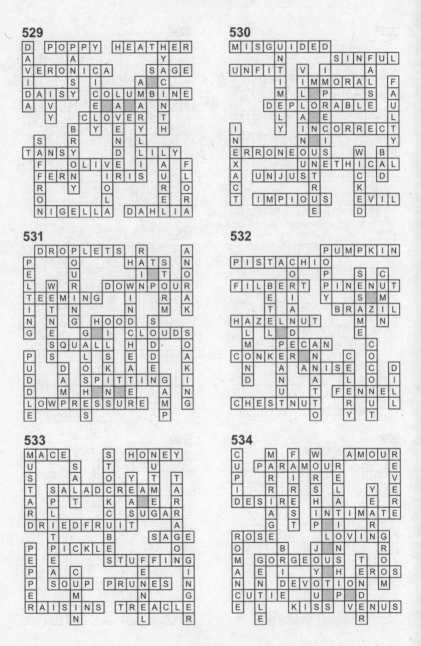

529

DA POPPY HEATHER
VERONICA SAGE
DAISY COLUMBINE
CLOVER
TANSY LILY
OLIVE F
FERNY IRIS L
NIGELLA DAHLIA

530

MISGUIDED
SINFUL
UNFIT
IMMORAL F
DEPLORABLE A
INCORRECT
ERRONEOUS
UNETHICAL
UNJUST
IMPIOUS EVIL

531

DROPLETS
HATS
DOWNPOUR
TEEMING
HOODS
CLOUDS
SQUALL
SPITTING
LOWPRESSURE

532

PUMPKIN
PISTACHIO
FILBERT PINENUT
BRAZIL
HAZELNUT
PECAN
CONKER ANISE
FENNEL
CHESTNUT

533

MACE HONEY
SALADCREAM
SUGAR
DRIEDFRUIT
SAGE
PICKLE
STUFFING
SOUP PRUNES
RAISINS TREACLE

534

AMOUR
PARAMOUR
DESIRE
INTIMATE
ROSE LOVING
GORGEOUS
EROS
DEVOTION
CUTIE
KISS VENUS

638

Solutions

535

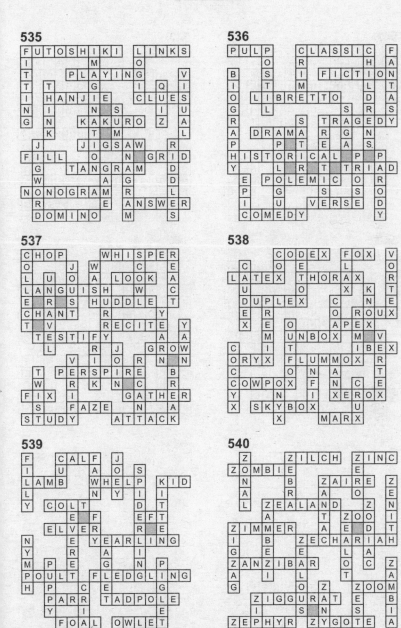

536

537

538

539

540

Solutions

541

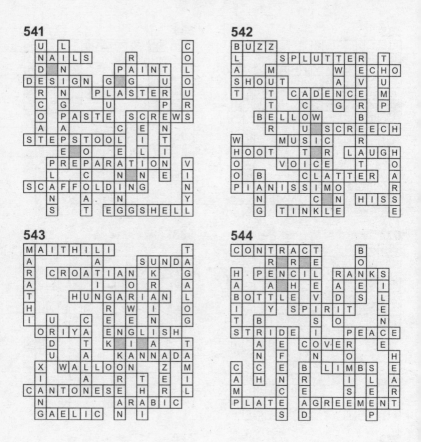

542

543

544